The Structural Basis of Antibody Specificity

MICROBIAL AND MOLECULAR BIOLOGY SERIES

J. R. S. Fincham (*John Innes Institute*): **Genetic Complementation**

J. Lascelles (*University of Oxford*): **Tetrapyrrole Biosynthesis and Its Regulation**

A. L. Lehninger (*The Johns Hopkins University*): **The Mitochondrion**

O. Maaløe and N. O. Kjeldgaard (*University of Copenhagen*): **Control of Macromolecular Synthesis**

D. Pressman and A. L. Grossberg (*Roswell Park Memorial Institute*): **The Structural Basis of Antibody Specificity**

The Structural Basis of Antibody Specificity

David Pressman
Allan L. Grossberg
Roswell Park Memorial Institute

W. A. BENJAMIN, INC.
ADVANCED BOOK PROGRAM
Reading, Massachusetts

London • Amsterdam • Don Mills, Ontario • Sydney • Tokyo

International Standard Book Number
Hardbound: 0–805–38052–3

Library of Congress Catalog Card Number 67–19436

First printing, 1968
Second printing, with corrections, October 1973

Manufactured in the United States of America

ISBN 0-8053-8052-1
ABCDEFGHIJ-CO-79876543

EDITOR'S FOREWORD

This book is the fifth to appear in a series of monographs on Microbial and Molecular Biology. The purpose of this series is to encourage and sponsor the publication of carefully selected and edited short monographs on topics in the forefront of research in these fields.

Each book in the series will present a more comprehensive review of its topic, and a broader perspective, than is ordinarily possible in a review article. The presentations are intended to be sufficiently detailed, and thoroughly enough documented and illustrated, so that the advanced student will be able to obtain a comprehensive and up-to-date grasp of an actively developing area without having to refer extensively to original papers. To facilitate access to especially important experimental detail or theoretical development, reprints of key papers will at times be included.

These volumes are not primarily reference works, and they will differ from the traditional monograph in not necessarily covering every relevant reference. The rapid proliferation of the scientific literature makes it increasingly difficult for the experienced investigator, let alone the graduate student, to rely on his coverage of original articles to keep him informed of important advances across the general field of microbial and molecular biology. Hence the editor and publisher believe that appropriate reviews are of increasing value; and for this purpose it seems to us more important that the reviews be critical and lucid than that they be exhaustive. Accordingly, we encourage the authors to be selective, to speculate on immediate problems and on directions of future advance, and to editorialize in much the same way as they would in lecturing to their own students.

I hope that this series of volumes will be of value to the scientific community. Criticisms and suggestions will be welcomed.

BERNARD D. DAVIS

Boston, Massachusetts
June 1967

PREFACE

This monograph is based on a series of lectures of the same title given by one of us for a special biophysics course at the University of Rochester. Similar lectures have been given from time to time by both of us to groups of professional chemists and biologists, and to undergraduate and graduate students. Depending on the background of the audience, the lectures covered the chemical nature of antibodies and their combining sites and certain related topics. The reception with which these lectures were met and the questions asked during and following their presentation indicated the desirability of a monograph which would cover these subjects for both chemists and biologists at a basic level and in greater depth than is usual in microbiology and immunology courses. We were therefore already inclined to write such a monograph when approached by the Editor of this series. The present volume is written primarily for the advanced biological science student who has some knowledge of immunological nomenclature and who desires to know more details of antibody structure and specificity. It is concerned primarily with anti-hapten antibodies, which permit analysis of the structural specificity and the chemical nature of specific binding regions. It is also designed to demonstrate to the chemistry student that the simple structural relationships and concepts with which he is familiar are the important considerations in the specificity of biological receptor sites.

No attempt has been made to be all inclusive. Certain topics are discussed at length whereas others, even controversial ones, are merely mentioned or not discussed at all.

The first two chapters are intended to introduce the student to the chemical concepts which are involved in antibody-antigen interaction. Chapter 1 describes the nature of the two components and the forces involved in the interaction. Chapter 2 introduces the concepts of chemical equilibria necessary for obtaining quantitative information on antibody-hapten interaction. The principles of such methods are described, but descriptions of experimental methods are relegated to Appendixes I and II in order to maintain the continuity of the textual presentation. Chapter 2 concludes with a specific example of the kind of quantitative information that is obtained, in order to lead the student into the more detailed examples which follow in Chapter 3.

Chapter 3 discusses a large number of individual anti-hapten systems in detail, in terms of the structural features important for antibody-hapten combination. To aid in understanding and in the visualization of the chemical structures involved, liberal use is made of drawings of structural formulas as well as the names of the compounds concerned. The examples discussed have been drawn largely from studies by the authors and their associates. Studies by others are included where pertinent, but no attempt has been made to be all inclusive in providing citations to the literature. Although there are many inter-relationships between the various systems as summarized at the end of Chapter 3, each system may be considered alone. Liberal use is made of cross references between sections of the chapter so that consistencies in the information derived from several systems are made apparent. A list of references to many anti-hapten systems which have been studied but which are not discussed is provided in Appendix III.

Chapter 4 takes up the important problem of the basis of the heterogeneity of antibody sites and provides several detailed examples of analysis of such heterogeneity.

Chapter 5 discusses the nature of the antibody site itself, as revealed by chemical modification of several anti-hapten antibodies. The chapter concludes with a summary of the amino acid residues thus far implicated in these sites.

Chapter 6 provides a short description of what is presently known of the polypeptide chain structure of γG-immunoglobulins and discusses at some length the evidence relating the antibody site to this structure. It is intended to provide the student with no more than an introduction to this rapidly expanding area of investigation, since current work is adding almost daily to knowledge of the subject.

The final chapter introduces the student to an additional large area of investigation concerned with the use of antibodies to map out the structures of both small and large molecules in aqueous solution. The importance of water of hydration in these structures is stressed. This area is important to both the chemist and the biologist: It provides chemists with a method of investigation potentially more powerful than the usual physical chemical approach, and it provides biologists with a means of investigating the structures of many macromolecules—polysaccharides, proteins, and nucleic acids—under conditions in which their biologically important reactions actually take place.

The preparation of this monograph has entailed discussions with many individuals who have generously given of their time to provide us with critical comment and encouragement. In this regard, we should like especially to thank our colleagues Dr. Yasuo Yagi, Dr. Oliver Roholt, Dr. Isaac Witz, and Dr. Jake Bello. We wish to thank Dr. M. J. Crumpton and Dr. A. J. Rowe for Figures 7.6 and 1.2, respectively.

Special thanks go to Miss Gail McBride who spent many hours editing the manuscript and critically reviewing its style. A similar service was generously provided by Mrs. George Tritsch. All the above have reviewed the content and format of the book. Errors of omission and commission, of course, are solely the responsibility of the authors.

Our secretary-typists, Miss Cheryl Goodman, Miss Diane Matla, and Miss Janet Stevens, were of unfailing energy and good humor in seeing the initial manuscript through its many revisions to the final product.

To our Editor, Dr. Bernard Davis, we express thanks for very valuable criticism.

Our wives and children are due much for their helpful encouragement, forbearance, and understanding throughout the period of preparation of this book. To them it is gratefully dedicated.

DAVID PRESSMAN
ALLAN L. GROSSBERG

Buffalo, New York
October 1967

CONTENTS

INTRODUCTION

The most striking feature of antibody molecules is their great specificity: the ability to combine tightly with certain structures but not with other closely related structures. Insight into the basis for this specificity was provided at the beginning of the twentieth century, in general terms, by Paul Ehrlich (1906) who adapted Emil Fischer's (1894, 1898) "lock-and-key" theory of enzyme-substrate interaction to immune reactions. He stated that the affinity of an antigen for the corresponding specific antibody depended on complementarity of surface structure, analogous to that of a lock and its key. This analogy is frequently expressed without the realization of how nearly correct it really is.

Since Ehrlich's time, studies in immunochemistry have helped greatly to elucidate the structural features of immunological specificity and to provide it with a firm chemical basis. Many physical chemists devoted much effort to analyzing the equilibria involved in the neutralization of toxins, and in the precipitation of antigens, by antibodies. As early as 1907 Arrhenius described such reactions in terms of simple chemical equilibria. Marrack (1934, 1939) and Heidelberger (1935, 1939) first proposed that such reactions are due to the multivalent nature of both antigen and antibody. Subsequently it has been borne out that antibody is essentially bivalent and precipitating antigens have at least two combining sites.

The idea that the antibody molecules are formed so that they are structurally complementary to the immunizing antigen or hapten was proposed in the early 1930's by Breinl and Haurowitz (1930), Alexander

(1931), and Mudd (1932). Structural chemical principles were applied by Erlenmeyer and Berger (1932), by Marrack (1934, 1939), by Hooker (1937), and by Pauling *et al.* (1943) to the nature of the combination of antibody with antigen or hapten.

Antibody formation is induced by immunogenic macromolecules, and the biological function of antibodies generally involves interaction with such antigens. However, precise studies on antibody specificity are not possible with naturally occurring macromolecules, because each molecule contains a variety of antigenic determinants which induce, and react with, antibodies of different specificity. Progress in this area has depended on the possibility of making antibodies practically at will against any number of different substances of known chemical structure (haptens), which can be covalently attached to macromolecular carriers. The reactions of antibodies directed against simple substances of known composition were initially exploited by Karl Landsteiner and his collaborators in the early 1900's (Landsteiner, 1945) to build up a background of knowledge concerning the structural basis of immunological specificity. Subsequently many other investigators contributed to this background. These earlier studies were largely qualitative. In the early 1940's Professors Linus Pauling and Dan Campbell and their co-workers (the present authors among them) initiated studies designed to provide more quantitative information on the role played by various chemically defined structures in antibody-hapten interaction. Such investigations, also taken up subsequently by others, provide much of the material covered in the present volume.

The significance of studies on hapten-antibody interactions extends beyond the bounds of immunology. As Ehrlich pointed out, the lock-and-key analogy is equally applicable to the interactions of drugs with their receptors. Today we are confident that a similar surface complementarity at a molecular level underlies the specificity of numerous other processes of the greatest importance for biology, such as cell-cell interactions in morphogenesis, cell-cell interactions in fertilization, the adsorption of viruses to susceptible cells, as well as the interactions of enzymes with substrates and with allosteric regulators. Anti-hapten antibodies may thus be regarded as models for the study of biological receptor sites in general.

Another approach to antibody specificity is that of protein chemistry, concerned with analyzing the structure of the antibody molecule. Following the initial investigations by R. R. Porter and his co-workers in England in the 1950's on the enzymatic fragmentation of the γ-globulin molecule, many such studies are now being pursued in various laboratories. Certain aspects of this work are briefly included in the present volume. We shall also discuss the use of haptens to help determine the amino acid and peptide composition of the combining sites of antibodies.

From a chemist's point of view antibodies are important not only as naturally occurring substances with biochemical reactivity, but also as analytical reagents to identify a substance, to differentiate between very closely related substances, or even to determine quantitatively how much of a particular substance is present. Antibodies have an advantage in that they offer a means of preparing a large variety of specific chemical reagents by a single general method. Each such reagent may be further purified or defined so that it will react with only the particular substance of interest. It can even be labelled, as with fluorescein or a radioactive isotope, so that it can be located at a microscopic level.

Antibodies can also be used to determine the structure and configuration of simple substances in aqueous solution. This use is of great potential importance for those interested in designing compounds which will have particular biological activities since such pharmacological activity must depend on the structure of a molecule under physiological conditions, rather than in crystalline form or as diagrammatically represented on paper. Evidence of this kind will be presented in this volume for many compounds.

The Structural Basis of Antibody Specificity

1

NATURE OF ANTIBODY-ANTIGEN INTERACTION

The reaction of an antibody molecule with the antigen against which it is directed is caused by physical chemical interaction between certain reactive parts of these two molecules. The general nature of these reactive parts, and the kinds of forces that are involved in the interaction, are discussed in this chapter.

1.1 THE ANTIBODY MOLECULE

The antibody molecule is a protein which has the property of being able to combine very selectively with the antigen against which it is directed. Antibodies found in the circulation are globulins (immunoglobulins) with a wide range of electrophoretic mobilities. They fall into broad major general classes which are currently designated as IgG, IgM, IgA[1] based on antigenic properties of the molecules. Further subdivision will probably be necessary. The antibody molecules most studied are of the 6S γ-globulin type (IgG immunoglobulin), with a molecular weight of 150,000–160,000. The molecule is composed of two halves, which appear to be identical. Each half is made up of two polypeptide chains—one of molecular weight 55,000–60,000, called the heavy chain, and the other

[1] *Bulletin World Health Organization,* **30**, 447–450 (1964). Another class, IgD, has recently been described by Rowe and Fahey (1965).

of molecular weight 20,000–24,000 called the light chain. The chains are held together by disulfide bonds and by noncovalent interactions.

There are two regions in a 6S antibody molecule which are able to combine with an antigenic group. Both combining regions appear to be directed against the same antigenic grouping. The molecule seems to exist in a compact form when free (and perhaps when combined with simple haptens) and in an extended form when combined with large antigens in the region of antigen excess. A schematic arrangement of the above-mentioned component features of the molecule is depicted in Fig. 1.1. Electron micrographs showing actual antibody molecules are in Fig. 1.2.

1.2 ANTIBODY-ANTIGEN INTERACTION

When antigen combines with antibody enough energy of binding must be available to hold them together. Under the conditions of most immunological reactions, that is, at pH 7–8, the antibodies are negatively charged, and nearly all protein antigens are negatively charged. Thus the energy of binding must be sufficient to overcome the Coulombic repulsion between the two.

When antibody binds to antigen there is no formation of a covalent chemical bond between atoms of the two molecules. Instead the binding energy is derived from two sources. The first is the relatively weak nonspecific attractive forces which exist between atoms, ions, and molecules. The second is due to outside forces in which interaction between solvent molecules pushes the antigen and antibody together. The forces involved are due to (a) charge interaction, (b) hydrophobic interactions which result from the reduction of water-nonpolar interfacial areas, (c) London dispersion forces (van der Waals attraction), (d) hydrogen bond formation, (e) dipole interaction, and (f) entropy increases involved in stripping water from charged and polar areas. The contribution of each kind of force depends on the individual system under consideration. In one system the combining energy may be derived predominantly from one type of force and in another system from a different type of force. In some systems several forces may be equally important.

The attractive forces are effective only over short distances. The binding of antigen to antibody requires that the atoms in the binding region of the antibody come very close to the corresponding atoms of the binding region of the antigen so that these short range forces can be effective. Forces due to solvent interaction also require a close fit to be effective. The combining region of the antibody must fit closely over enough of the antigenic region to produce sufficient binding force to hold the molecules together.

The selectivity (or specificity) of the reaction is particularly important.

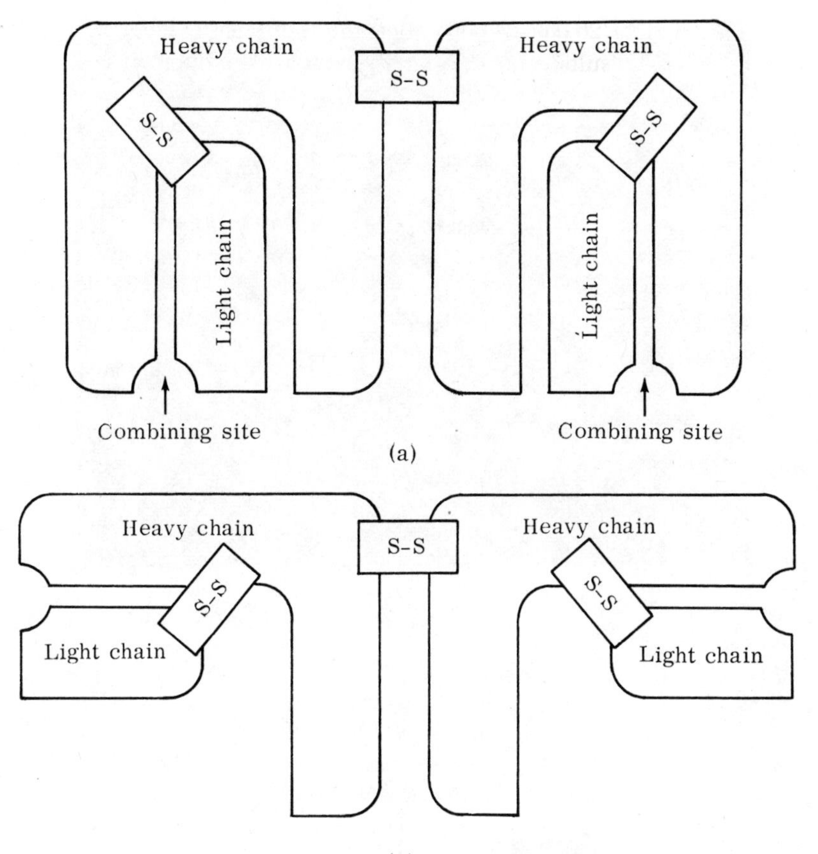

FIGURE 1.1 **The antibody molecule in schematic representation. (a) Folded form. (b) Extended form (in the presence of an excess of a large antigen). This representation makes use of the multichain composition as shown by Edelman (1959), the arrangement of the chains as suggested by Porter (1962), and the shape of the molecule as described by Feinstein and Rowe (1965). See also Almeida *et al.* (1963) and Lafferty and Oertelis (1963).**

An antibody will react with the antigen against which it is directed and with certain very closely related substances. Very small differences in structure of the antigen affect the reaction, however, so that the antibody as a rule does not react as well with less closely related substances.

Part of the selectivity comes from the requirement that the antibody have a close steric fit around the antigenic grouping in order that the short range forces can be effective. Groupings with shapes much different from the antigenic structure do not fit the antibody site and cannot bind to it. The rest of the selectivity arises from the fact that the distribution of groups on the antibody must correspond to a complementary

(a)

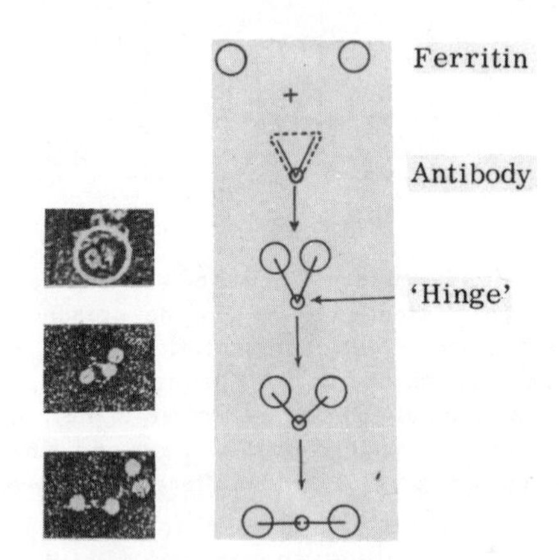

(b)

FIGURE 1.2 Electron microscope pictures of anti-ferritin antibody molecules alone or in combination with antigen. (a) The free molecules (note compact form). (b) Complexes of anti-ferritin antibodies with ferritin showing the spreading of the antibody molecule when combined with two ferritin molecules. [From Feinstein and Rowe (1965).]

distribution of groups on the antigen, again in order that the short range interatomic forces can be effective. An antigen which fits the antibody combining region sterically but does not have the correct groups in proper positions will not combine.

1.3 STERIC FIT

In Fig. 1.3a is depicted schematically a portion of an antigenic grouping together with a portion of the antibody combining region directed against it. The close complementary structural fit is seen. There is an arrangement of groupings on the antigen involving a negative charge, a proton donor group, a dipole and a nonpolar region. The antibody fits closely around this and has the complementary positive charge, proton acceptor, dipole, and nonpolar region in such positions as to interact with the corresponding groups on the antigen. The result is a good fit of the two regions with a good binding arrangement.

Figure 1.3b shows the effect of a change in degree of steric fit on the specificity of the reaction. An antigen of a somewhat different shape from that in Fig. 1.3a is depicted with, however, the same arrangement of groups on it. It can be seen that, owing to the presence of a large inactive structure in the antigen region, the groups on the antibody that was formed against the antigen of Fig. 1.3a can no longer come close

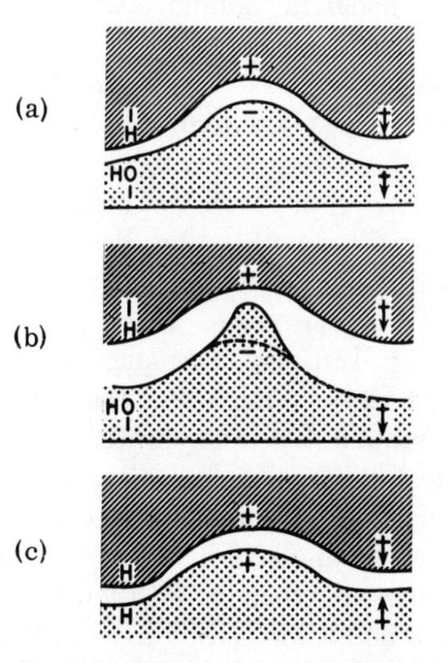

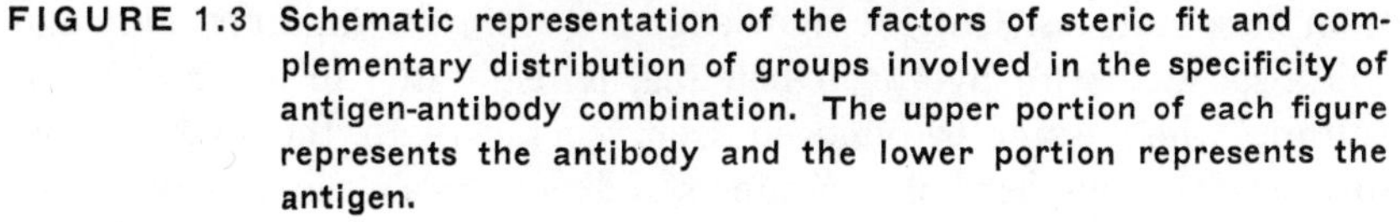
FIGURE 1.3 Schematic representation of the factors of steric fit and complementary distribution of groups involved in the specificity of antigen-antibody combination. The upper portion of each figure represents the antibody and the lower portion represents the antigen.

enough to the ones on the differently shaped antigen to form a strong bond. Thus there is no effective combination.

Figure 1.3c shows the same antibody in juxtaposition to another substance which has the correct steric shape for combination, but whose various groups do not attract, and may even repel, the contiguous groups of the antibody. In this case also there is no effective combination.

1.4 FORCES INVOLVED IN ANTIBODY-ANTIGEN INTERACTION

1.4a Charge interaction. The charge interaction results from interaction of a charged group on the antigen with its complementary but oppositely charged group on the antibody. The energy of the reaction depends inversely on the square of the distance between charges and inversely on the dielectric constant of the medium. Corrections for the apparent change in the dielectric constant of the medium when two charges approach closely to each other in aqueous solution have been worked out by Schwartzenbach (1936). The charged groups on the antibody are limited by the fact that the antibody is protein and thus negative groups must be carboxylate and positive groups must be due to lysine, arginine, histidine, or N-terminal amino groups. A charged group against which an antibody is directed is not limited to groups found on the naturally occurring amino acids and thus can be due to any negatively or positively charged group. There appears to be no limit to the types of groups against which an antibody can be directed.

1.4b Hydrophobic forces. The hydrophobic forces are the same type of forces that cause oil drops suspended in water to coalesce. They arise from the effect of various groups on the structure of water. When a nonpolar surface is in contact with water, the water molecules adjacent to it are not in as low a free-energy state as when they are entirely surrounded by other water molecules. If the amount of nonpolar-water interface is reduced by bringing nonpolar surfaces together, water molecules are displaced from contact with the nonpolar surface and are then completely surrounded by other water molecules. Originally it was presumed that the water molecules adjacent to the nonpolar surface cannot form as many hydrogen bonds as they can when they are entirely surrounded by other water molecules. The driving force for bringing the two nonpolar surfaces together would then stem from the energy of the additional hydrogen bonds formed by the water after it was displaced from these surfaces. Current knowledge is that the driving force, although still associated with hydrogen bonding, is really due to an increase of entropy when water is removed from contact with the hydrophobic surfaces. The hypdrophobic groups stabilize a very well ordered water arrangement in the region of immediate contact with the nonpolar surface. Subsequent shift of water molecules away from the hydrophobic groups results in sufficient disarray and corresponding increase of entropy to drive the hydrophobic parts together.

1.4c Van der Waals attraction. The van der Waals attraction is due mainly to London dispersion forces which result from the polarization of two atoms as they approach each other. The cloud of electrons around each nucleus is distorted so that there is a resultant attraction between the electrons of one atom and the positive nucleus of the other. This van der Waals attraction exists between all atoms. For example, these are the forces between molecules of a gas which cause the pressure volume relationship of a gas to deviate from those of the perfect gas laws (and follow the van der Waals equations). The maximum forces between various groups are proportional to the products of their polarizabilities. These relative values of the polarizabilities for several groups, taking hydrogen as unity, are given in Table 1.1.

1.4d Hydrogen bond formation. The hydrogen bond results from the attraction of a hydrogen atom attached to one electronegative atom (the proton donor) for the unshared electron pair of another (the proton acceptor). Thus the proton on an oxygen or nitrogen atom will interact with the unshared electron pair on any other oxygen, nitrogen, or other electronegative atom. However, since the reactions take place in water,

TABLE 1.1 Polarizabilities Relative to Hydrogen for Estimating Relative van der Waals Forces of Groups

Group	Relative polarizability
—H	1.0
—F	0.8
—Cl	5.7
—Br	8.5
—I	13.5
$—CH_3$	5.5
$—C_2H_5$	10.0
$—C_6H_5$	24.8
$—C_{10}H_7$	41.7
—C≡N	5.3
—OH	2.5
$—C(=O)CH_3$	10.2

these groups in both antigen and antibody are already hydrogen bonded to water. These bonds to water must be broken before the new ones between the antigen and antibody can form. The overall energy of a given reaction depends on the energies of the individual bonds being formed and broken. The hydrogen bond has an energy of 0 to 5 kcal/mole, depending on which structures are being bonded.

1.4e Dipole interactions. The dipole interaction is the attraction between dipolar arrangements in the molecules. Since atoms of different elements have different electronegativities, there is an unequal sharing of electrons when they are bonded. This results in the formation of an electrical dipole which is attracted by any other dipole lined up properly.

1.4f Entropy increase. Another force that may act between antigen and antibody molecules results from the fact that a charged group in an aqueous environment has water bound to it. When two oppositely charged groups interact, some of this bound water is released. A decrease in free energy of the system occurs because the water molecules assume a more random orientation when they are released. This greater randomness means an increase in entropy and results in a driving force to hold the molecules together.

1.5 VAN DER WAALS RADII

The closeness with which nonbonded atoms can approach each other is limited by the van der Waals outlines of the atoms. The distance from the center of an atom to its steric outline is called its van der Waals radius. This value, which is characteristic for each element, is determined from the distances between nonbonded atoms in crystals of various substances. Van der Waals radii for various atoms are given in Table 1.2.

1.6 ANTI-HAPTEN ANTIBODIES

Much information concerning complementarity of fit between antigen and antibody derives from the studies of antibodies against simple substances of known composition. Such studies were initiated by Obermeyer and Pick (1904) and by Landsteiner and Lampl (1917). These investigators coupled a substance of known chemical structure to a protein and used this conjugated protein as an immunogen for the formation of antibodies. They were able to demonstrate that antibodies are formed which react with the chemically defined group. Such a group is called a *hapten* from the Greek meaning "to be stuck on." Antibodies against a hapten can be studied by their interactions with substances

TABLE 1.2 Van der Waals Radii and Covalent Bond Radii of Atoms

Atom	Van der Waals radius (Å)	Covalent bond radius (Å)
H	1.2	0.30
O	1.4	0.74[a] 0.62[b]
S	1.85	—
F	1.35	0.64
Cl	1.80	0.99
Br	1.95	1.14
I	2.15	1.33
C		0.77[a] 0.67[b]
CH_3	2.0	—
½ thickness of a benzene ring	1.70	

[a]Single bond.
[b]Double bond.

of known configuration which are structurally related to the original hapten. The structural features of the hapten which are of importance to the interaction can thus be evaluated.

As an example, antibodies can be formed against the *p*-azobenzoate group. To prepare the antigen, *p*-aminobenzoic acid is diazotized and coupled to a protein such as bovine γ-globulin according to the following reactions:

$$HOCO\langle\bigcirc\rangle NH_2 + 2HCl + NaNO_2 \longrightarrow HOCO\langle\bigcirc\rangle NNCl + NaCl + 2H_2O$$

$$HOCO\langle\bigcirc\rangle NNCl + \text{bovine } \gamma\text{-globulin} + 2NaOH \longrightarrow$$

$$NaOCO-C_6H_4-N{=}N\text{-bovine } \gamma\text{-globulin} + NaCl + 2H_2O$$

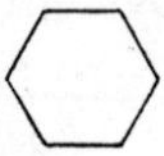

The diazonium group replaces a hydrogen atom on a tyrosine, histidine, lysine, or N-terminal amino acid residue of the protein to form an azo bond.

When the conjugated protein is injected into rabbits (or other animals), antibodies are formed which react with the benzoate group as shown by the following set of observations:

1. If the conjugated protein used for injection is added to the resulting antiserum a precipitate of antigen and antibody is obtained.
2. If the unconjugated protein is added to the antiserum some precipitate is also formed, composed of this protein and antibodies formed against the antigenic groups on it.
3. If a completely different protein, such as ovalbumin, is added to the antiserum no precipitate is formed, showing lack of interaction.
4. However, if *p*-azobenzoate groups are coupled to the ovalbumin the product does give a precipitate with the antiserum, showing the presence in the serum of antibodies directed against the *p*-azobenzoate groups.
5. If ovalbumin coupled with groups of a different substance (for example, *p*-azobenzenearsonate groups) is added, there is no precipitate. Thus the antibody formed reacts with ovalbumin altered with homologous hapten but not with that altered nonspecifically by other substances. This demonstrates the specificity of the anti-hapten reaction.

A very important aspect of interaction in the anti-hapten systems is that the formation of a precipitate with the homologous antigen is inhibited by hapten. Thus the precipitation of anti-benzoate antibody by ovalbumin coupled with azobenzoate groups is inhibited by the addition of benzoate ion. The benzoate ion competes with the antigen for the combining regions of the antibody, but benzoate does not form a precipitate when it complexes with the antibody; hence, the competition by hapten prevents precipitate formation by the antigen. Substances structurally related to benzoate also combine with the antibody, but substances not related closely enough to benzoate do not do so. This method of hapten inhibition of precipitation can be used to study the interaction of haptens with the antibody, as will be described more fully in Chapter 2.

By the use of various simple haptens it is possible to study the antibodies directed only against the haptenic group, and not against the protein carrier, and thus to obtain a great deal of information about the kind of group which will fit the antibody site. Study of the effect of structural variation of the group on its interaction with antibody gives detailed information about the nature of the interaction and about the nature of the combining region of the antibody.

1.7 ANTI-PROTEIN ANTIBODIES

Studies of anti-hapten antibodies afford a great simplification over those involving antibodies against proteins. First, a given antigenic region of proteins is not clearly defined. Second, a protein usually has a multiplicity of antigenic regions each of which may well be different in structure from the others as shown in Fig. 1.4. A protein gives rise to antibodies directed against its several groupings and in different amounts for each grouping. Thus, when certain amounts of antigen are added to a portion of antiserum, antibodies against certain groups may be in excess while for other groups the antigenic group is in excess. This makes it impossible to talk about a zone of equivalence between antigen and anti-protein-antibody (see Section 7.2). Third, the combination of hapten with antibody can be measured by methods which give good thermodynamic information about the strength of the reaction. Such methods are not available or are difficult to apply to protein-anti-protein interaction.

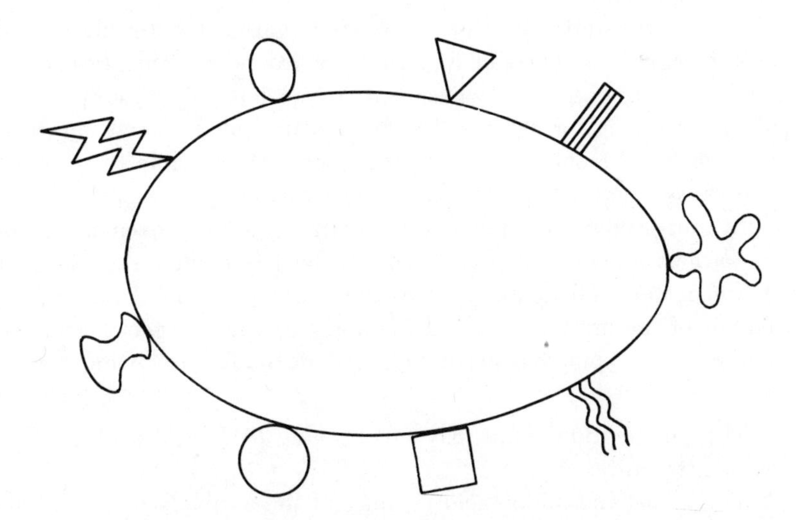

FIGURE 1.4 Schematic representation of a protein with a multitude of antigenic sites, each of which induces the formation of antibody capable of reacting with it. Thus an anti-protein antiserum does not contain a single type of antibody molecule reactive with the protein as a whole, but is composed of molecules directed against individual antigenic sites. Individual animals will produce antibodies reacting with certain but not all of the antigenic sites, and other individuals will produce antibodies reacting with other sites.

1.8 HETEROGENEITY AS A COMPLICATION INVOLVED IN THE STUDY OF ANTI-HAPTEN ANTIBODIES

Even in the much simpler case in which all the antibodies being studied are directed against a known hapten, there are complications. First, the antibody may be directed against haptens attached to different parts of the carrier protein molecule, and the environment around each hapten may vary somewhat. This process gives rise to different antibodies (carrier specificity), although all of the antibodies detected by use of a particular haptenic antigen would be those directed against the common haptenic group. This difficulty may be partly overcome by using as carrier proteins those which contain only one amino acid residue available for a certain coupling reaction, or by use of a synthetic polypeptide containing only one type of amino acid residue. However even such antibodies are heterogeneous (Eisen *et al.*, 1964).

Another problem is that the hapten can be oriented in different ways with respect to the surface of the antigen molecule. It can extend from it, lie on its face against the carrier protein, or lie on its side as shown in Fig. 1.5, and the antibodies directed against these different orientations would be different.

Moreover, the antibody may be directed against different parts of the hapten group as depicted in Fig. 1.6. For example, antibodies may be directed against one side, against various portions of the outline of the haptenic grouping, or against the face, as indicated. These antibodies will all have different properties, since some will be able to react with certain cross-reacting haptens while others will not.

With anti-protein antibodies, the situation becomes even more complex. Various parts of the protein are involved, and the antigenic groupings are not as well defined as are the simple haptens.

The fit of the antibody around the antigen is not perfect because the requirement of complementarity is limited by the following physical aspects:

1. The polypeptide chain may not be able to fold closely about the antigenic structure.
2. The atoms and amino acid residues of the antibody may not follow the outline of the hapten exactly because of their size.

Thus, since the atoms of the antibody molecule occupy space, as is determined by their van der Waals radii, and are bound to each other in the molecule, they are limited in their closeness of fit around the antigenic structure. Moreover, the atoms making up the antibody and its combining region are of the same size as the atoms making up the hapten

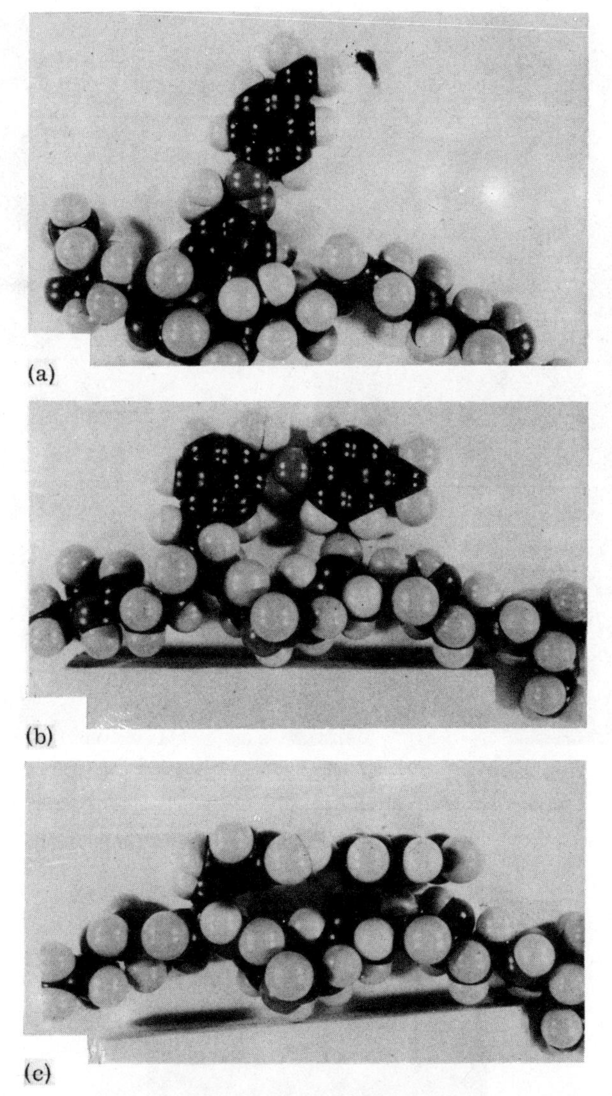

FIGURE 1.5 Different orientations of a haptenic group with respect to the surface of the antigen molecule. The representation is of a *p*-azobenzoate group (a) when extended from the surface of the carrier protein, (b) lying on its side, and (c) lying on its face.

and thus do not make a matrix which can fit the hapten very precisely, as shown in Fig. 1.7.

Another complicating feature is that in an anti-hapten serum there are several different classes of protein with anti-hapten antibody activity.

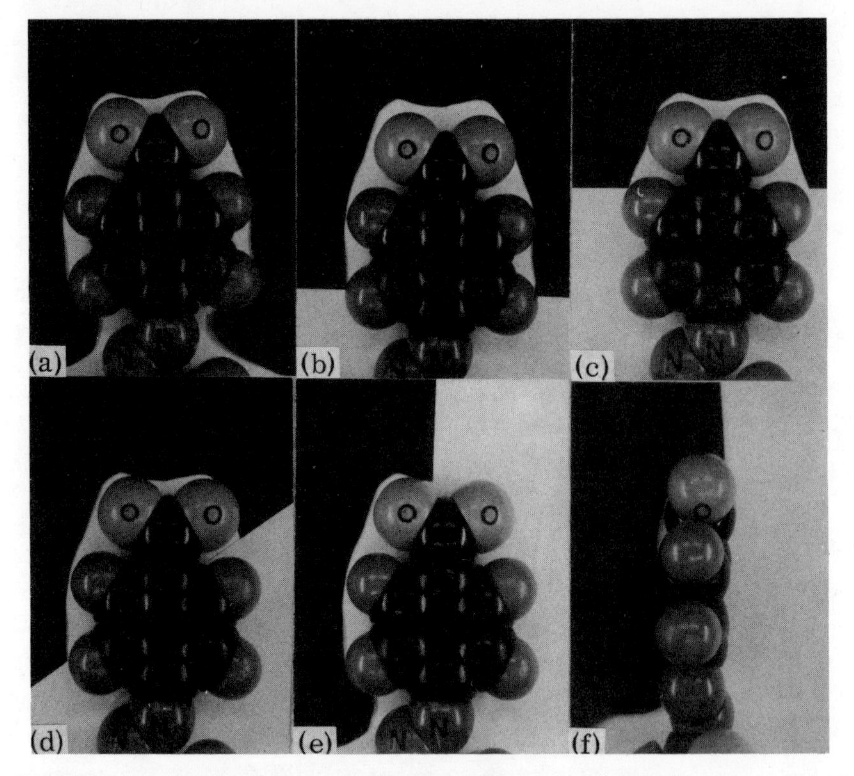

FIGURE 1.6 Various portions of the p-azobenzoate haptenic group against which antibody sites are directed.

FIGURE 1.7 Inherent imprecision of the fit of the antibody site around the homologous hapten due to the same size of the units (atoms) composing the site and the hapten.

These probably have different combining regions even though they may be directed against the same part of a hapten in the same orientation and in the same carrier protein environment. Indeed, antibodies entirely of the 6S γ-globulin class show a heterogeneity of combining regions.

Methods have been devised to deal with this heterogeneity, so that much information has been obtained about hapten-antibody interaction in spite of it. These methods are discussed in Chapter 2 and in Chapter 4.

1.9 THE SIZE OF THE ANTIBODY SITE

The region which makes up the combining site of an antibody molecule appears to be at least large enough to be complementary to a hapten group such as the *p*-azobenzoate group. It is difficult to determine very precisely the size of the region directed against a given group because of the heterogeneity of the population of antibody molecules which react with the hapten. Each antibody molecule is directed against only part of the immunogen. Thus it is difficult to define how much of the hapten and its immediate environment is involved for any one antibody molecule. This problem will be considered further in Section 4.6.

1.10 THE RATE OF COMBINATION OF HAPTEN WITH ANTIBODY

The reaction of antibody with the hapten against which it is directed or with antigen is an extremely rapid one. It appears that the reaction is diffusion controlled; that is, it occurs as rapidly as the hapten and the antibody combining site meet in the diffusion process, which is essentially as fast as it is possible for a reaction to take place. Most organic interactions to form covalent bonds are slower by rate constants a million times lower. In order to measure such rapid reactions, very special types of measurement techniques are used. For example, Froese *et al.* (1962) and Froese and Sehon (1965) have used the temperature jump method of Eigen as described in Czerlinski *et al.* (1959), and Day *et al.* (1962, 1963) have used a stopped-flow fluorometric method. Accurate measurements have been made with antibodies directed against the *p*-azobenzenearsonate group and with antibodies to the 2,4-dinitrophenyl group. The rapidity of reaction of anti-protein antibody with the protein antigen has been demonstrated by Heidelberger *et al.* (1940).

2

THE DETERMINATION OF ANTIBODY-HAPTEN COMBINATION

This chapter is devoted to (1) a discussion of the principles of chemical equilibrium which underlie the methods used for determining quantitatively the strength of antibody-hapten interaction, and (2) a description of how information is obtained about structure-specificity relationships. The methods are outlined in principle and certain critical evaluations are given.

The description of results of studies with a particular antibody (against the *p*-azobenzoate group) is limited to findings which most clearly demonstrate the principles involved. A more comprehensive discussion of findings with this antibody, as well as many others, is given in Chapter 3.

2.1 EQUILIBRIA INVOLVED IN ANTIBODY-HAPTEN COMBINATION

The strength of combination of a hapten with an antibody site is measured by determining the equilibrium constant of the following reaction:

$$\text{Hapten} + \text{antibody site} \rightleftarrows \text{Hapten antibody complex}$$
$$\text{H} + \text{Ab} \rightleftarrows \text{HAb}$$

The equilibrium constant K_H is given by the equation

$$K_H = \frac{(HAb)}{(H)(Ab)} \tag{2.1}$$

Frequently it is useful to describe the effect of a structural change in the hapten on combination by comparing the combination of a substance of interest with the combination of a reference hapten. Then the relative combining constant K_{rel} is given by the following equation

$$K_{rel} = \frac{K_H}{K_{ref\ hapten}} \tag{2.2}$$

It has been found that antibody preparations are generally heterogeneous, in that many species of antibody binding sites are present, so that there exists a distribution of binding constants which describes the observed binding activity of the preparation toward a given hapten. In this situation, an average binding constant, K'_H, can be determined by measuring binding at several different concentrations of hapten and making a calculation with the assumption that the distribution of the binding constants follows a particular function (see Appendix I).

2.2 THE METHOD OF EQUILIBRIUM DIALYSIS

The equilibrium constant K_H can be determined directly by the method of equilibrium dialysis in which a solution of a known amount of antibody in a dialysis bag is equilibrated with a solution of hapten in buffer.[1] At equilibrium, the difference in total concentration of hapten inside and outside the dialysis bag is due to the amount of hapten bound by the antibody. The concentration of free hapten inside the bag is the same as the concentration of hapten outside the bag. From these values, together with the known concentration of the antibody inside the bag, it is possible to calculate a value for K_H according to Eq. 2.1. Such a determination of K_H requires that the hapten be determined analytically, and for this purpose a colored or radioactive hapten is usually used.

The method of equilibrium dialysis measures combining constants accurately only within a relatively narrow range (about 10^3–10^6). With higher constants essentially all the hapten is bound until the antibody is saturated, and the free hapten concentration prior to saturation is too low to be determined accurately. With lower binding constants, on the other hand, the concentration of free hapten required to produce combination is so high that the difference between the free hapten and total

[1] As a matter of historical interest, this method was utilized as early as the 1930's. See Marrack and Smith (1932), and Haurowitz and Breinl (1933).

hapten inside the bag is too small to be determined accurately at feasible antibody concentrations.

The relative combining constant K_{rel} is obtained according to Eq. 2.2, after a K_H has been determined for each hapten.

2.3 THE METHOD OF FLUORESCENCE QUENCHING

Another method of determining the equilibrium constant directly is that of fluorescence quenching (Velick *et al.*, 1960; Eisen, 1964b). This method depends on the fact that the tryptophan residues of protein molecules exhibit fluorescence when excited by ultraviolet light, and the fluorescence of antibody is quenched when particular haptens (or antigens) are bound by the antibody. The extent of quenching is related to the proportion of antibody sites that are combined with hapten, so that the method, in principle, provides a way of determining the factors in Eq. 2.1. The quenching is most effectively attained when the adsorption spectrum of the hapten overlaps the fluorescence emission spectrum of tryptophan (330–360 mμ); thus haptens which are yellow-colored are most effective.

The measurements are made by adding small increments of hapten solution to the antibody and measuring the fluorescence after each addition. The titration data thus obtained are plotted in a manner that allows calculation of both the concentration of binding sites in the antibody solution and the value of K_H. Heterogeneity of binding sites must be taken into account. The methods of titration and of calculation have been fully described by Eisen (1964b).

The method is simple and rapid (10–20 minutes for a titration) and requires only a small amount of antibody (20–200 μg). It is especially useful for measurement of antibody-hapten interaction in systems such as those anti-2,4-dinitrophenyl systems (Section 3.14) which exhibit values of $K_H > 10^7$. Such high values of K_H cannot be accurately measured by the method of equilibrium dialysis.

Fluorescence quenching can also be used to obtain values of K_{rel} according to Eq. 2.2.

There are certain disadvantages to the method: it requires specifically purified antibody (or at least a globulin fraction highly enriched in antibody), whereas the method of equilibrium dialysis can be performed with a globulin fraction containing only a few percent of antibody; it is limited to yellow-colored haptens, so that it is not as generally applicable as equilibrium dialysis; the degree of quenching differs from antibody preparation to antibody preparation so that an independent determination of K_H by another method such as equilibrium dialysis is often required to establish the validity of the method for a given system.

2.4 THE METHOD OF COMPETITIVE EQUILIBRIUM DIALYSIS

The relative combining constant K_{rel} can also be determined by competitive equilibrium dialysis. In this method the ability of a hapten to displace a colored, or radioactive, or otherwise measurable reference hapten from the antibody is determined by equilibrium dialysis. The constant of a weakly binding substance can be determined by using it as a competitor in high concentration. An example of the use of this method is given in the paper by Nisonoff and Pressman (1958c). Heterogeneity of binding sites is a factor which must be taken into account in this method also.

2.5 THE METHOD OF HAPTEN INHIBITION OF PRECIPITATION

The third and most usual method of determining K_{rel} is the method of inhibition of precipitation. When a simple hapten is added to a mixture of antigen and antibody, the amount of precipitate obtained is less than that obtained in the absence of hapten. The higher the concentration of hapten, the less is the amount of precipitate obtained. The decrease in amount of precipitate is due to competition of the hapten with antigen for antibody sites.

Precipitation is obtained only with substances which contain more than one antigenic group per molecule. Since an antibody is bivalent, the addition of a multivalent antigen gives a precipitate of a three-dimensional framework of complexes of alternating antigen and antibody molecules (Fig. 2.1). The addition of increasing amounts of antigen to a constant amount of antibody gives increasing amounts of precipitate up to a certain maximum. A further increase in amount of antigen over the optimum amount gives reduced amounts of precipitate, because the antigen-antibody complexes become smaller in the region of antigen excess. The antibody molecules become saturated with antigen which is not shared with other antibody molecules. The smaller complexes are more soluble, so less precipitate is formed. Likewise, in the region of far antibody excess there may exist soluble complexes composed of antigen molecules saturated with antibody molecules and not cross-linked to other antigen molecules.

A simple hapten is univalent; since it cannot cross-link it cannot form a precipitate with antibody and thus cannot lead to the formation of larger complexes. However, it can compete with multivalent antigen for antibody sites and inhibit precipitation.

In using the method of hapten inhibition of precipitation to determine

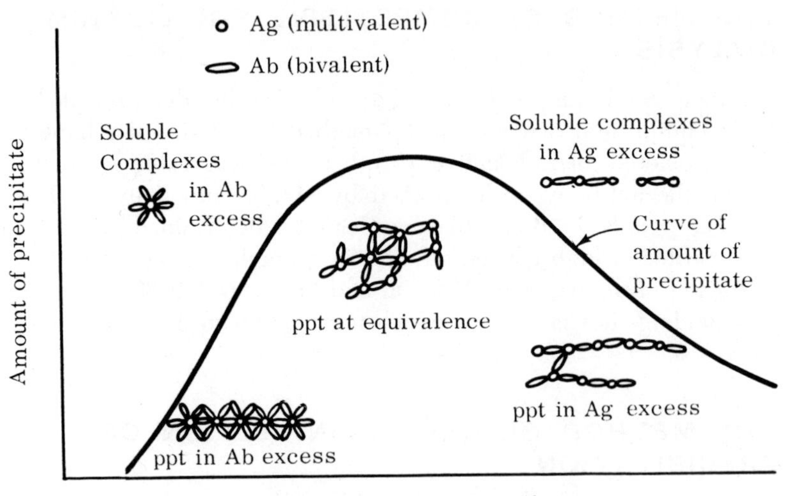

FIGURE 2.1 Curve of the amount of precipitate formed as a function of the amount of antigen added to a constant amount of antibody. The compositions of the soluble complexes and precipitate are shown for the regions of antibody excess, equivalence, and antigen excess (see Pauling, 1940).

K_{rel}, comparison is made between the effects of a hapten (H) and a reference hapten (H_{ref}), each at several concentrations, on the amount of precipitate obtained. The method of calculation is given in Appendix II; it takes into account the heterogeneity of the antibody preparation.

As an approximation, neglecting heterogeneity, the concentration of hapten and reference hapten required to give any particular degree of inhibition of precipitation (say 50%) can be used to determine the relative binding constant. At this degree of inhibition the concentration of free antibody is identical in the presence of H and H_{ref}. The same is true for the concentration of hapten-antibody complex. Equation 2.2 therefore becomes

$$K_{rel} = \frac{K_H}{K_{\text{ref hapten}}} = \frac{(HAb)_{50\%}}{(H)_{50\%}(Ab)_{50\%}} \Big/ \frac{(H_{ref}Ab)_{50\%}}{(H_{ref})_{50\%}(Ab)_{50\%}} = \frac{(H_{ref})_{50\%}}{(H)_{50\%}} \tag{2.3}$$

In the usual experimental situation, total antibody concentration is small in comparison to total hapten concentration; hence the concentration of the free hapten is essentially that of total hapten. Then, for practical purposes, Eq. 2.4 holds:

$$K_{rel} = \frac{\text{(total concentration of ref hapten added to give 50\% inhibition)}}{\text{(total concentration of hapten added to give 50\% inhibition)}} \quad (2.4)$$

The determination of K_{rel} by the method of hapten inhibition of precipitation has the advantage that smaller amounts of antibody are required than for dialysis equilibrium. In addition, the method is convenient to perform, and accurate constants are obtained even for haptens which are relatively poor in binding activity, because they can be tested at a high concentration.

2.6 RELATIVE CHANGE IN FREE ENERGY

In the discussions in this book concerning the effect of change in structure of a hapten on the degree of interaction of the hapten with antibody, we have found it useful to consider both relative change in free energy (ΔF_{rel}) and the relative equilibrium constant K_{rel}. These are related through the Eq. 2.5.

$$-\Delta F_{rel} = RT \ln K_{rel}$$
$$(\text{At } 5°\text{C}, \ -\Delta F_{rel} = 1280 \log_{10} K_{rel}) \quad (2.5)$$

Thus the relative change in free energy is linear with the logarithm of the relative binding constant. For example, if the substitution of a certain group for a hydrogen atom in a hapten changes the binding constant by a factor of two, then there is a change in the free energy of the reaction amounting to 380 cal; if a different change in structure changes the binding constant by a factor of four, the change in the free energy of the reaction is 760 cal. We like to use relative equilibrium constants because the number itself seems to give a more graphic representation of magnitude than does the relative free energy, as shown in Table 2.1. Relative free energies are useful for comparing a particular change in a large number of systems, or in cases in which values in relation to various reference compounds are desired. For example, they are useful in comparing the effects of a particular substitution in a host of compounds, such as the effect of an ortho chloro substitution on the combining strengths of many variously substituted benzoates.

The percent change in the standard free energy, which is sometimes used, is rather meaningless and does not describe the real contribution of the structural change of the hapten to the energy of combination. The absolute change in standard free energy, ΔF_{rel}, on the other hand, is meaningful.

TABLE 2.1 Corresponding Values of K_{rel} and ΔF_{rel}

K_{rel}	ΔF_{rel} (cal)
20	−1660
10	−1280
2	− 380
1	0
0.5	380
0.1	1280
0.02	2180
0.01	2560
0.005	2940
0.001	3840
0.0005	4220

2.7 THE EFFECT OF SERUM ALBUMIN

In the above methods of determining antibody-hapten combination constants, it is important that specifically purified antibody or the globulin fraction of antiserum be used rather than the whole serum, or else that correction be made for the effect of serum albumin. A large proportion of the total protein of whole serum is albumin which has the property of binding many substances. It thus may bind a given hapten in sufficient amount to produce a significant change in the concentration of free hapten. A correction can be made in the data obtained with whole serum, however, by determining the extent of binding to albumin for the particular hapten of interest. In the method of inhibition of precipitation, the effect is negligible for haptens which bind relatively poorly to the antibody, since the amount of hapten bound to albumin, in the concentration range required to give inhibition, is not a significant proportion of the total hapten present. It is only for those substances which are bound to antibody at very low concentrations, that is, bound very strongly to the antibody, that the albumin binding becomes important. Then the true binding constant is larger than the one observed in the presence of albumin.

2.8 OTHER METHODS

There are other methods of determining antibody-hapten interaction. These include spectral shift for bound hapten (Froese *et al.*, 1962), fluorescence enhancement of bound hapten (Winkler, 1962), the inhibition of complement fixation (Wasserman and Levine, 1961), or the elution of antibody from specific solid absorbents by hapten (Kitagawa *et al.*, 1965). These methods will not be discussed here but information can be obtained from the references given.

2.9 PURIFICATION OF ANTIBODIES

As noted in Section 2.7, the use of purified antibody is often desirable in studying antibody-hapten combination by the methods described in this chapter and is a necessity when the method of fluorescence quenching is applied (Section 2.4). In addition, studies on the chemical nature of antibody sites (Chapter 5) are often facilitated by the use of specifically purified antibody.

Methods of antibody purification depend on the separation of antibodies from other proteins in the serum (or globulin fraction of serum) by the formation of an insoluble antibody-antigen complex. Serum components such as complement which adhere to such a complex are first removed by adsorbing them on an antigen-antibody precipitate of a heterologous specificity.

The method of choice is to use an insoluble antigen as a specific immunoadsorbent. Such specific immunoadsorbents have been prepared by coupling the protein or hapten to cellulose (Campbell *et al.*, 1951; Lerman, 1953; Gurvich *et al.*, 1957), to ion exchange resins (Isliker, 1953) or to polystyrene (Manecke and Gilbert, 1955; Gyenes *et al.*, 1958; Yagi *et al.*, 1960). Although such immunoadsorbents often have rather low capacity for antibody, specific adsorbents with quite satisfactory high capacity have been prepared using as insoluble carrier either a specifically treated cellulose (Gurvich *et al.*, 1961) or a polymerized protein (Onoue *et al.*, 1965). With the use of such immunoadsorbents, separation of antibody from serum is simple and more complete than by methods which depend on precipitation with a soluble antigen.

The dissociation of an antigen-antibody complex into its two components can generally be achieved by acidification to a pH less than 3 in the cold, using either a glycine buffer of pH 2.4 (Singer *et al.*, 1960; Singer, 1964) or 1 *M* propionic acid (Tanigaki *et al.*, 1966). For anti-hapten antibodies, it is usually possible to dissociate the complex at pH 7 in a 0.1 *M* solution of the appropriate hapten (Section 2.5). Once the complex has been dissociated, and when an insoluble immunoadsorbent is used, the antigen can be separated from the soluble antibody easily by centrifugation or filtration.

When a soluble antigen is used it can be removed in several ways from the solution of dissociated antigen-antibody complex depending on the particular system. In certain instances soluble antigen can be separated from antibody by chromatography on a column of a suitable ion exchange resin (Koshland *et al.*, 1959; Grossberg and Pressman, 1964) or by gel filtration (Givol *et al.*, 1962; Givol and Sela, 1964). In other instances the antigen may be precipitated due to its particular properties. For example, an azofibrinogen antigen is precipitated under conditions in which antibody is soluble (Karush and Marks, 1957). A very negatively charged protein can be precipitated with a positively charged substance such as streptomycin (Farah *et al.*, 1960; Eisen, 1964c). Protein antigens can be precipitated with a bifunctional organic mercurial which reacts with sulfhydryl groups; the method for adding such groups to proteins in general has been developed by Singer *et al.* (1960) and use of the method is described by Singer (1964).

Another method of separating antigen from antibody is to use a coupled gelatin as antigen and to fragment it with the enzyme collagenase so that it can be removed from antibody by gel filtration or dialysis (Givol and Sela, 1964).

2.10 EXAMPLES OF INFORMATION OBTAINABLE

As an example of the use of the method of inhibition of precipitation, let us look at the properties of antibody against the *p*-azobenzoate group (see Section 1.6).

The contribution of the various parts of the benzoate group to combination with this antibody can be evaluated by studying the effect on K_{rel} of changing the individual parts. For example, the effect of replacing hydrogens of the benzene ring by chlorine and by the *p*′-hydroxyphenylazo group has been studied.

The effect of benzoate, *o*-chlorobenzoate, *m*-chlorobenzoate, *p*-chlorobenzoate, and *p*-(*p*′-hydroxyphenylazo)benzoate ions on the amount of precipitate obtained with an optimum amount of antigen in a particular experiment is shown in Fig. 2.2. The amount of precipitate obtained is plotted against the molar concentration of the haptens added. These haptens decrease the amount of precipitate obtained, but to different extents. From the curves we see that the *p*-(*p*′-hydroxyphenylazo)benzoate is by far the most effective in reducing the amount of precipitate. The next most effective is *p*-chlorobenzoate, followed by *m*-chlorobenzoate, and the unsubstituted benzoate. The least effective is the *o*-chlorobenzoate. By calculation of K_{rel} for these substituted benzoates (relative to unsubstituted benzoate) we obtain the values 23 for *p*-(*p*′-hydroxyphenylazo)benzoate, 2.8 for *p*-chloro, 1.8 for *m*-chloro, and 0.17 for *o*-chloro, as shown in Table 2.2, where the values of ΔF_{rel} are also listed. The method for calculating such values of K_{rel} and ΔF_{rel} is described in Appendix II.

The van der Waals outline (from van der Waals radii) of the *p*-azo-

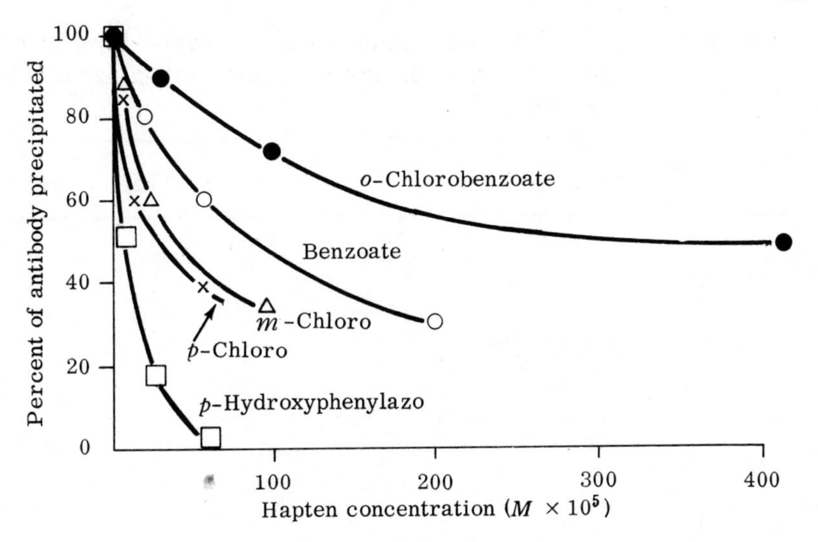

FIGURE 2.2 Inhibition of specific precipitation of anti-*p*-azobenzoate antibody by haptens (Pressman *et al.,* 1954). Plot of fraction of antibody precipitated against concentration of various haptens.

benzoate group, against which the antibodies are directed, is shown in Fig. 2.3. The antibodies act as though they fit closely against it (Fig. 2.4a). For example, the antibodies combine well with benzoate ion, which fits well within a site formed around the van der Waals outline of the *p*-azobenzoate ion (Fig. 2.4b).

The antibodies combine best of all with *p*-(*p*′-hydroxyphenylazo)-benzoate, with a value for K_{rel} of 23 (ΔF_{rel}: -1700 cal). This is because the antibodies are directed not only against benzoate but also against the azobenzoate and the part of the protein to which the azobenzoate is attached. *p*-(*p*′-Hydroxyphenylazo)benzoate contacts a large portion of an antibody site because it has the *p*-azobenzoate structure plus the benzene ring of tyrosine (Fig. 2.3).[2]

When a different substituent such as chloro is present in the para position, it occupies the region directed against the azo group of the homologous hapten present in the injected antigen (Fig. 2.4c) and thus *p*-chlorobenzoate also combines better than benzoate ($K_{rel}=2.8$). Not only is the chlorine accommodated but it adds to the combining energy since it is larger than the hydrogen, more polarizable, and can exert a greater van der Waals interaction with the antibody than does the hydrogen.

With chlorine in the meta position, the substituted benzoate also combines more strongly than does benzoate ($K_{rel}=1.8$) but less strongly

[2] Tyrosine is one of the residues to which diazonium compounds couple. Other residues are histidine, lysine, and N-terminal amino.

TABLE 2.2 Effect of Substituents on the Benzene Ring of Benzoate for Combination in the Anti-*p*-azobenzoate System[a]

Hapten	K_{rel}	ΔF_{rel} (cal)
Benzoate	1.0	0
p-(*p*′-Hydroxyphenylazo)benzoate	23	−1700
p-Chlorobenzoate	2.8	− 550
m-Chlorobenzoate	1.6	− 300
o-Chlorobenzoate	0.17	950

[a]Data from Pressman *et al.* (1954).

than does *p*-chlorobenzoate. The chlorine group is appreciably larger than the hydrogen as shown in Fig. 2.4d. It extends 1.3 Å further from the benzene ring and would interfere in a combination in which an antibody fitted closely around a hydrogen. The meta chloro substituent is accommodated in this case either because the antibody does not fit closely enough in this region to cause interference, or because the greater van der Waals attraction more than compensates for any interference due to reduced fit. Individual pools of serum differ in their combining properties to the extent that with some, K_{rel} for *m*-chlorobenzoate is greater than 1.0, and with others it is less than 1.0.

Replacing one of the ortho hydrogens of benzoate by chlorine results

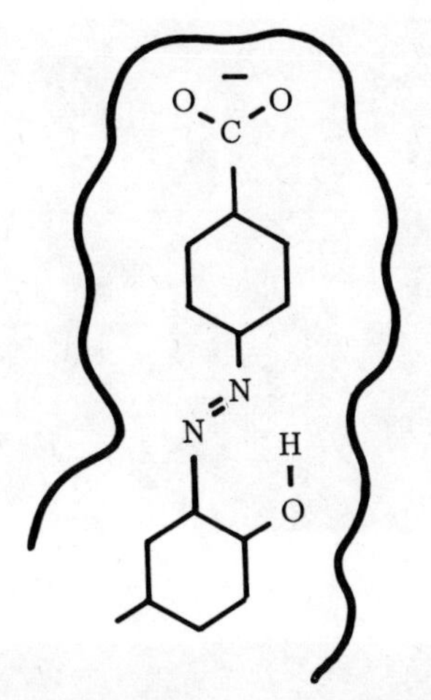

FIGURE 2.3 Van der Waals outline of the *p*-azobenzoate antigenic group (shown as attached to a tyrosine residue).

in a K_{rel} value of 0.17 ($\Delta F_{rel} = +950$ cal). This is a large decrease in combining power and is due to steric interaction. The steric effect can arise in two different ways. First, the larger chlorine may not fit into the part of the antibody directed against the smaller hydrogen (Fig. 2.4e). Second, since the carboxylate and benzene ring of benzoate are coplanar owing to resonance, the ortho chloro group or other ortho substituents may tilt the carboxylate group out of the plane of the benzene ring and change the accommodation of the carboxylate group (Fig. 2.5). This effect has been shown by other physical chemical studies. For example, ortho substituted benzoates have abnormally high dissociation constants compared to other benzoates, and this difference is attributed to a decrease in carboxylate-benzene resonance due to the induced tilt of the carboxylate. Moreover, direct determination of the structure of *o*-chloro- and *o*-bromobenzoic acids by x-ray crystallography (Ferguson and Sim, 1961 and 1962) has shown that in these compounds the carboxyl groups are tilted out of the plane of the benzene ring by 14° and 18°, respectively.

2.11 STRUCTURAL FEATURES OF SIGNIFICANCE IN THE COMBINATION OF ANTIBODY WITH HAPTEN

By studying the combination of various compounds with antibody to the *p*-azobenzoate group (Fig. 2.3), much information has been obtained about the specificity of combination of the antibody. For example, the importance of the carboxylate group has been determined by replacing

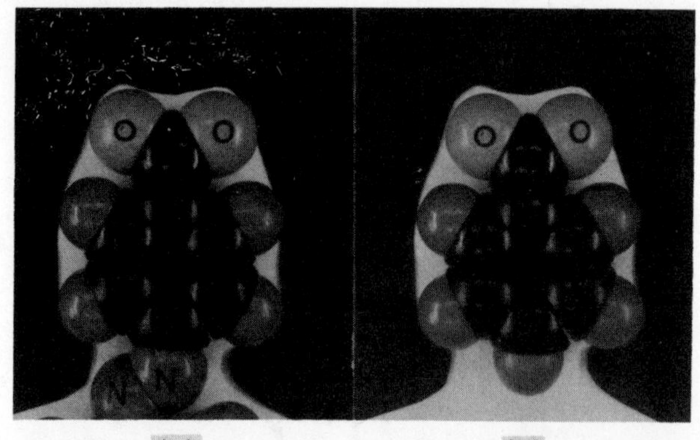

(a) (b)

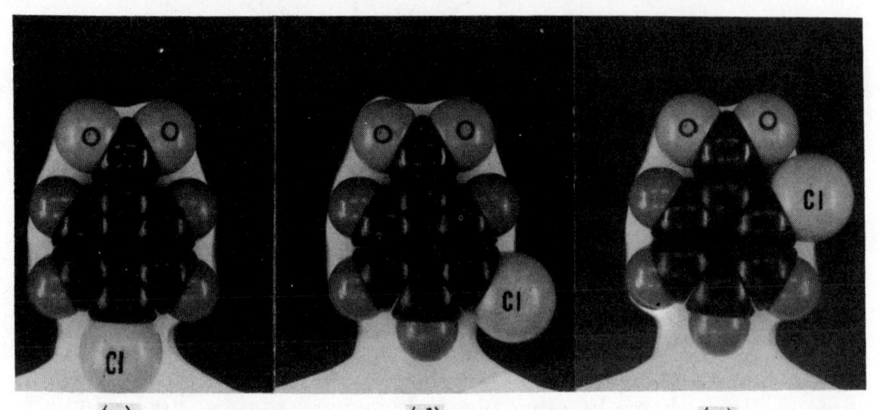

(c) (d) (e)

FIGURE 2.4 Schematic fit of the antibody site of anti-*p*-azobenzoate antibody around (a) *p*-azobenzoate, (b) benzoate, (c) *p*-chlorobenzoate, (d) *m*-chlorobenzoate, (e) *o*-chlorobenzoate.

FIGURE 2.5 Tilt of the carboxylate group out of the plane of the benzene ring by the ortho chlorine atom of *o*-chlorobenzoate.

it with other groups. These replacements include charged groups such as sulfonate and arsonate, or the uncharged nitro group, which has essentially the same size and shape as carboxylate but no charge. It has been found that the carboxylate group itself is very important for combination. Compounds with a negatively charged group of a markedly different shape do not combine, nor do those with an uncharged group. Similarly, replacing the ortho and meta hydrogens by groups of different size indicates the closeness of fit of the antibody around the hapten.

Replacement of the azo group by various other groups gives further information on specificity. The importance of the benzene ring has been determined by replacing it with aliphatic groups, with the saturated cyclohexane ring, or with heterocyclic five- and six-membered rings. These and other details of structure which contribute to specificity in this system and in several other systems are discussed in the next chapter.

3

STRUCTURAL FEATURES IMPORTANT FOR ANTIBODY-HAPTEN INTERACTION IN SOME SIMPLE SYSTEMS

Structural features important for the interaction of hapten and anti-hapten antibody have been studied quantitatively by the method of hapten inhibition of precipitation in many antibody systems and by equilibrium dialysis or competitive equilibrium dialysis in a few. Only antibodies directed against very simple structures are discussed in this chapter. The structural formulas of the haptens against which they were prepared are shown in Fig. 3.1. The values of K_{rel} and ΔF_{rel} for the combination of these antibodies with a large number of haptens are given in tables and figures also in this chapter.

In each of these systems there are features of structure which contribute to the combination with the antibody. The magnitude of the contribution and the relative importance of these features are the determining factors in the selective reactivity of antibodies. This selective reactivity is what is meant by specificity.

3.1 GENERAL CHARACTERISTICS OF SYSTEMS STUDIED

The specificity of the carboxylate group attached to a benzene ring is shown by antibodies against the *o*-azobenzoate group, the *m*-azo-

SYSTEM	STRUCTURAL FORMULA OF THE HAPTEN
Anti-*o*-azobenzoate	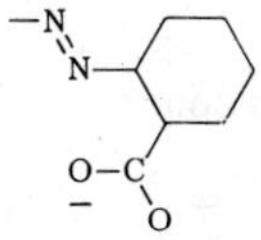
Anti-*m*-azobenzoate	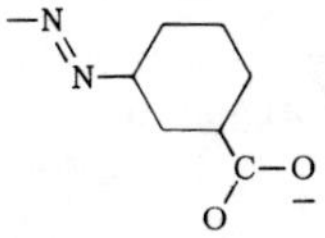
Anti-*p*-azobenzoate	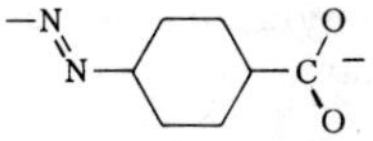 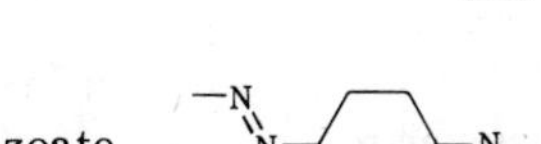
Anti-*p*(*p*′-azophenylazo)benzoate	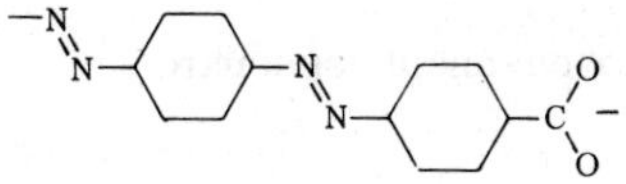
Anti-3-azonitrobenzene	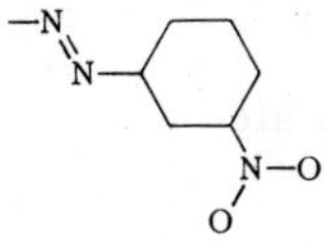
Anti-4-azonitrobenzene	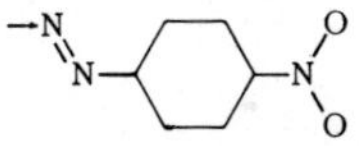 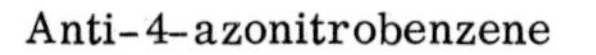 
Anti-*p*-azophenyltrimethyl-ammonium	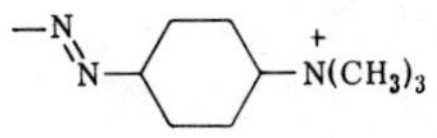 $\overset{+}{N}(CH_3)_3$
Anti-3-azopyridine	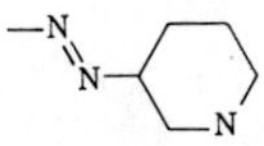
Anti-azobenzene	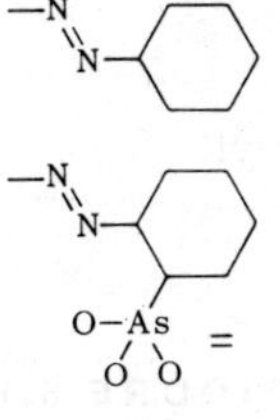
Anti-*o*-azobenzenearsonate	

FIGURE 3.1 The systems described.

SYSTEM	STRUCTURAL FORMULA OF THE HAPTEN
Anti-*m*-azobenzenearsonate	
Anti-*p*-azobenzenearsonate	
Anti-*p*(*p*′-azophenylazo)-benzenearsonate	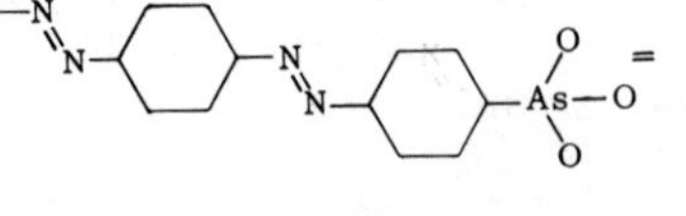
Anti-*p*-azobenzenephosphonate	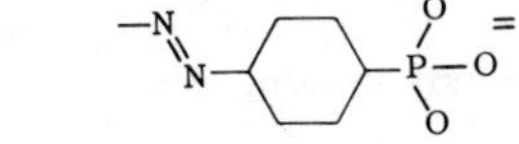
Anti-5-azoisophthalate	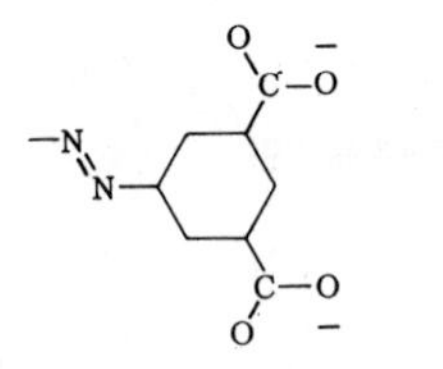
Anti-4-azophthalate	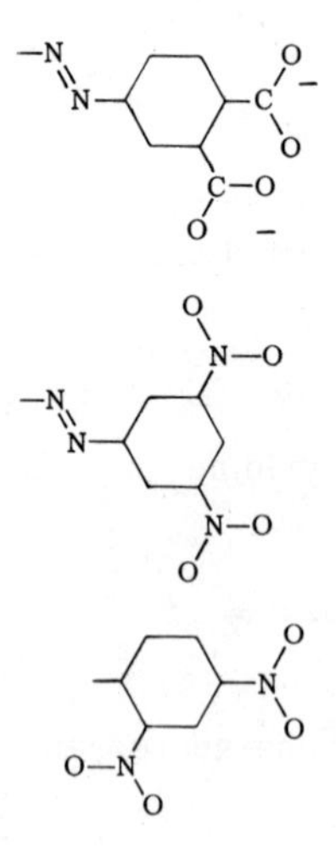
Anti-azo-3,5-dinitrobenzene	
Anti-2,4-dinitrophenyl	

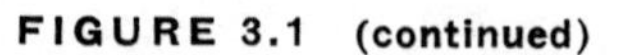

FIGURE 3.1 (continued)

SYSTEM	STRUCTURAL FORMULA OF THE HAPTEN
Anti-azo-3-nitro-5-carboxybenzene	
Anti-*p*-azosuccinanilate	
Anti-*p*-azomaleanilate	
Anti-*p*-azofumaranilate	
Anti-*p*-azo-N-methylsuccinanilate	
Anti-β-*p*-azobenzoylpropionate	
Anti-*p*-azohippurate	
Anti-phenyl(*p*-azobenzoylamino)acetate	
Anti-*p*-azophenyl-β-lactoside	

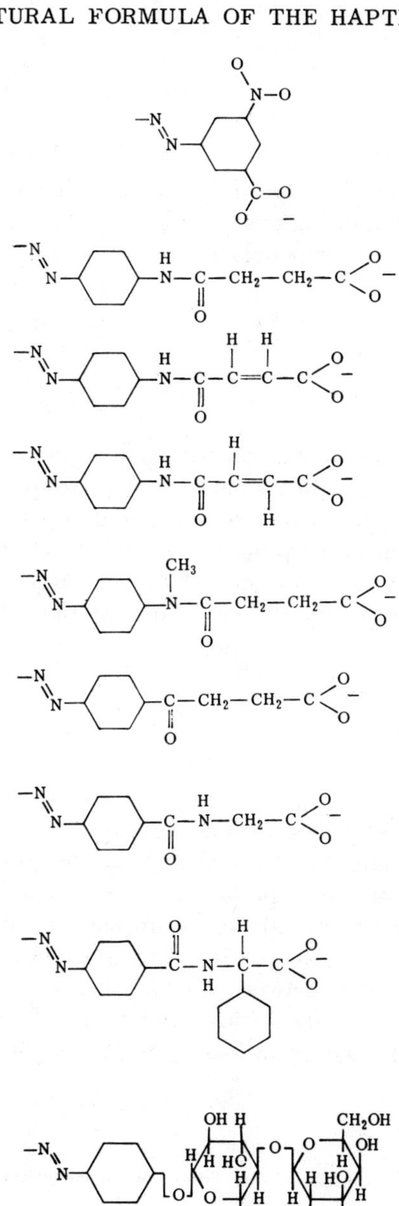

FIGURE 3.1 (continued)

benzoate group, and the *p*-azobenzoate group. These antibodies also

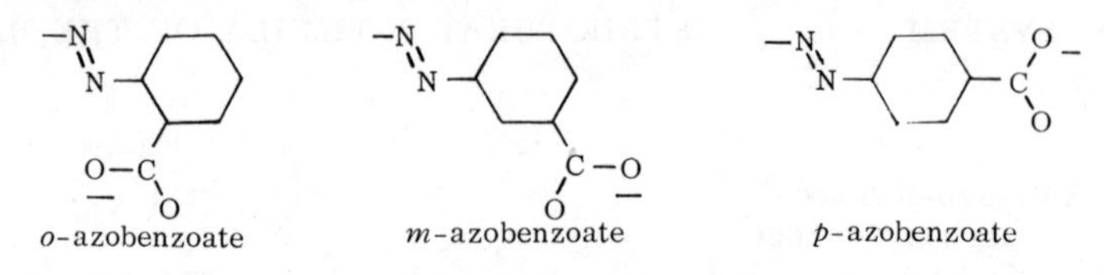

o-azobenzoate *m*-azobenzoate *p*-azobenzoate

show the effect on antibody specificity of coupling the benzoate group through various positions to the carrier protein. The antibody against the *p*-azophenylazobenzoate group demonstrates the effect on specificity

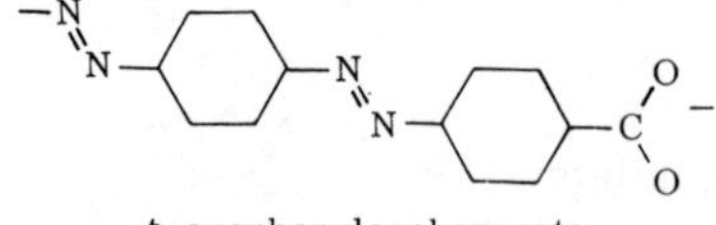

p-azophenylazobenzoate

of displacing the terminal azobenzoate group from the protein carrier by an additional azobenzene group. All of these haptens bear a negative charge on the carboxylate group at the hydrogen ion concentration at which their properties have been determined.

The importance of an uncharged group as a specific determinant is shown by antibodies against the 3-azonitrobenzene group, and against

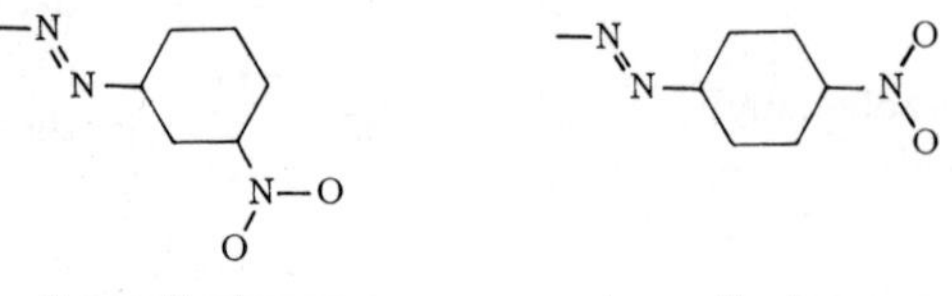

3-azonitrobenzene 4-azonitrobenzene

the 4-azonitrobenzene group. When these are compared with antibodies against the charged carboxylate groups, it is shown that the nitro group is just as important in its systems as is the carboxylate in its systems. Moreover, although from known atomic dimensions the nitro group appears isosteric with the carboxylate group, there is essentially no cross reaction between the nitrobenzene and the benzoate systems.

The specificity of the positively charged trimethylammonium group is shown by antibody against the *p*-azophenyltrimethylammonium group.

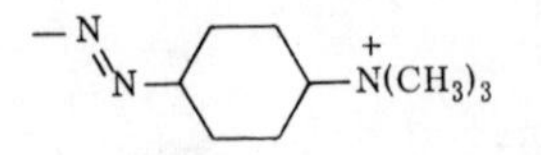

p-azophenyltrimethylammonium

This group is a quaternary base and has a positive charge at all pH values. The antibody has been shown to have a negative carboxylate ion group in its combining site.

The annular nitrogen of pyridine contributes greatly to specificity of interaction, as is shown by antibody against the 3-azopyridine group.

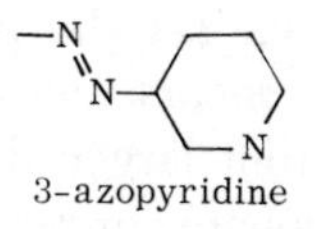

3-azopyridine

Pyridine is hydrated in aqueous solution and the water of hydration acts as part of the structure of the pyridine group against which the antibody is directed. The antibody specificity is strongly determined by the hydrated nitrogen group.

Antibodies against azobenzene yield information about closeness of fit of antibodies around an unhydrated structure related to pyridine.

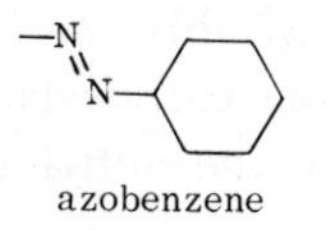

azobenzene

The properties of the arsonate group as a determinant are shown by antibodies against *o*-azobenzenearsonate, *m*-azobenzenearsonate, *p*-azobenzenearsonate, and *p*-(*p*′-azophenylazo)benzenearsonate. The ben-

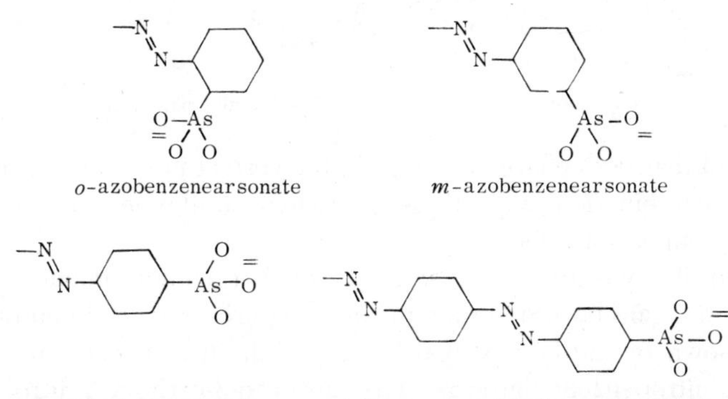

o-azobenzenearsonate   *m*-azobenzenearsonate

p-azobenzenearsonate   *p*-(*p*′-azophenylazo)benzenearsonate

zenearsonic acids ionize to the singly charged group —AsO_3H^- at around pH 3. At the alkaline side of neutrality the singly charged group ionizes into the doubly charged group —$AsO_3^=$; the pK of the second hydrogen is around 8. Thus both the singly charged and doubly charged forms of benzenearsonate are present at physiological pH values. There is evidence that some antibodies are directed against the singly charged arsonate and others against the doubly charged arsonate. The anti-benzenearsonate antibodies cross react extensively with benzenephosphonate, which is structurally related to benzenearsonate.

Antibody against the *p*-azobenzenephosphonate group has a very

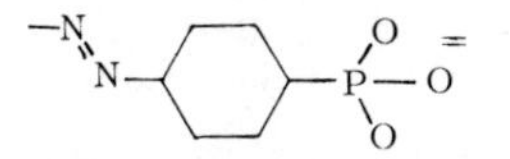

p-azobenzenephosphonate

close relationship to antibody against the *p*-azobenzenearsonate group. It reacts strongly with the benzenearsonate ion. The arsonate group is only a few tenths of an angstrom larger than the phosphonate group. However, the benzenephosphonate group has an acid dissociation constant tenfold greater than the corresponding benzenearsonate and seems to stimulate the formation of antibody primarily against the doubly charged form rather than against both forms as with the benzenearsonate group. Comparison of these two systems provides a means of studying the antibodies formed against the different states of ionization of the arsonate.

The specificity of antibodies directed against haptens with two negative charges on neighboring carboxylates is shown by the anti-5-azoisophthalate system, and by the anti-4-azophthalate system. It has

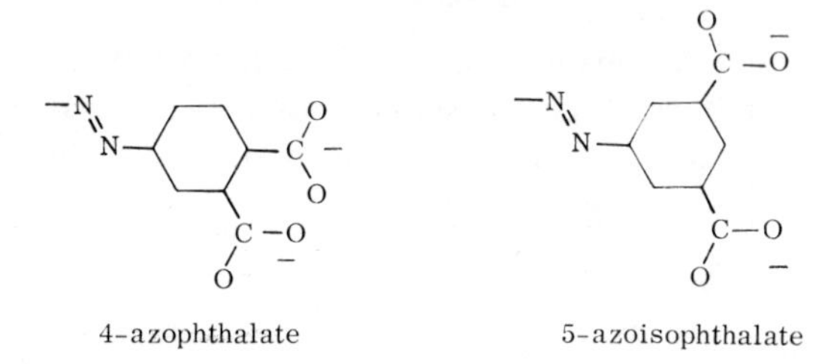

4-azophthalate 5-azoisophthalate

been found that both charged groups in the correct positions are required for good combination with these particular antibodies; a single carboxylate group is not sufficient.

When antibody is directed against two uncharged determinants present in a hapten, again both determinants are required for good combination. This is shown by antibodies against azo-3,5-dinitrobenzene, and against the 2,4-dinitrobenzene group. The anti-azo-3-carboxy-5-nitrobenzene

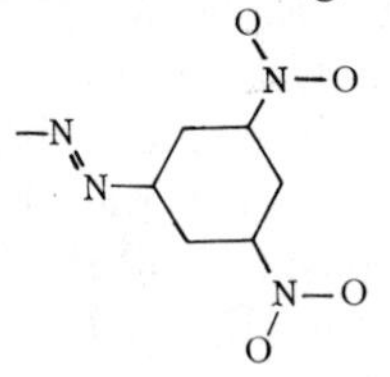

azo-3,5-dinitrobenzene

2,4-dinitrobenzene

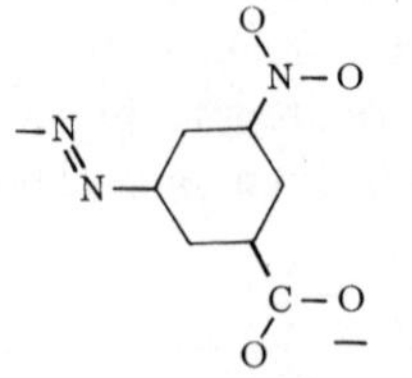

azo-3-carboxy-5-nitrobenzene

system, which is intermediate between the anti-azo-3,5-dinitrobenzene and the anti-5-azoisophthalate system (which has carboxyl groups in the 3 and 5 positions), also requires both determinant groups, one a carboxyl and the other a nitro.

The determinants so far listed are of a rigid fixed configuration. Information is available also on antibodies against a group of haptens composed of a flexible side chain attached to the benzene ring. Antibodies have been prepared against *p*-azosuccinanilate, against *p*-azo-N-methylsuccinanilate, against *p*-azo-β-benzoylpropionate, against *p*-azohippurate,

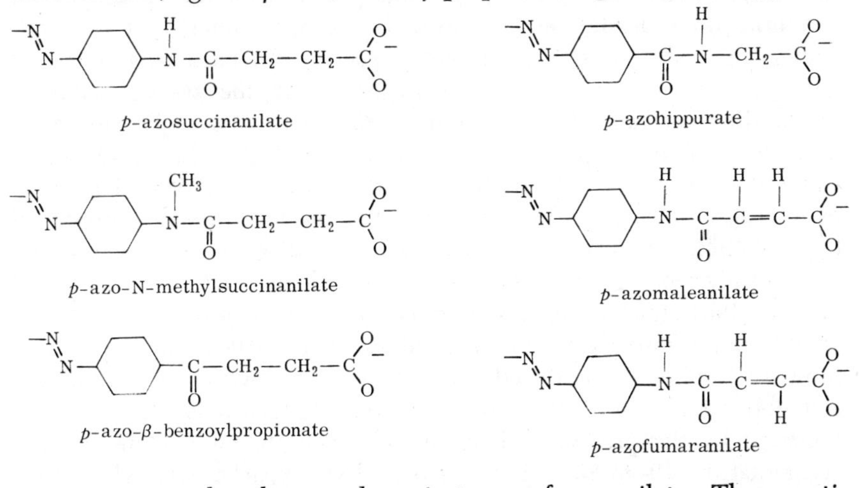

p-azosuccinanilate

p-azohippurate

p-azo-N-methylsuccinanilate

p-azomaleanilate

p-azo-β-benzoylpropionate

p-azofumaranilate

against *p*-azomaleanilate, and against *p*-azofumaranilate. These antibodies are of interest because they yield information about the configuration of flexible side chains in aqueous solution. They have provided evidence that succinanilate and β-benzoylpropionate are coiled in aqueous solution. In addition, the anti-*p*-azo-N-methylsuccinanilate system has shown that the methyl group contributes greatly to antibody specificity.

Antibody against the phenyl(*p*-azobenzoylamino)acetate group is of

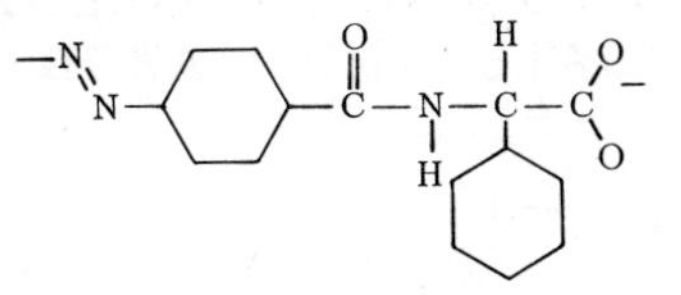

phenyl(*p*-azobenzoylamino)acetate

interest since this group exists in two optically active forms which differ in the arrangement of the four different groups around the α carbon of the acetate. The significance of the steric configuration of the hapten is evident, since the D form of this hapten is not accommodated by antibody against the L form and vice versa.

Antibody against the *p*-azophenyl-β-lactoside group yields information

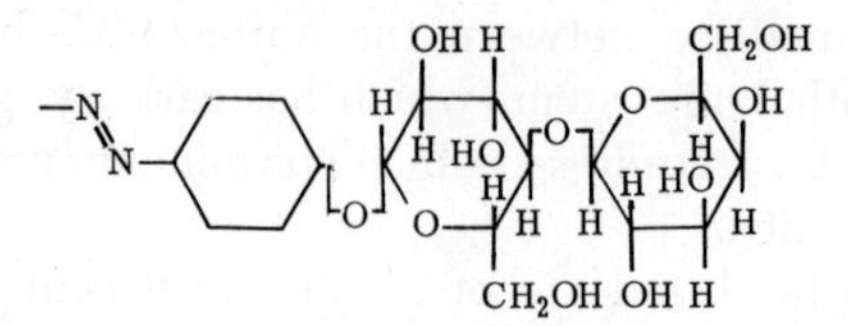

p-azophenyl-β-lactoside

on a very important group of haptens, since many naturally occurring antigenic substances are carbohydrates. The anti-lactoside antibody is able to distinguish small changes in the structure of the carbohydrate.

A note on heterogeneity. It must be borne in mind that the antibodies directed against the haptenic structures in each of the above-mentioned systems are heterogeneous. Moreover, the average value of the binding constant (K'_H) differs from animal to animal. For example, different individuals produce antibodies against *p*-azobenzoate whose value of K'_H vary severalfold (Nisonoff and Pressman, 1958a). The value of K'_H can even change dramatically with time for antibodies produced by an individual. Thus in the case of antibodies directed against the 2,4-dinitrobenzene group, it has been clearly demonstrated by Eisen and Siskind (1964) that antibodies produced several months after an initial single immunization can have K'_H values up to 10,000-fold larger than those of antibodies produced within the first few weeks. Antibodies from individual rabbits directed against *p*-azobenzenearsonate have been observed by the present authors (unpublished) to increase in binding constant from 10- to 20-fold over a period of a year, during which time weekly intravenous injections of antigen were given.

The structural relationships described in this chapter are for heterogeneous populations of antibodies. The populations can be fractioned, as described in Chapter 4, to give subpopulations whose characteristics differ.

3.2 ANTIBODIES TO THE *o*-AZOBENZOATE, *m*-AZOBENZOATE, AND *p*-AZOBENZOATE GROUPS

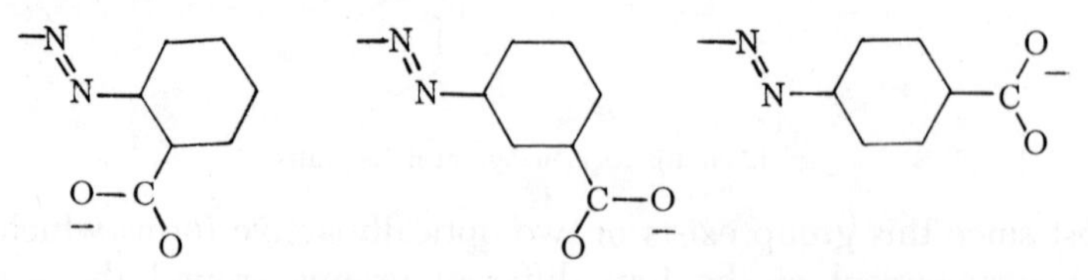

The antibodies directed against the *o*-, *m*-, and *p*-azobenzoates react as though they are formed closely around the van der Waals outlines of these haptens. The van der Waals outlines are shown in Fig. 3.2.

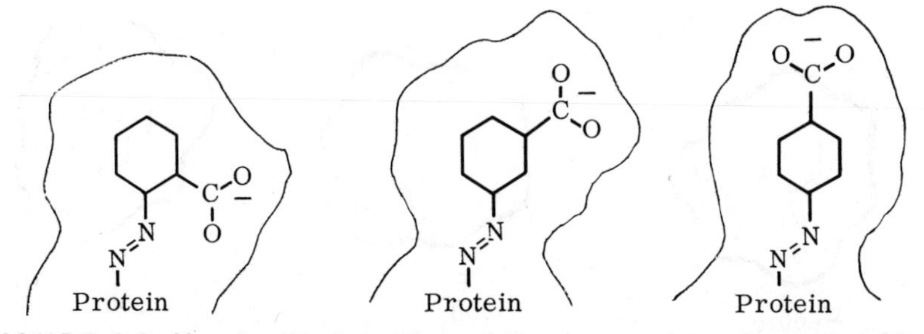

FIGURE 3.2 Van der Waals outlines of the *o*-, *m*-, and *p*-azobenzoates. [From Pressman *et al.* (1954).]

All three antibodies combine well with benzoate ion but differ markedly in their combination with the *o*-, *m*-, and *p*-chlorobenzoates. Each antibody combines best with the chlorobenzoate in which the chlorine atom is in the position occupied by the azo group of the azobenzoate hapten against which the antibody is directed. In this position—the attachment-homologous position—the chlorine contributes to the binding by interacting with the region of the antibody which is directed against and accommodates the azo group. When the chlorine occupies a different position, it decreases binding by interfering sterically with the region of the antibody directed against the smaller hydrogen. Chlorine extends 1.3 Å further than hydrogen from the benzene ring; it is a little over half as thick as the benzene ring, whereas hydrogen is only one sixth as thick. Consequently, of the three monochloro substituted benzoates, the anti-*o*-azobenzoate antibody combines best with the *o*-chlorobenzoate, the anti-*m*-azobenzoate antibody combines best with the *m*-chlorobenzoate, and the anti-*p*-azobenzoate antibody combines best with the *p*-chlorobenzoate.

These relationships are shown graphically in Fig 3.3, in which the van der Waals outline of each chlorobenzoate (shown as a solid black line) is superimposed on the van der Waals outline of the azo hapten against which the antibody is directed (shown as a shaded line). The regions of overlap designate regions of steric interference. The observed relative change in free energy of combination (ΔF_{rel}), relative to unsubstituted benzoate, is also shown on each diagram.

Similar results concerning closeness of fit are obtained with methyl as the substituent (Fig. 3.4). In each system, again, the best combination is obtained when the methyl is in the position of the azo group of the immunizing hapten.

A much better evaluation of the closeness of fit of each antibody around the benzoate grouping is obtained from the extent of combination with the various chloro substituted (p'-hydroxyphenylazo)benzoates, as shown in Fig. 3.5 in which the van der Waals outline of the inhibiting

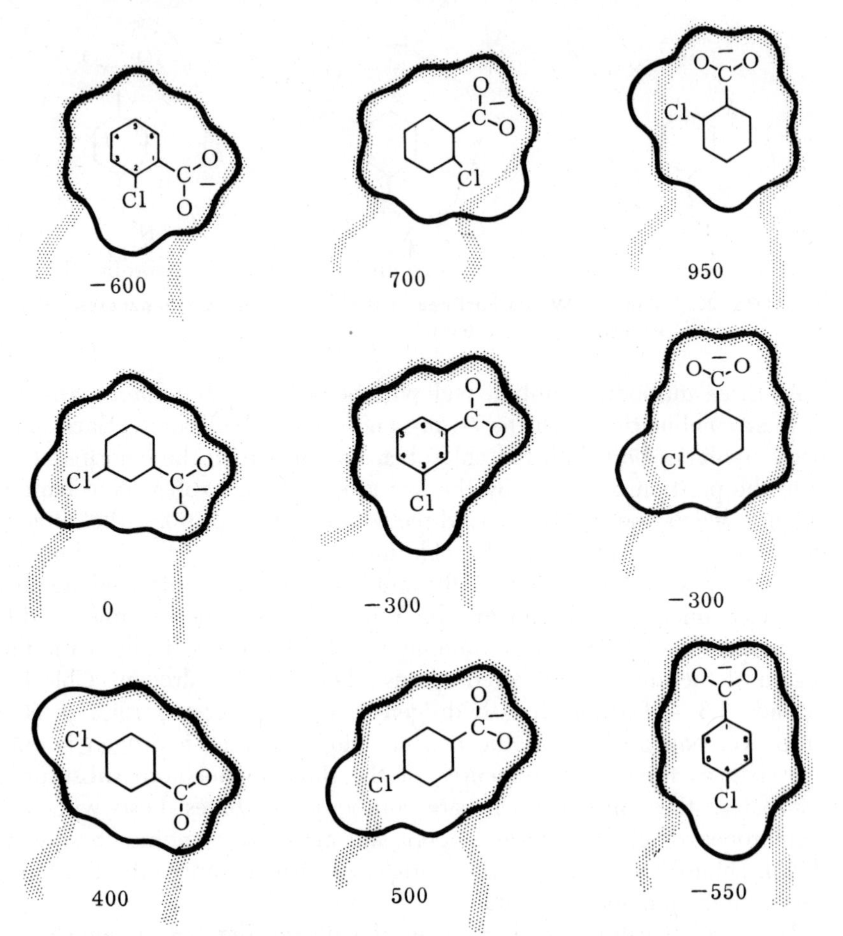

FIGURE 3.3 Combination of *o*-, *m*-, and *p*-chlorobenzoates with anti-*o*, -*m*-, and -*p*-azobenzoate antibody. The van der Waals outline of the chlorobenzoate is superimposed on the outline of the injected haptenic group. Degree of overlap indicates steric interference. Values given are for ΔF_{rel}, relative to unsubstituted benzoate. [From Pressman *et al.* (1954).]

hapten (solid black line) is superimposed on that of the immunizing hapten (shaded line). With these compounds the carboxylate is fixed in combination with the region of the antibody directed against the carboxylate and the azo group is fixed in combination with the region of the antibody directed against the azo group. Thus the actual change in free energy of interaction that occurs when a hydrogen is replaced by a chlorine in each position can be defined. As may be seen in Fig. 3.5, there probably is steric hindrance at the positions in which the van der

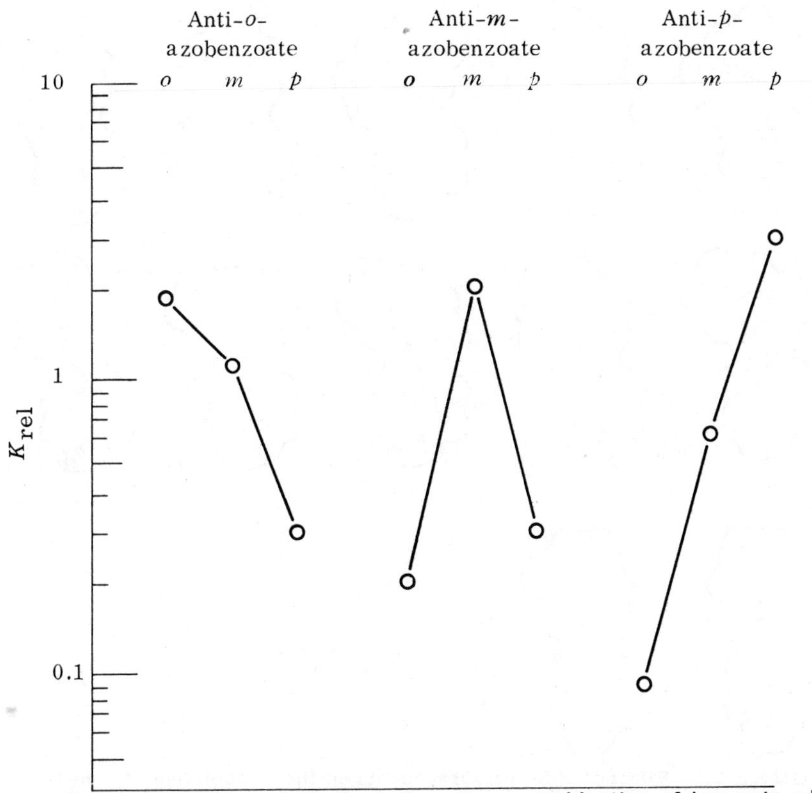

FIGURE 3.4 Effect of methyl substituents on combination of benzoate with anti-*o*-, -*m*-, and -*p*-azobenzoate antibodies. [Data from Pressman and Siegel (not previously published).]

Waals outline of the inhibiting hapten overlaps that of the immunizing hapten. Values for ΔF_{rel}, relative to unsubstituted benzoate ion, are given under each combination.

Figure 3.6 summarizes the effect of chlorine substituents in various positions on the free energy of combination of the *p*-(*p*′-hydroxyphenylazo)benzoate residue with antibody. These substituent values are obtained as the difference in the relative free energies of combination of the unsubstituted (*p*′-hydroxyphenylazo)benzoate and the chloro substituted azo derivative. A large free energy contribution indicates that antibody fits closely around the position of substitution and thus that the substituent exerts a large steric effect.

With the anti-*o*-azobenzoate antibody, the closest fit of the antibody around the benzene ring is in the 3 and 4 positions, and there is a little interference with combination by a substituent in the 6 position (ortho

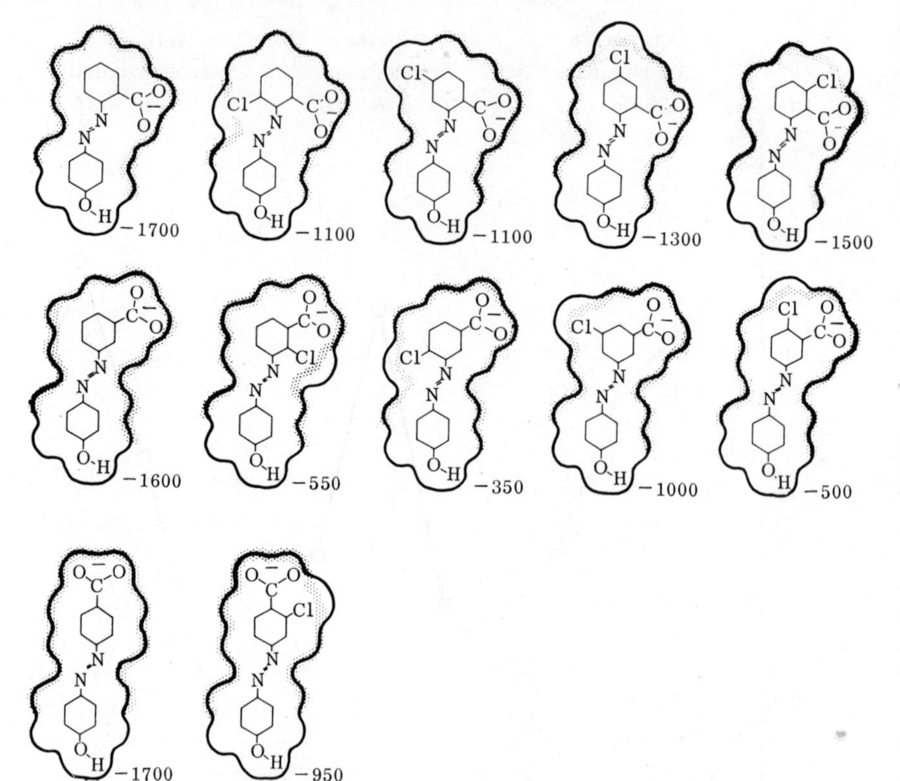

FIGURE 3.5 Effect of chlorine substituents on the combination of p'-hydroxyphenylazobenzoates with anti-azobenzoate antibodies. The van der Waals outline of the inhibiting hapten is shown superimposed on the outline of the injected haptenic group. Values given are for ΔF_{rel}. [From Pressman *et al.* (1954).]

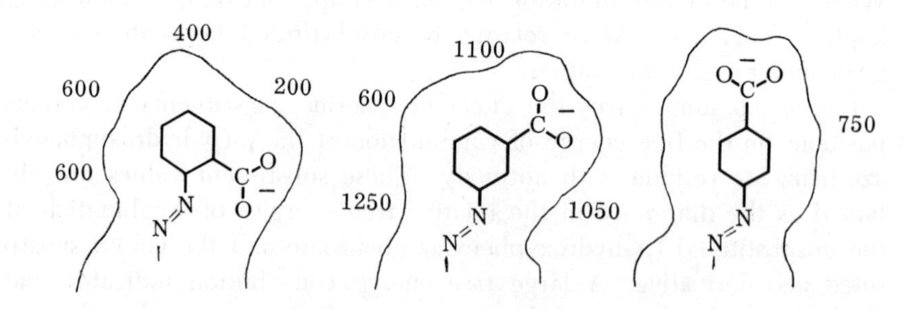

FIGURE 3.6 Effect of chloro substituents on the combination of p'-hydroxyphenylazobenzoates with antibody. Values given are ΔF_{rel} for the chlorine in the indicated position. [From Pressman *et al.* (1954).]

to the carboxylate group). In the anti-*m*- and *p*-azobenzoate systems there is a very close fit of antibody around the benzene ring in the position ortho to the carboxylate. This difference in effect between the *o*-azobenzoate system on the one hand and the *m*- and *p*-azobenzoate systems on the other may well be due to the fact that the ortho chloro substituent twists the carboxylate group out of the plane of the benzene ring (Fig. 2.5) in the meta and para systems. The carboxylate group of the ortho chloro hapten may no longer fit well into an antibody site which is directed against the coplanar carboxylate grouping of the immunizing antigen. In the case of the anti-ortho antibodies, the antibodies are directed against the *o*-azobenzoate in which the carboxylate group is already tilted out of the plane of the benzene ring. The presence of a chloro group in the 6 (ortho) position apparently has no further effect on tilting, since it exerts only a small effect on the combining constant.

The haptenic group in these systems is joined to the protein of the immunizing antigen through an azo linkage. In view of the large protein moiety on the other side of the azo linkage, one might not expect a close fit of the antibody about the azo group. However, in the case of the *o*- and *m*-azobenzoate systems, when substituents are placed ortho to the azo linkage of the inhibiting haptens, large effects are observed on the combination of hapten with antibody. The 3-chloro-2-(*p*′-hydroxyphenylazo)benzoate is the poorest inhibitor for the *o*-benzoate system and the 2- and 4-chloro-3-(*p*′-hydroxyphenylazo)benzoates are very poor inhibitors in the *m*-benzoate system (Fig. 3.5). There must be a very tight fit of antibody about the azo linkage of the unsubstituted hapten for substituents in positions adjacent to the azo linkage to exert such a large influence. The tight fit around the azo linkage may indicate that the antibody is directed against an antigen which has the hapten lying along the surface of the protein. In such a case, the positions adjacent to the azo group would be more exposed for interaction with antibody than if the hapten extended perpendicularly from the surface of the antigen and was engulfed by the antibody (Fig. 1.6). The degree of engulfment in the latter case would have to be limited unless the site were flexible. Otherwise combination could not take place at all if the degree of engulfment were as complete as in Fig. 1.6a.

3.2a Orientation of monochlorobenzoate ions in combination with antibody. As noted previously, data on combination of the monochlorobenzoate ions with antibody do not give as clear a picture of the tightness of fit around the benzoate group as do the data with the *p*-hydroxyphenylazochlorobenzoates. The orientation of a simple monochlorobenzoate in the antibody site is determined by its carboxylate group and by the carboxylate-complementary region of the antibody. Then, as shown in Fig. 3.7a, b, for combination with anti-*m*-azobenzoate anti-

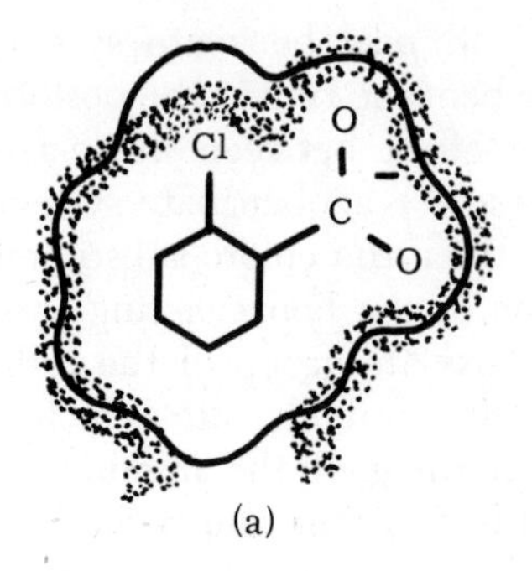

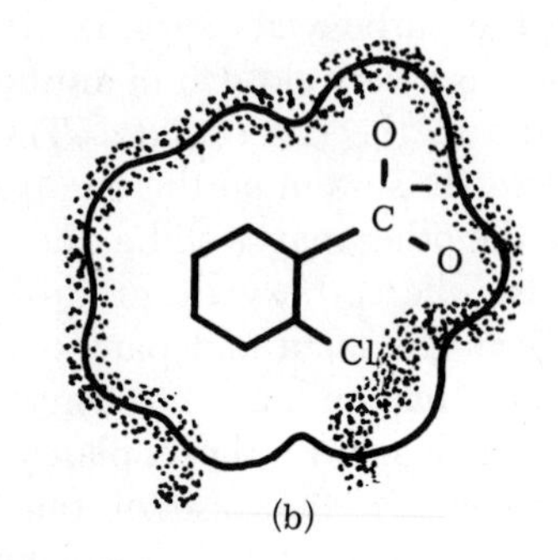

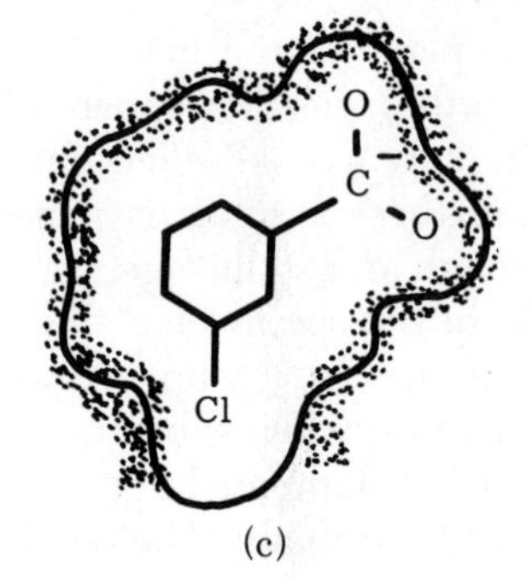

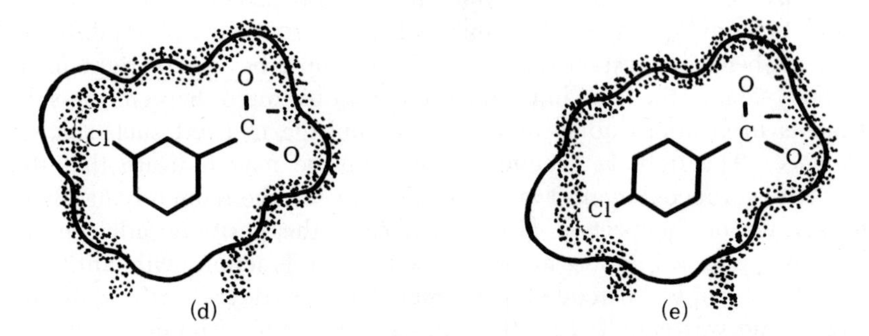

FIGURE 3.7 Combination of monochlorobenzoates (solid black lines) with anti-*m*-azobenzoate antibody. In (a) and (b), *o*-chloro can occupy one of two positions with neither favored; in (c) and (d), *m*-chloro can occupy one of two positions, with (c) favored; in (e), *p*-chloro can occupy only one position.

body, the ortho chloro group can occupy one of two possible ortho positions. A meta chloro group can occupy one of two possible meta positions (Fig. 3.7c, d). The para chloro group can occupy only one position Fig. 3.7e. However, even in those cases where the substituent can occupy the region of the antibody complementary to the azo group of the immunizing hapten (and the hapten does favor combination in that orientation), there is still some contribution of the second orientation. For example, although *m*-chlorobenzoate combines best with the anti-meta system when the chlorine is in the 3 position (Fig. 3.7c) there is some limited combination with the chlorine in the 5 position (Fig. 3.7d).

An estimate of the contribution of the less favored orientation can be made by observing the effect of the chlorine substituent on the free energy of combination of the (*p'*-hydroxyphenylazo)benzoate. In the case of *o*-chlorobenzoate combining with anti-ortho antibody, the replacement of the hydrogen by a chlorine in the unfavored position (the 6 position) causes a change of 200 cal in free energy of combination (Fig. 3.6). However, there is a change of −1000 cal in the favored position. The −1000 cal is obtained from the sum of −600 cal [Fig. 3.3 (the observed relative free-energy change of *o*-chlorobenzoate as compared to benzoate ion in combining with antibody)] plus a statistical term −400 cal, the value of $RT \ln 2$, which corrects for the fact that the unsubstituted benzoate ion can fit into the antibody complementary region in two ways (with either one face or the other of the benzene ring up). The chlorobenzoate with the chlorine in the favored position can fit with only one face up. The difference in free energy for combination in the favored and unfavored orientations, 1200 cal [200−(−1000)], represents a factor of 10 in distribution between the two possible combinations. Similarly, in the combination of *m*-chlorobenzoate with anti-meta antibody the replacement of a hydrogen by a chlorine in the unfavored position (5 position) causes a change in the free energy of combination of 600 cal as determined above (Fig. 3.6), and a change of −700 cal in the favored position [−300 observed (Fig. 3.3) plus −400 due to the statistical term]. The difference, 1300 cal, again represents a factor of 10 in distribution between the favored and unfavored orientations.

The values of the contributions of the less favored orientations, as calculated above, are minimum ones since the values used were those observed when the chlorine substitution was made on the azobenzoate residue. The effect of a chlorine substituent on the combination of benzoate with antibody is generally less than the effect of the substituent on the combination of the azobenzoate with the same antibody. There is a looser fit between chlorobenzoates and antibody than between azochlorobenzoates and antibody. The reason is that when a single substituent is present there can be a shift in the orientation of the benzene ring and carboxylate group in the combining region of the antibody to accommodate the chloro substituent as shown in Fig. 3.8. This shift can reduce the magnitude of the steric interaction. However, when the azo group and a second ring are present, the orientation of the hapten is more definitely fixed by the carboxyl and the azo groups, so that

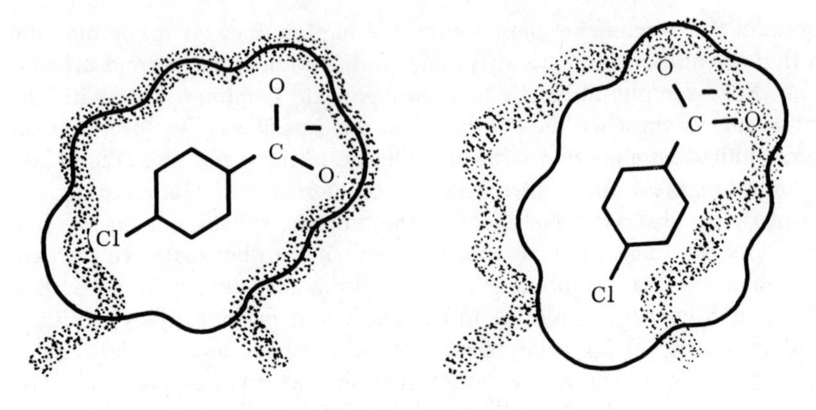

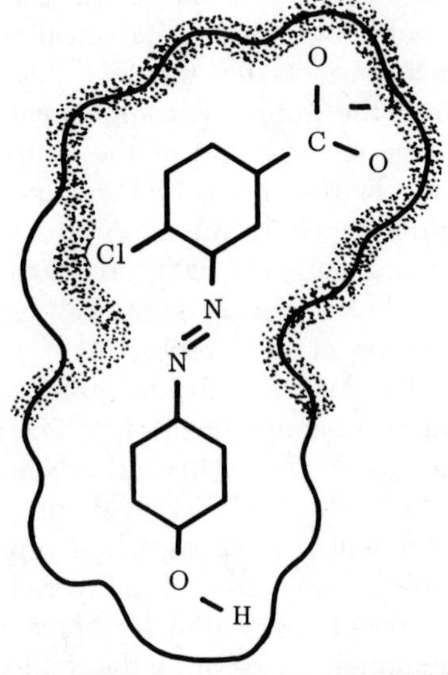

FIGURE 3.8 Shift of hapten where only one substituent is present to permit better accommodation. The para chloro group is then accommodated by the region directed against the azo group. This shift is not possible in the 3-azo-4-chlorobenzoate.

there is very little reorientation and the full steric effect is observed.

In the case of a looser fit, it is difficult to predict a favored orientation. Such cases are those in which the substituent cannot occupy the region of the antibody complementary to the azo group of the immunizing hapten; that is, in the combination of *o*-chlorobenzoate with the anti-meta antibodies or *m*-chlorobenzoate with anti-ortho antibodies. The ΔF_{rel} which is observed for the monochlorobenzoates is of lesser magnitude than the ΔF_{rel} observed with the azochlorobenzoates. The greatest changes in ΔF_{rel} takes place when either the chlorine substituent or the benzene ring itself can shift toward the part of the combining region of the antibody directed against the azo group of the injected antigen. Thus *p*-chlorobenzoate reacts with anti-meta antibody with a ΔF_{rel} value of +500 cal whereas when the azo group is attached to give 3-azo-4-chlorobenzoate, ΔF_{rel} is +1250 cal. The monochloro compound reacts appreciably better (750 cal) indicating that shifting of the hapten occurs as described above, resulting in decreased steric effects. With anti-ortho antibody, however, no such rotation of *p*-chlorobenzoate can occur, and the reduction in ΔF is only 200 cal. The relatively large reduction for *m*-chlorobenzoate in the anti-ortho system and *o*-chlorobenzoate in the anti-meta system indicates that some shift takes place with these compounds also. No statement can be made as to a preferred orientation of the chlorine group since either it or the benzene ring can be displaced toward the azo-complementary region of the antibody, depending on which is in the adjacent position.

In the combination of *o*-chlorobenzoate with the anti-*p*-azobenzoate antibody there is no chance of shift into the azo-specific region and the free energy is not decreased.

3.2b The effect of two substituents. The effect of two substituents on the binding of a hapten with antibody is very closely tied to the ability of the hapten to shift its orientation. When two substituents are on the benzoate group, one in the para position and one in the ortho position, K_{rel} for interaction with anti-para antibody is essentially the product of the K_{rel} values of the groups taken separately (Table 3.1). Thus K_{rel} observed for the 2,4-dinitrobenzoate is 0.06, which is the same as the calculated product (0.07) of the K_{rel} values of *p*-nitrobenzoate and of *o*-nitrobenzoate. However, when the two substituents are on opposite sides of the molecule—for example, in 3,5-dinitrobenzoate or in trimesate, which has carboxylate groups in the 3 and 5 positions—the observed K_{rel} values are very much smaller than the calculated values, that is, 0.004 as against 0.16 for the 3,5-dinitrobenzoate and 0.0004 as against 0.64 calculated for the trimesate ion. This appears to be due to a very close fit of the antibody around the periphery of the benzoate ion. The constant observed for a single meta nitro or meta carboxylate group is the result of a structural displacement of the benzoate to accommodate the meta substituent. This greatly decreases the ability of the antibody to accommodate a nitro or carboxyl group on the opposite side (in the 5 position) and results in a very low combining constant.

3.2c The specificity directed toward the carboxylate group. As is shown in Table 3.2, K_{rel} values for benzenesulfonate and benzenearsonate with the anti-*p*-azobenzoate antibody are less than 0.001. In these compounds the carboxylate of benzoate has been replaced by the

TABLE 3.1 The Effect of Two Substituents on Combination in the Anti-*p*-azobenzoate System

Hapten	K_{rel} (observed)	K_{rel} (calculated)[a]
o-Nitrobenzoate	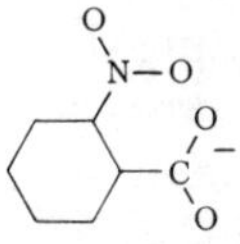 0.006	
m-Nitrobenzoate	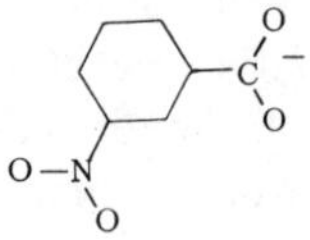 0.40	
p-Nitrobenzoate	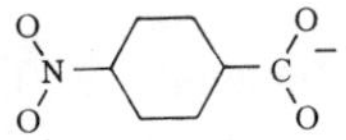 11.5	
Isophthalate	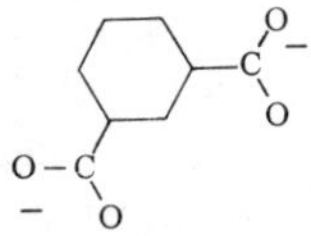 0.83	
2,4-Dinitrobenzoate	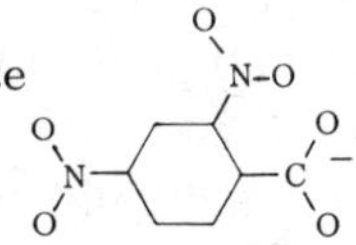 0.06	0.07 (0.006 × 11.5)
3,5-Dinitrobenzoate	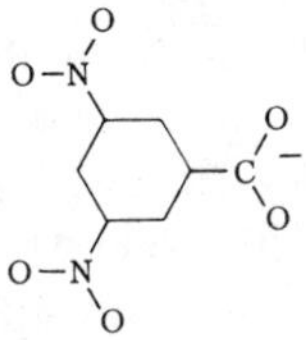 0.004	0.16 (0.4 × 0.4)
Trimesate	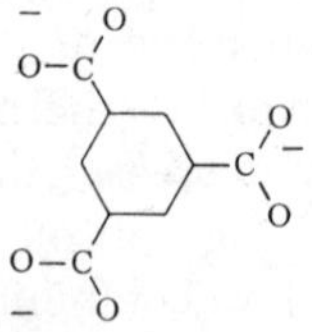 0.0004	0.64 (0.8 × 0.8)

[a] Calculated as the products of the K_{rel} values for each substituent on the basis of additivity of ΔF_{rel} values. (From Pressman *et al.*, 1954.)

TABLE 3.2 Importance of the Nature of the Charged Group for Combination in the Anti-*p*-azobenzoate System[a]

Hapten	K_{rel}	ΔF_{rel} (cal)
Benzoate	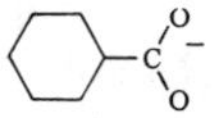 1.00	0
Benzenesulfonate	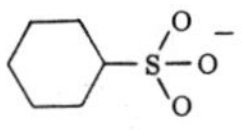 < 0.001	> 3800
Benzenearsonate	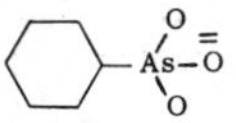 < 0.001	> 3800
p-(*p*′-Hydroxyphenylazo)benzoate	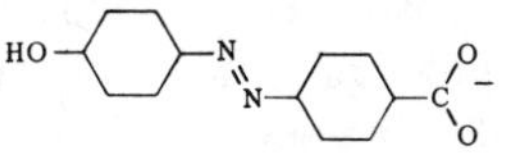 34	−1900
p-(*p*′-Hydroxyphenylazo)benzenesulfonate	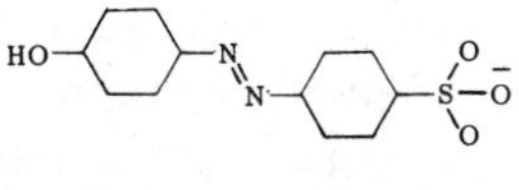 0.12	1200
p-(*p*′-Hydroxyphenylazo)benzenearsonate	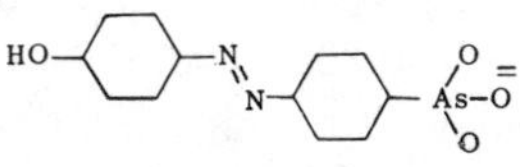 < 0.002	> 3400

[a]Data from Pressman *et al.* (1944).

sulfonate or by the arsonate group. Effective combination with the antibody apparently requires the carboxylate group. Even though the sulfonate and arsonate groups are charged, they produce a ΔF_{rel} value of over 3800 cal.

The sulfonate group does combine somewhat better than the arsonate. This is shown with the haptens having the structure more closely related to the injected hapten, such as with the *p*-hydroxyphenylazo, in the para position. This group contributes about −1900 cal to ΔF of the interaction. The *p*-(*p*′-hydroxyphenylazo)benzenesulfonate shows measurable combination, giving a value of 3100 cal for the increase in ΔF_{rel} when carboxylate is replaced by sulfonate. The arsonate still combines too poorly to be measured readily.

Anti-*o*-azobenzoate antibody does accommodate the sulfonate group; K_{rel} for benzenesulfonate is 0.30 in this system (Siegel and Pressman, unpublished). The reason for this probably is that the carboxylate of the ortho azobenzoate group of the injected hapten is tilted and the antibody is directed against the tilted carboxylate. It can thus accommodate the thicker and larger sulfonate.

3.2d Importance of the benzene ring. The benzene ring is a large structural feature and contributes a large amount of van der Waals and nonpolar interaction energy, making it an important feature for combination—for example, with the anti-*p*-azobenzoate antibody system (Table 3.3), replacing the benzene ring of benzoate by methyl to give acetate or by ethyl to give propionate results in K_{rel} values of <0.001. Displacing the benzene ring from its original position by a methylene group as in phenylacetate also reduces its effectiveness. In this latter molecule, the benzene is displaced laterally and at an angle from the carboxylate group, as compared to its position in benzoate. Further displacement as in phenylpropionate makes little additional change. The cyclohexyl group when substituted for benzene does not contribute much to the binding, although it has the same hydrophobic effect as a benzene ring; K_{rel} is only 0.002. It does not have benzene's polarizability and it is also much thicker, since the ring is puckered rather than planar.

3.2e Replacement of the benzene ring by heterocyclic rings. When the benzene ring of benzoate is replaced by heterocyclic rings such as thiophene, furan, pyrrole, and pyridine, appreciable combination with anti-benzoate antibodies still takes place. These rings are coplanar with a carboxylate group and are themselves planar as is the case with the benzene of benzoate ion. The values of K_{rel} for the combination of 2-thiophenate, 3-thiophenate, 2-furoate, and 2-pyrrolate and the three pyridine carboxylates, isonicotinate, nicotinate, and picolinate, with anti-*o*-, -*m*-, and -*p*-azobenzoate antibodies are shown in Table 3.4. The thiophene ring is very close in steric configuration to benzene as indicated by the fact that thiophene forms mixed crystals with benzene and is thus able to fit into the crystal lattice of benzene. The sulfide group of thiophene is about the size of an ethylene group—equivalent to two carbons of the benzene ring. When the benzene ring is replaced by a thiophene ring and attached to the carboxylate with the sulfur in the 2 position, K_{rel} for combination with anti-*p*-azobenzoate antibody is 1.12, whereas when the sulfur is in the 3 position it is 0.72. The order is re-

TABLE 3.3 The Importance of the Benzene Ring for Combination in the Anti-*p*-azobenzoate System[a]

Hapten		K_{rel}	ΔF_{rel} (cal)
Benzoate	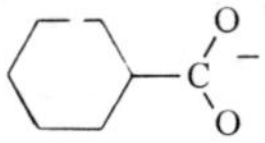 $C_6H_5{-}COO^-$	1.00	0
Phenylacetate	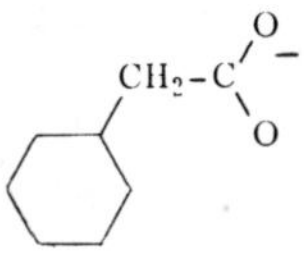 $C_6H_5{-}CH_2{-}COO^-$	0.002	3500
Phenylpropionate	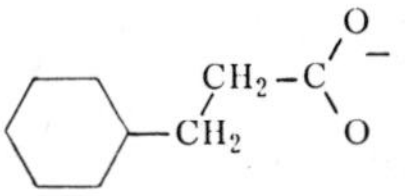 $C_6H_5{-}CH_2{-}CH_2{-}COO^-$	0.005	3000
Cyclohexanecarboxylate	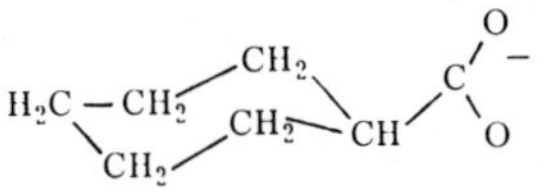 $H_2C(CH_2CH_2)_2CH{-}COO^-$	0.002	3500
Acetate	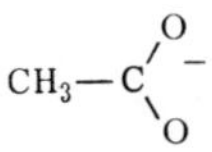 $CH_3{-}COO^-$	≪ 0.001	≫ 3800
Propionate	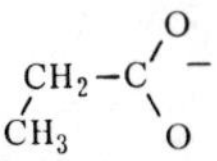 $CH_3{-}CH_2{-}COO^-$	≪ 0.001	≫ 3800

[a] Data from Pressman *et al.* (1954), Pressman and Siegel (unpublished), and Pressman *et al.* (1944).

versed with anti-*o*-azobenzoate antibody. It is very interesting that the anti-*p*-azobenzoate antibody can differentiate between the two positions of sulfur in the thiophene ring. When the heterocyclic ring contains the NH or O group as in pyrrolate or furoate, the combining power with the anti-*p*-azobenzoate antibody drops. These latter two rings combine much better than the cyclohexane carboxylate but are not as close to benzene in configuration as is the thiophene ring.

The six-membered pyridine ring is particularly effective in its combina-

TABLE 3.4 Effect of Replacement of Benzene Ring of Benzoate by Heterocyclic Rings[a]

		Anti-X_o	Anti-X_m	Anti-X_p
Benzoate		1.0	1.0	1.0
2-Thiophenate		0.50	0.72	1.12
3-Thiophenate		0.70	0.69	0.72
2-Furoate		0.17	0.13	0.19
2-Pyrrolate		0.20	0.07	0.15
Picolinate		0.065	0.05	0.09
Nicotinate		0.11	0.58	0.43
Isonicotinate		0.08	0.24	1.71
α-Naphthoate		11.5	1.5	0.22
β-Naphthoate		0.27	1.7	3.1

[a]Data from Pressman and Siegel (unpublished).

tion with anti-*p*-azobenzoate antibody. However, the values of K_{rel} for the combination of isonicotinate, nicotinate, and picolinate with this antibody depend on the relative position of the carboxylate and the nitrogen in the ring. For example, when the nitrogen group is para to the carboxylate in the anti-*p*-azobenzoate systems, K_{rel} is 1.71, whereas when it is in the meta position, K_{rel} is 0.43, and in the ortho position, 0.09. It has been shown that the ring nitrogen is hydrated; the attached water acts as a large substituent and thus accounts for this behavior of the pyridine ring (see Section 3.6). The binding of pyridine compounds to the anti-*o*- and anti-*m*-azobenzoate antibodies is in accord with this phenomenon as discussed in Chapter 7.

3.2f Replacement of the benzene ring by a naphthalene ring. When the benzene ring of benzoate is replaced by a naphthalene ring to give the α- and β-naphthoate ions, there is combination with all three antibodies (Table 3.4). The α-naphthoate acts as a 2,3-disubstituted benzoate, whereas the β-naphthoate acts as a 3,4-disubstituted benzoate. The naphthalene ring displays an increased van der Waals interaction due to a greater polarizability than the benzene ring. The effects of replacing the benzene with naphthalene on combination with the three anti-benzoate antibodies are given in Table 3.4. The α-naphthoate combines best with anti-ortho antibody and least with anti-para antibody. The β-naphthoate combines best with anti-para antibody and least with the anti-ortho antibody.

3.2g Contribution to binding energy by various substituents in the attachment-homologous position. When a substituent replaces a hydrogen of the benzene ring in the position occupied by the azo group of the immunizing hapten, the combining constant is greater than when the replacement is in a different position. In this position the substituent occupies the region of the antibody site directed against the azo group. How it interacts with that part of the antibody determines its effect. The effect of a substituent also depends on a particular system and varies to some extent with the pool of antiserum. However, strong correlations do appear. The data for the various anti-benzoate systems are in Table 3.5. When the substituent is the *p*-hydroxyphenylazo group the strength of combination is greatly increased; K_{rel} is around 20. This reflects the presence in this substituent of the azo group against which the antibodies were directed. The series of substituents, methyl, chloro, bromo, and iodo, show increasing values of K_{rel} in that order for the anti-*m*- and anti-*p*-azobenzoate systems. There is a slight deviation from this order in the anti-ortho system, in that the chlorine has a K_{rel} value which is a little larger than that of bromine. This discrepancy is probably due to a greater tilting of the carboxylate group by bromine when it is in the ortho position. The order recorded for these substituents in

Table 3.5 is that of increasing van der Waals attraction, which accounts well for the increased combining activity.

When the nitro group is the substituent in the attachment-homologous position, K_{rel} values vary appreciably and seem to depend on the batch of serum used. For example, values of 11.8, 7.9, and 2.8 were observed with three different pools of anti-*p*-azobenzoate serum. In general, however, the nitro group increases K_{rel} appreciably for the anti-*m*- and anti-*p*-azo-

TABLE 3.5 Effect of Substituents in the Attachment-Homologous Position on Combination in the Anti-*o*-, -*m*-, and -*p*-azobenzoate Systems

Substituent	K_{rel} in the system: (*o*-azobenzoate, $-N{=}N-C_6H_4-COO^-$)	(*m*-azobenzoate, $-N{=}N-C_6H_4-COO^-$)	(*p*-azobenzoate, $-N{=}N-C_6H_4-COO^-$)
None	1.0	1.0	1.0
H_3C-	1.7	1.9	2.6
$Cl-$	2.9	3.0	2.8
$Br-$	2.5	4.8	5.1
$I-$	4.2	6.0	6.5
H_3C-O-	3.3	3.0	3.8
O_2N-	1.1	1.4	2.8
$^-OOC-$	0.6[a]	0.75[a]	2.1[a]
$HO-$	0.31	1.1	2.3
H_2N-	0.76	1.4	1.9
$H_3C-CO-NH-$	1.2	7.8	7.4
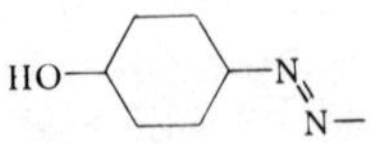 $HO-C_6H_4-N{=}N-$	19	—	23

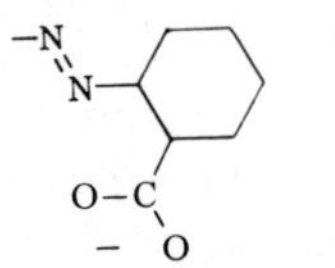

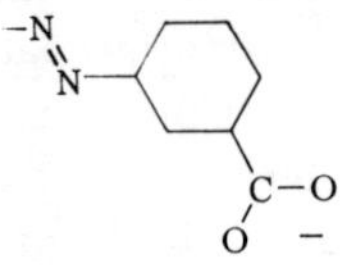

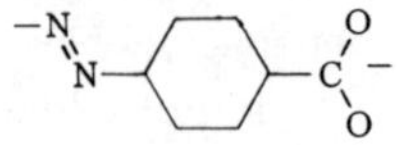

[a]Values listed are one-half the observed values, to correct for the entropy effect of two carboxyl groups since these compounds can fit into the site in either one of two orientations. Data from Pressman *et al.* (1954) and Pressman and Siegel (unpublished).

benzoate systems. The acetamino group in this position is also very effective in increasing K_{rel} for these systems. The low values of K_{rel} for a carboxylate in the anti-ortho and anti-meta systems may reflect the presence of a negative charge in the antibodies close to the attachment-homologous regions.

The amino group is universally very poor in providing increased interaction energy when in the attachment-homologous position. With anti-*o*-azobenzoate antibody it gives a K_{rel} value of less than 1.0. The observation that K_{rel} is below 1.0 with this antibody when the ortho substituent is hydroxyl or amino, and only slightly above 1.0 when the substituent is acetamino, may be due to the formation of hydrogen bonds between these substituents and the benzoate carboxylate, thereby affecting its tilt.

3.2h Exceptional binding of certain ortho substituted benzoates with anti-*p*-azobenzoate antibody. In general the order of effectiveness of position of a particular substituent on benzoate for combination with anti-*p*-azobenzoate antibody is $p>m>o$. The amino group is an exception; the dependence of K_{rel} on the position of the amino group is in the order $o>p>m$ (Pressman *et al.*, 1944). Indeed, K_{rel} for *o*-aminobenzoate is 1.5, whereas most substituents in the ortho position decrease K_{rel} to a value considerably below 0.1, presumably through steric hindrance. A possible explanation for this phenomenon is that there is a hydrogen bond between the carboxylate group and the group in the ortho position which provides the hydrogen atom as shown in Fig. 3.9. How this structural feature achieves its effect is not clear. Other groups capable of forming a hydrogen bond show similar ortho effects. Thus, K_{rel} for OH in the ortho position is 0.46; for acetamino ($NHCOCH_3$) K_{rel} is 0.25; even the very large *o*-N-phenylamino (NHC_6H_5) gives a K_{rel} value of 0.43 compared to 0.003 for the comparably large *o*-benzoyl (COC_6H_5) which has no hydrogen atom to contribute for hydrogen bond formation.

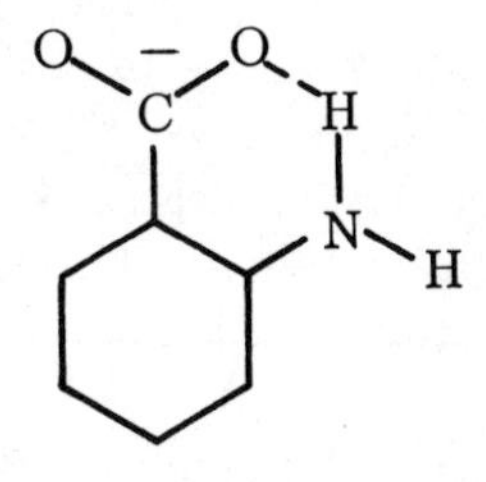

FIGURE 3.9 Hydrogen bonding in *o*-aminobenzoate.

3.3 ANTIBODIES TO THE *p*-(*p'*-AZOPHENYLAZO)-BENZOATE ION

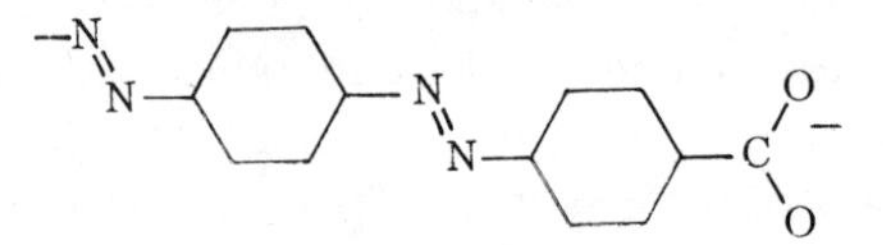

The antibody to this ion is related to the anti-*p*-azobenzoate antibody. However, it differs in that it is in addition directed against a second benzene ring and azo group. The closeness of fit of the antibody around the first ring is shown by the extent of its combination with the ortho, meta, and para substituted benzoates, where the substituent is chloro, methyl, iodo, nitro, carboxy, or acetamino (Fig. 3.10). For each substituent the magnitude of K_{rel} is in the order $p>m>o$, as observed with the anti-*p*-azobenzoate antibody. All substituents in the para position show an increased combining constant over the unsubstituted benzoate.

Substitution in the ortho position causes a large reduction of combining constant, reminiscent of the situation with anti-*p*-azobenzoate antibodies. This again may be due to the tilt of carboxylate out of the plane of the benzene ring. The relatively high K_{rel} for ortho acetamino, 0.13, compared to the low values observed with ortho nitro, ortho carboxy, or ortho iodo is similar to the effect of hydrogen bonding substituents in the position ortho to carboxylate with the anti-*p*-azobenzoate system.

There is a tight fit of anti-azophenylazobenzoate antibodies about the meta position of the first ring, since in general a meta substituent reduces combining power relative to benzoate. This is true of each substituent tested except the meta acetamino group. This group, which contains a chain of four atoms, can assume configurations in which a large portion of the group extends into the space surrounded by the para or azo-specific portion of the antibody and thus can contribute to the binding energy.

It is interesting to compare the differences between the effects of a nitro group and a carboxylate in the meta position of benzoate in this system. These substituted benzoates have K_{rel} values of 0.12 and 0.90, respectively. Since the two groups are nearly identical in size and shape, the larger K_{rel} value produced by the *m*-carboxylate may be due to some type of charge interaction between this group and a positively charged group on the antibody.

3.3a Closeness of fit around the first azo group. The effect of substitution of various groups in the para position of benzoate on the K_{rel} value for combination with this antibody is shown in Table 3.6. The

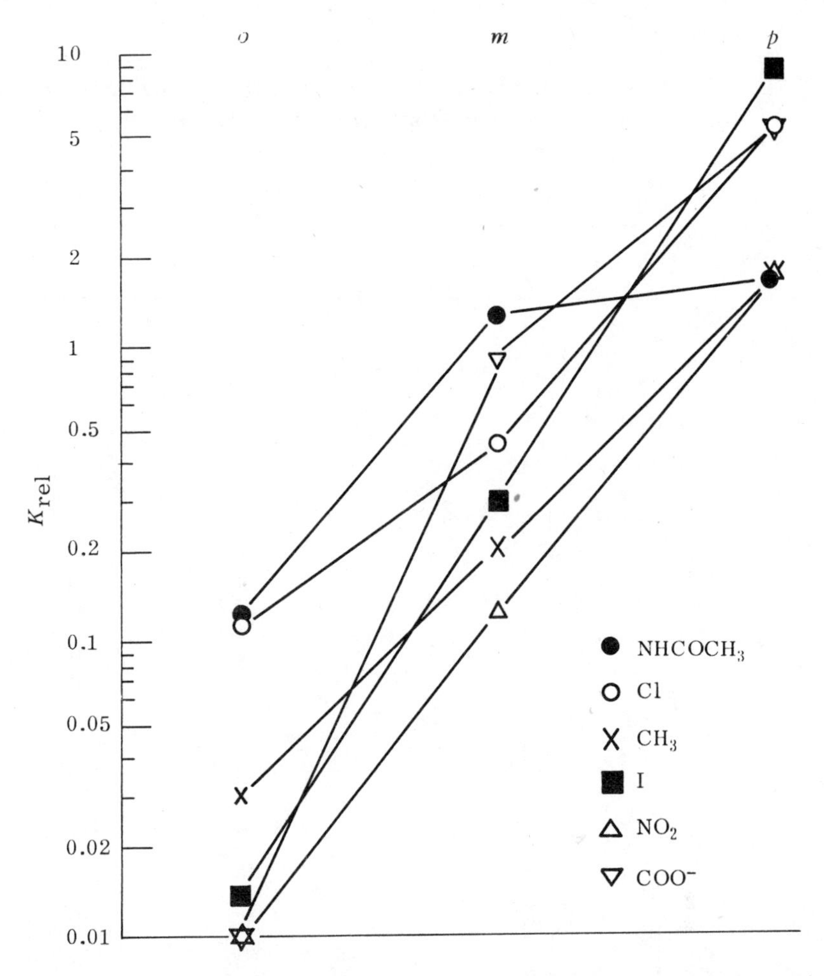

FIGURE 3.10 Effect of substituents on the combination of benzoate with anti-*p*-(*p*-azophenylazo) benzoate antibody. [Data from Nisonoff and Pressman (1957a).]

large relative combining constant of *p*-phenylbenzoate ($K_{rel}=6.8$) shows that the antibody is able to accommodate a rather large group in the azo-specific portion of the combining site.

By far the most effective haptens are the *p*-phenylazo derivatives of benzoate; this is consistent with the fact that these compounds are the most closely related structurally to the haptenic group on the immunizing antigen.

The K_{rel} values for para halogen substituted benzoates are in the order fluoro$<$chloro$<$bromo$<$iodo. This is also the order of increasing polarizability and size of the halogen atom and is consistent both with

TABLE 3.6 Combination of Para-Substituted Benzoates in the Anti-*p*-(*p*′-azophenylazo)benzoate System[a]

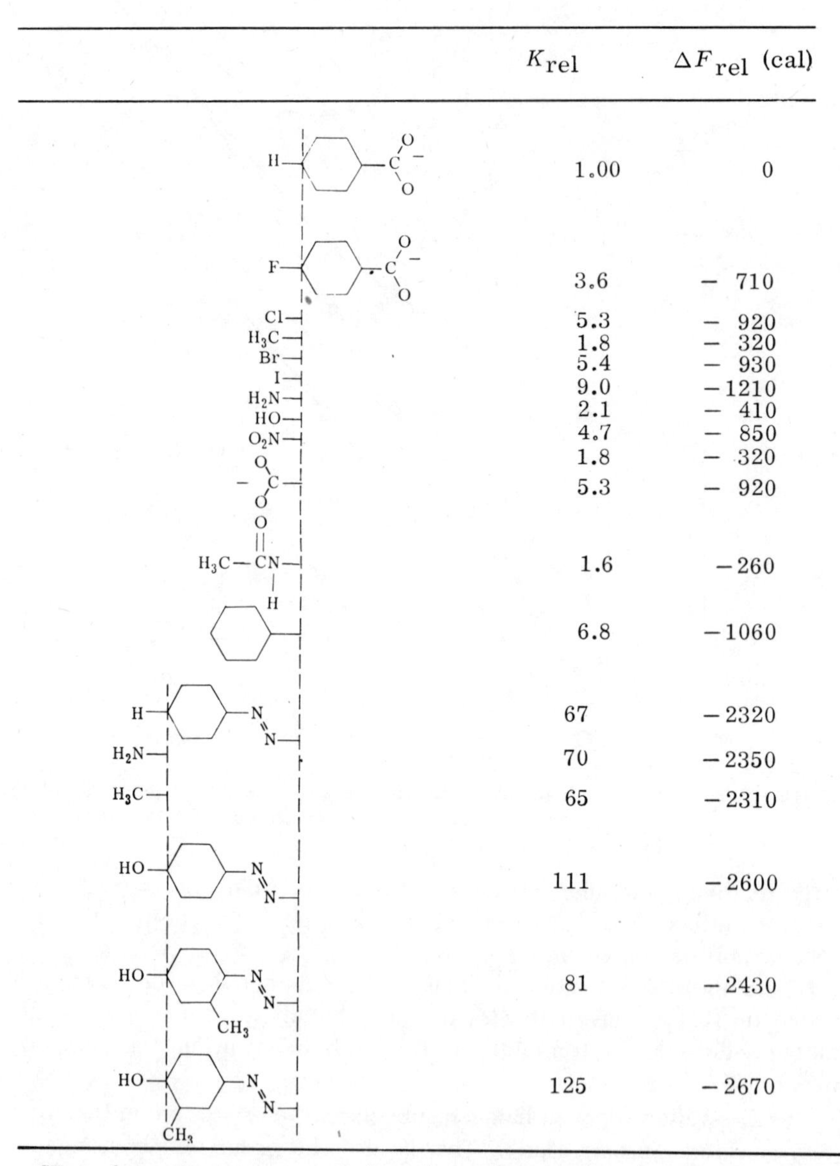

	K_{rel}	ΔF_{rel} (cal)
H—	1.00	0
F—	3.6	−710
Cl—	5.3	−920
H_3C—	1.8	−320
Br—	5.4	−930
I—	9.0	−1210
H_2N—	2.1	−410
HO—	4.7	−850
O_2N—	1.8	−320
$^{-}O_2C$—	5.3	−920
H_3C—C(=O)N(H)—	1.6	−260
	6.8	−1060
H—, N=N—	67	−2320
H_2N—	70	−2350
H_3C—	65	−2310
HO—, N=N—	111	−2600
HO—, CH_3, N=N—	81	−2430
HO—, CH_3, N=N—	125	−2670

[a]Data from Pressman *et al.* (1954) and Nisonoff and Pressman (1957a).

increasing van der Waals attraction and water displacement. However, since methyl is close to bromo in size and has a K_{rel} value of only 1.8, one third that of bromo, it would appear that the additional effect, at least of the bromo group, is due to van der Waals attraction rather than water displacement.

3.3b Additivity of steric effects. The 3,5-disubstituted benzoates are of special interest in connection with the study of closeness of fit. Table 3.7 shows the observed K_{rel} values together with values calculated from the combining constants of the corresponding mono substituted benzoates on the basis that the changes in free energy accompanying the substitution of more than one group are additive, that is, that the resultant relative combining constant is the product of the individual constants.

In general the agreement is good. In the case of 3,5-dinitrobenzoate and 3-nitro-5-chlorobenzoate, in which substituents are present on both sides of the benzene ring, the agreement is strong evidence that combination is taking place by means of a close fit against the face of the benzene ring and a looser fit around the sides (Fig. 1.7f). It is only with a fit of this type that one would expect the steric effects of the two substituents to be additive.

If combination occurred with the antibody fitting very closely around the hapten or completely surrounding it, one would expect an enhanced steric effect from two meta substituents. A close fit is indicated by the fact that even a single meta substituent causes a decrease in the combining constant. Therefore if the antibody surrounds the hapten, a second meta substituent would show an enhanced steric effect, since any looseness of fit would have already been taken up by the first meta substituent. Such an enhancement was not observed. This is in contrast to the anti-*p*-azobenzoate system in which the K_{rel} values, relative to benzoate, for *m*-nitrobenzoate and 3,5-dinitrobenzoate were found to be 0.40 and 0.004, respectively (Table 3.1). The enhanced steric effect in the anti-*p*-azobenzoate system indicates more of a surrounding fit of antibody than in the anti-*p*-(*p*′-azophenylazo)benzoate system.

3.3c Closeness of fit about the second benzene ring. The fit about the second benzene ring appears to be much looser than that about the first. This is indicated by the small effect of methyl substituents in the ortho′ and meta′ positions of *p*-(*p*′-hydroxyphenylazo)benzoate ion (Table 3.6). The ortho′ methyl substituent causes a small decrease in K_{rel} from 111 to 81, whereas the *m*′-methyl substituent increases K_{rel} slightly from 111 to 125. The substitution of a methyl group in the ortho or meta position of the *first* benzene ring causes decreases of K_{rel} to values considerably below 1.0 (Fig. 3.10).

The total contribution of the azo group and of the second benzene

TABLE 3.7 Additivity of Effect of Substituents on Combination in the Anti-*p*-(*p'*-azophenylazo)benzoate System[a]

Benzoate		K_{rel} (observed)	K_{rel} (calculated)
m-Chloro-		0.43	—
p-Chloro-		5.3	—
o-Nitro-		< 0.01	—
m-Nitro-		0.12	—
p-Nitro-		1.8	—
3-Nitro-4-chloro-		0.41	0.64 (0.12 × 5.3)
3-Nitro-5-chloro-		0.070	0.052 (0.12 × 0.43)
3,5-Dinitro-		0.024	0.014 (0.12 × 0.12)

TABLE 3.7 *(continued)*

Benzoate	K_{rel} (observed)	K_{rel} (calculated)
2,4-Dinitro-	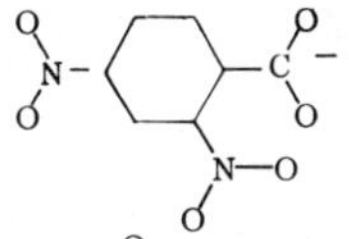 0.014	< 0.018 (< 0.01 × 1.8)
2,5-Dinitro-	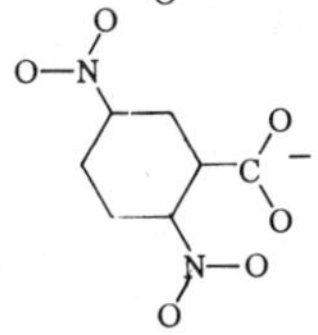 0.013	< 0.001 (< 0.01 × 0.12)
2,4,6-Trinitro-	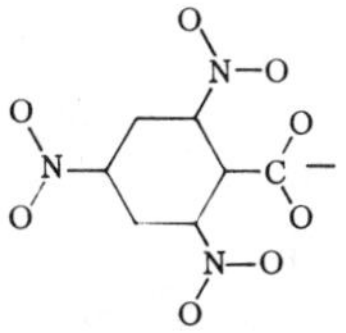 < 0.01	0.000 (< 0.01 × < 0.01 × 1.8)

[a]Data from Pressman *et al.*, (1954) and Nisonoff and Pressman (1957a).

ring to ΔF of combination, as shown by the data for *p*-phenylazobenzoate, is −2300 cal. In view of the loose fit around the second ring, it seems reasonable to attribute a large part of this energy to the contribution of the azo group. This is supported also by the fact that the chloro group, which is no larger than the azo group and differs sterically from it, causes a change in ΔF_{rel} of −920 cal—almost half as large as that of the entire *p*-phenylazo group.

3.3d Closeness of fit around the second azo grouping. It is apparent (Table 3.6) that the fit around the second azo grouping is rather loose, since replacement of the para hydrogen atom of *p*-phenylazobenzoate by amino or methyl does not change K_{rel} appreciably; the introduction of a para hydroxy group increases the strength of combination slightly (by about 280 cal).

3.3e Specificity of antibody against the charged group. The combining constant of anti-*p*-azophenylazobenzoate antibodies is found to be essentially zero with benzenesulfonate, *p*-arsanilate, and benzenephosphonate (Table 3.8). These substances fail to inhibit precipitation even at 0.01 *M* concentration. Ionized phenols, however, do combine. *p*-Nitrophenolate has a K_{rel} value of 0.23; *p*-cyano- and *p*-acetylphenol combine, but have lower constants.

The fact that benzenesulfonate, benzenephosphonate, and *p*-arsanilate

TABLE 3.8 Importance of the Nature of the Charged Group for Combination in the Anti-*p*-(*p'*-azophenylazo)benzoate System[a]

Hapten[b]	Structure	K_{rel}	ΔF_{rel} (cal)
Benzoate	$C_6H_5-COO^-$	1.00	0
Benzenesulfonate	$C_6H_5-SO_3^-$	< 0.01	> 2500
p-Arsanilate	$H_2N-C_6H_4-AsO_3^{=}$	< 0.01	> 2500
Benzenephosphonate	$C_6H_5-PO_3^{=}$	< 0.01	> 2500
"H-Acid"-*p*-azobenzoate	(H-Acid)—N=N—$C_6H_4-COO^-$	89	−2480
"H-Acid"-*p*-azonitrobenzene	(H-Acid)—N=N—$C_6H_4-NO_2$	< 0.01	> 2500
p-Nitrophenolate	$O_2N-C_6H_4-O^-$	0.23	810
p-Cyanophenolate	$NC-C_6H_4-O^-$	~ 0.1	~ 1200
p-Acetylphenolate	$CH_3CO-C_6H_4-O^-$	~ 0.03	~ 2000
p-Propionylphenolate	$H_3C-CH_2-CO-C_6H_4-O^-$	0.04	2000

[a]Data from Nisonoff and Pressman (1957a).

[b]"H-Acid" is used so that the nitro compound is soluble. H-acid is

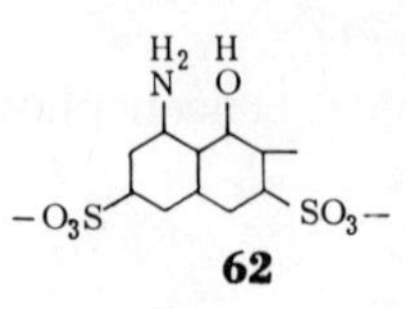

do not combine with the antibody, while phenolate ions and benzoate do, illustrates the specificity of this antibody with regard to the nature of the charged group. It constitutes evidence for a very tight fit around the carboxylate group of the hapten. Of the negatively charged substituents tested, only the O^- group is smaller than carboxylate and it is also the only negatively charged group other than carboxylate which permits effective combination with the antibody.

3.3f Importance of the benzene ring in juxtaposition to the carboxylate group. Just as in the anti-*p*-azobenzoate system, replacement of the benzene ring by methyl, benzyl, or cyclohexyl results in very low values for K_{rel} (Table 3.9). In addition the α- and β-naphthoates act as disubstituted benzoates, giving K_{rel} values of 0.03 and 2.0, respectively. The benzene ring can be effectively replaced by the 2-thiophene group ($K_{rel}=1.3$) and by the 4-pyridine group ($K_{rel}=2.2$). When the pyridine is attached to the carboxylate through the 3 or 2 positions, however, the values of K_{rel} are 0.38 and 0.03, respectively, showing the effect of the position of the pyridine nitrogen on the combination.

3.3g Evidence for the presence of a positive charge in the antibody site. An estimate of the contribution of the negative charge in the haptenic group to the free energy of combination has been obtained by measuring the combining power of the antibody with the two haptens, "H acid" *p*-azobenzoate and "H acid" *p*-azonitrobenzene (Table 3.8). The H acid residue was used so that the nitrobenzene group would be soluble. Since the nitro and carboxylate groups are nearly identical with respect to size, configuration, and their coplanarity with the benzene ring, but differ in that the former group has no charge, the relative combining powers of these two substances with antibody indicates the effect of the charge of the benzoate ion on combination. It was found that the H acid *p*-azobenzoate had a K_{rel} value of 89, whereas K_{rel} for the corresponding nitrobenzene derivative was less than 0.01, indicating that the negative charge of the carboxylate contributed over 4900 cal/mole to the combining energy. The great importance of a negative charge in the hapten strongly suggests the presence of a positive charge in the antibody site adjacent to the position occupied by the carboxylate group of the hapten.

Knowing the difference in free energy, it is possible to estimate the equilibrium distance between the negative charge of the carboxyl group and the hypothetical positive charge in the antibody site. The difference in free energy of combination (4900 cal) is set equal to Ne^2/Dr, which is the expression for the energy of attraction of two charges separated by a distance r, where D is the effective dielectric constant. N is the number of charges and e is the charge on the electron. For the effective dielectric constant of water in the short distance between

TABLE 3.9 Importance of the Benzene Ring for Combination in the Anti-*p*-(*p*′-azophenylazo)benzoate System[a]

Hapten		K_{rel}	ΔF_{rel} (cal)
Benzoate	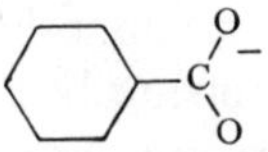 $C_6H_5-COO^-$	1.00	0
Acetate	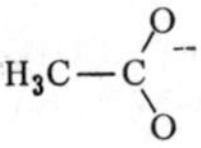 H_3C-COO^-	< 0.01	> 2500
Phenylacetate	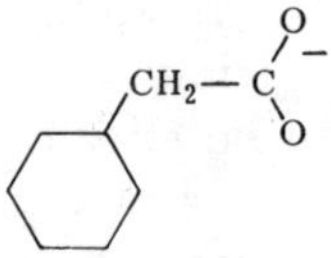 $C_6H_5-CH_2-COO^-$	< 0.01	> 2500
Cyclohexanoate	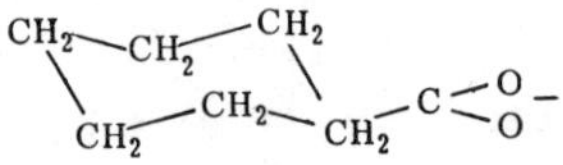 $(CH_2)_5CH-COO^-$	0.02	2160
α - Naphthoate	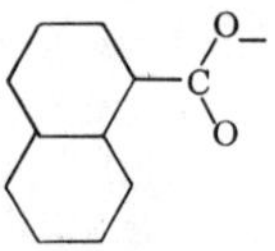 $C_{10}H_7-COO^-$	0.03	1920
β - Naphthoate	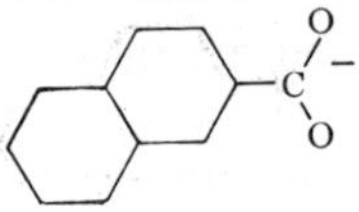 $C_{10}H_7-COO^-$	2.0	−380
2-Thiophenate	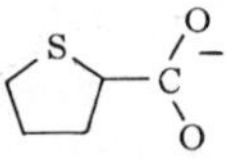 $C_4H_3S-COO^-$	1.3	−150
Picolinate	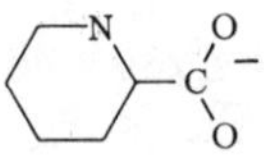 $C_5H_4N-COO^-$	0.03	1920
Nicotinate	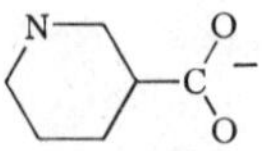 $C_5H_4N-COO^-$	0.38	530
Isonicotinate	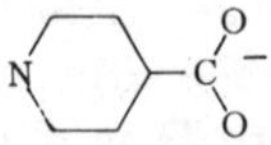 $C_5H_4N-COO^-$	2.2	−430

[a]Data from Nisonoff and Pressman (1957a).

charges, the function derived by Schwartzenbach (1936)[1] is used. This states that in the range of values of r between 5 and 10 Å the effective dielectric constant of water D is $(6r-11)$ with r in angstrom units. The value of r thus calculated amounts to a distance of less than 4.5 Å between the negative charge of the hapten and the positive charge in the antibody site. This closely approximates the minimum distance of approach (3.6 Å) for the charges when an ammonium and a carboxylate group are in contact. (The radius of the oxygen atom bearing the charge of the carboxylate is 1.4 Å and the radius of the positive ammonium group is 2.2 Å, giving a separation of charges of 3.6 Å.)

Further evidence for the presence of a positive charge in the antibody site is provided by the fact that phenols ionize at pH 8 or 9. At pH 8, phenol and *p*-cresol, which are essentially nonionized, do not combine

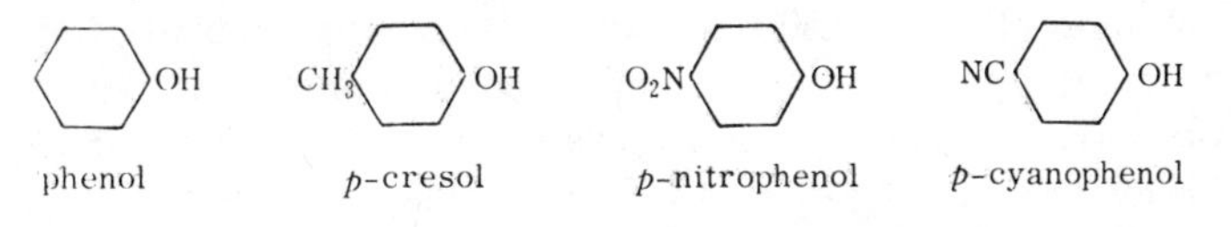

with the antibody. *p*-Nitrophenol and *p*-cyanophenol, which at pH 8 are ionized to the extent of 91 and 57%, respectively, show combining affinity due apparently to the phenolate ion structure which can be

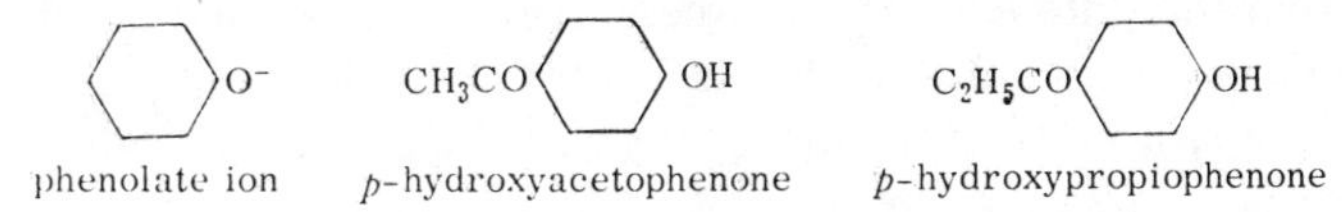

accommodated by the site. *p*-Hydroxyacetophenone and *p*-hydroxy-proprophenone, which are also ionized to a considerable degree at pH 8, combine measurably (Table 3.8).

3.4 CONTRIBUTION OF THE UNCHARGED NITRO GROUP TO COMBINING STRENGTH WITH ANTIBODY DIRECTED AGAINST IT

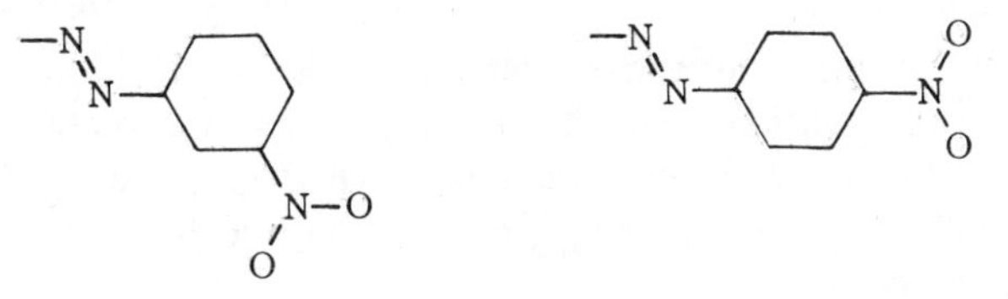

Antibodies directed against the 3-azonitrobenzene and the 4-azo-

[1] Schwartzenbach's calculations, which give the effective dielectric constant in aqueous medium as a function of the distance between singly charged groups, are based on the ionization constants of model compounds. His calculations are thus related to free energies rather than heats of combination, and his approximation includes the entropy changes resulting from the displacement of water from the charged groups when they combine.

nitrobenzene groups demonstrate that the uncharged nitro group contributes an appreciable amount to the energy of combination of a hapten with this antibody. This can be seen from the data in Tables 3.10 and 3.11. Since the nitrobenzenes and certain other compounds of interest related to these haptens are not very soluble, the substituted benzene residues were solubilized by the attachment of a succinamate or carboxylate group to give the substituted succinanilate or substituted benzoate. When unsubstituted, neither succinanilate nor benzoate combine.

A comparison of succinanilate with 3-nitrosuccinanilate in the anti-3-nitro system shows that substitution of a nitro group for a hydrogen atom in the 3 position increases the combining constant by a factor of 3000. This corresponds to a contribution to ΔF of combination by the nitro group of more than -4500 cal/mole. The large contribution of the nitro group is also seen in a comparison of binding of benzoate and *m*-nitrobenzoate. The ratio of K_{rel} values (>100) yields a contribution to ΔF of combination of over -1900 cal/mole. A more precise estimate of the negative value cannot be obtained because of the very low combining affinity of benzoate.

The contribution of the 4-nitro group in the anti-4-nitro system, obtained from the difference in the free energies of combination of 4-nitrosuccinanilate and succinanilate, is -4000 cal/mole. When obtained from a comparison of *p*-nitrobenzoate with benzoate the value is more negative than -2500 cal/mole.

The position of the nitro group in the hapten is important. The best combination is obtained when the nitro group and succinamate group are in the same relative positions as are the nitro and azo groups in the immunizing hapten. Thus in the anti-3-nitro system, 3-nitrosuccinanilate has the highest K_{rel} value of the isomeric nitro derivatives and K_{rel} for the 4-nitro derivative is 0.40; in the anti-4-nitro system, the 4-nitro derivative has the highest value of K_{rel} while K_{rel} for the 3-nitro derivative is only 0.002.

In each system, the nitrosuccinanilate is much more effective in inhibiting precipitation than the corresponding benzoate. This shows that the succinamate group interacts more strongly with the antibody region directed against the azo group of the injected antigen than does the carboxylate group.

The contribution of the nitro group to the free energy of interaction shows that a small uncharged group can make a large energy contribution to the antigen-antibody interaction. It is also noteworthy that the energy contribution is comparable in magnitude to that observed for charged groups in the combination of antibodies with haptens containing carboxylate groups. For example, the free energy of interaction of anti-

TABLE 3.10 Contribution of the Nitro Group to Combination with Antibodies Directed Against It[a]

	System (3-nitrophenyl-azo)		System (4-nitrophenyl-azo)	
Hapten[b]	K_{rel}	ΔF_{rel} (cal)	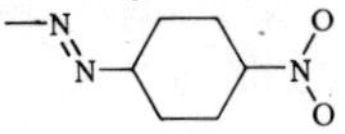 K_{rel}	ΔF_{rel} (cal)
Succinanilate 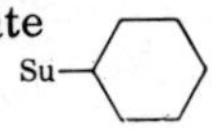	< 0.0003	> 4500	0.0007	4000
4-Nitrosuccinanilate 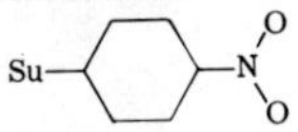	0.40	500	1.00	0
3-Nitrosuccinanilate 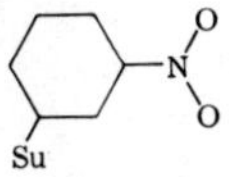	1.00	0	0.002	3500
4-Iodosuccinanilate 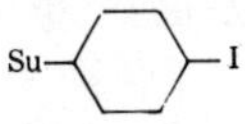	0.02	2200	0.05	1600
3-Iodosuccinanilate 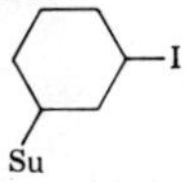	0.04	1800	0.003	3200
2-Iodosuccinanilate 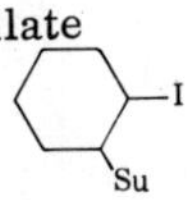	0.0007	4000	< 0.001	> 3800
4-Carboxysuccinanilate 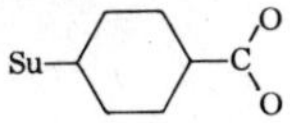	< 0.0003	> 4500	< 0.0003	> 4500
3-Carboxysuccinanilate 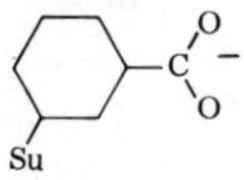	< 0.0003	> 4500	< 0.0003	> 4500

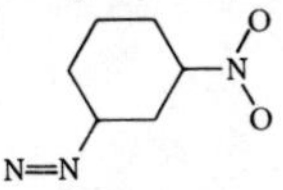

[a]Data from Nisonoff *et al.* (1959).

[b]Su is $^{-}O(O)C-CH_2-CH_2-C(=O)-NH-$

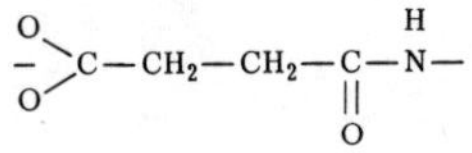

TABLE 3.11 Contribution of the Nitro Group to Combination with Antibodies Directed Against It[a]

Hapten[b]	System (3-nitrophenylazo) K_{rel}	System (3-nitrophenylazo) ΔF_{rel} (cal)	System (4-nitrophenylazo) K_{rel}	System (4-nitrophenylazo) ΔF_{rel} (cal)
4-Nitrosuccinanilate 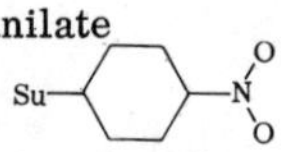	0.40	500	1.00	0
3-Nitrosuccinanilate 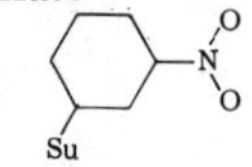	1.00	0	0.002	3500
4-Nitrobenzoate 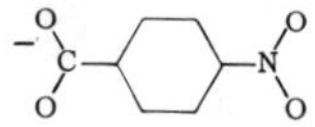	—	—	0.03	2000
3-Nitrobenzoate 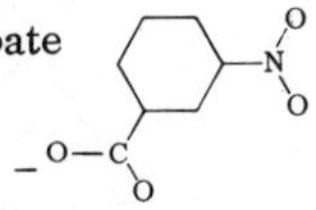	0.009	2600	0.004	3000
Benzoate 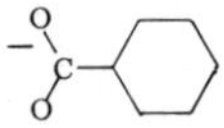	< 0.0003	> 4500	< 0.0003	> 4500
3,5-Dinitrosuccinanilate 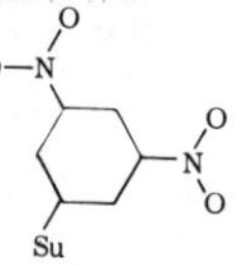	~ 0.1	~ 1300	0.06	1600
3-Nitro-5-carboxyl-succinanilate 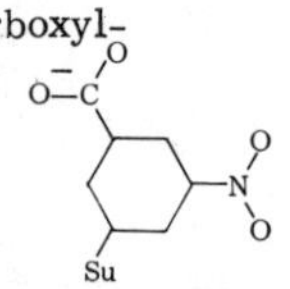	0.001	3800	0.002	3500
3,5-Dicarboxy-succinanilate 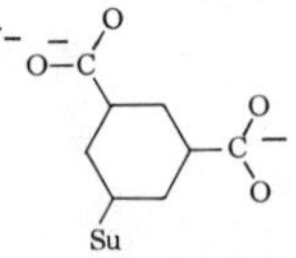	< 0.001	> 3800	0.0003	> 4500

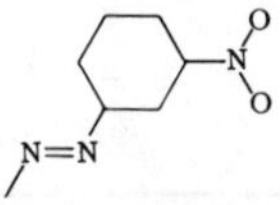

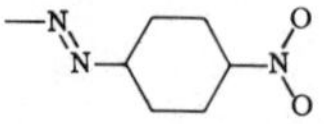

[a] Data from Nisonoff *et al.* (1959).

[b] Su is $^{-}O_2C-CH_2-CH_2-C(=O)-NH-$

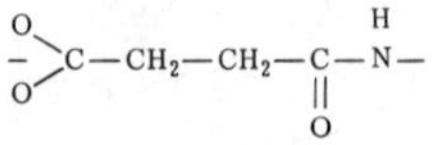

body with the nitro group in the anti-3-nitro or anti-4-nitro systems (-4 to -5 kcal/mole) is as large as that of anti-*p*-azobenzoate antibody with the carboxylate ion of the homologous hapten; the total free energy of combination of the latter antibody with *p*-iodobenzoate is -6 kcal/mole, to which the benzene ring and the iodine atom contribute an appreciable part. This latter value was obtained by determining K_H (cf. Eq. 2.1) for *p*-iodobenzoate by the method of dialysis equilibrium (Nisonoff and Pressman, 1958). Although uncharged, the nitro group is polar, which may be a contributing factor to the combination.

3.4a Substitution of carboxylate for the homologous nitro group. In both the anti-3-nitro and anti-4-nitro systems, replacement of the nitro by a carboxylate group in the same position results in a large decrease in K_{rel} (see 3-carboxysuccinanilate and 4-carboxysuccinanilate, Table 3.10). For each of these compounds, the K_{rel} value relative to that of the corresponding nitro derivative, is less than 0.001.

Since the nitro and carboxylate groups are almost identical in size and configuration, the large differences in K_{rel} must be attributed to the negative charge of the carboxylate. Whether a negative charge, which tolerates the approach of an uncharged nitro group but repells the negatively charged carboxylate, is present in the combining region of the antibody molecule, or whether the difference is due to markedly different degrees of hydration for the nitro and carboxyl groups in aqueous solution is not certain. It is quite probable that the carboxylate and nitro groups differ with respect to their degree of hydration in view of the fact that the former is charged.

3.4b Effect of substitution of iodine for a nitro group in the homologous position. In the anti-3-nitro and anti-4-nitro systems, the presence of an iodine atom in the nitro-specific position contributes markedly to the free energy of interaction with antibody in comparison to a hydrogen atom, but the value still is less negative by 1.6–1.8 kcal than that for the homologous nitro group. In the anti-3-nitro system, the ΔF_{rel} value for 3-iodosuccinanilate is more negative by 3.5 kcal/mole than that for succinanilate and in the anti-4-nitro system, the value for 4-iodosuccinanilate is more negative by 2.4 kcal/mole than that for the unsubstituted compound. These energies represent 60 to 65% of the values associated with substitution of a nitro group in each of the corresponding homologous positions. The effectiveness of an iodo group in each case is consistent with the hypothesis that the interaction of the nitro group with antibody is largely the result of nonpolar forces or van der Waals forces and not hydrogen bonding. An iodo group does not ordinarily form hydrogen bonds. It still contributes a large fraction of the energy of interaction of the homologous nitro group with each antibody. The remaining difference can probably be ascribed to a difference in complementarity rather than to the nature of the force of attraction.

3.4c Other observations. The anti-3-nitro antibody fits closely about the 3-nitrosuccinamate ion as shown by the fact that placement of a second nitro group on the opposite side (in the 5 position) interferes with combination and increases the free energy of combination by about 1.3 kcal/mole. If a carboxylate group is placed in the 5 position instead of the nitro group, there is a much greater increase (3.6 kcal/mole), due either to the hydration of the carboxylate, which may increase its effective size; or to the presence of a negative charge in or near the combining site of the antibody, which would repel the carboxylate-substituted hapten.

3.5 ANTIBODIES TO THE POSITIVELY CHARGED *p*-AZOPHENYLTRIMETHYLAMMONIUM GROUP

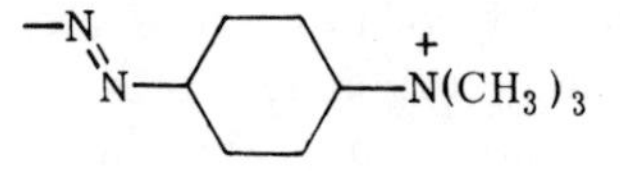

This antibody is directed against a positively charged group, whereas those described previously were directed against negative or neutral groups. The fit of the antibody around the *p*-azophenyltrimethylammonium group is not very close (Table 3.12), as shown by the fact that large substituent groups on the benzene ring are readily accommodated. Even an ortho methyl group is accommodated ($K_{rel}=1.05$) and a meta methyl group decreases binding very slightly ($K_{rel}=0.86$). In addition, an α-naphthyl group is accommodated so that the greater polarizability of the naphthalene ring becomes effective ($K_{rel}=2.0$). These findings indicate a loose fit at least along one side of the benzene ring.

The fit around the benzene ring is close enough so that when the methyl group is in the para position (the attachment-homologous position), the highest value for the methyl-substituted haptens is obtained ($K_{rel}=1.45$). Para acetamino and para amino substituents give K_{rel} values of 2.15 and 0.93, respectively. The azo group and a second benzene ring are important, however, since when the

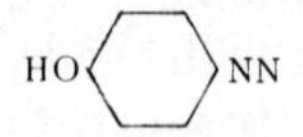

group is in the para position, K_{rel} is 13 (Table 3.12), and when the group is H acid azo, K_{rel} is 5.2 (see Table 3.14).

The fit of the antibody around the charged trimethylammonium group is also not very close, since the antibody will react with the related but

TABLE 3.12 Combination of Trimethylammonium Haptens in the Anti-*p*-azophenyltrimethylammonium System[a]

Hapten	K_{rel}	ΔF_{rel} (cal)
Phenyltrimethylammonium	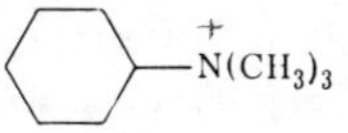 1.00	0
p-Methylphenyltrimethylammonium	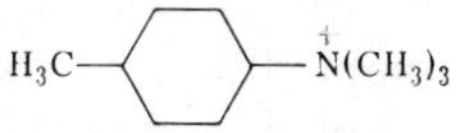 1.45	−200
m-Methylphenyltrimethylammonium	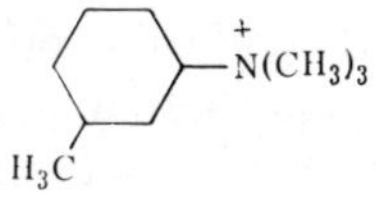 0.86	85
o-Methylphenyltrimethylammonium	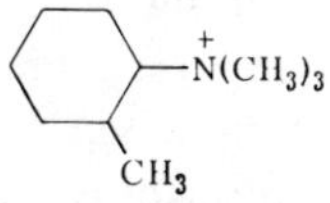 1.05	−25
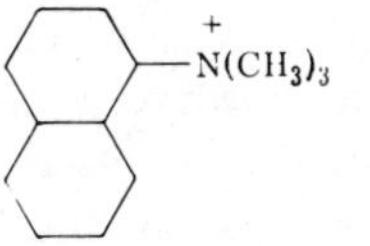 α-Naphthyltrimethylammonium	2.02	−390
p-Acetaminophenyltrimethylammonium	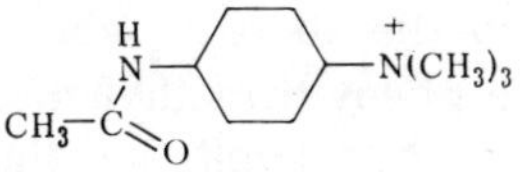 2.15	−420
p-Aminophenyltrimethylammonium	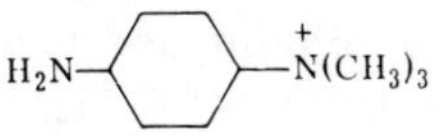 0.93	40
p-Hydroxyphenylazophenyltrimethylammonium	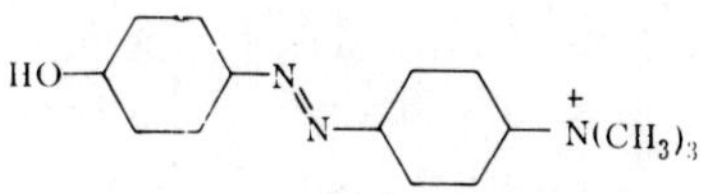 13	−1400

[a]Data from Pressman *et al.*, (1946).

larger trimethylphenylarsonium and triethylphenylammonium ions, with constants of 0.50 and 0.25, respectively (Table 3.13). The trimethylarsonium ion is 0.5 Å larger than the trimethylammonium group and the triethylammonium group is 1 Å larger in radius. The effectiveness of the trimethylphenylarsonium ion shows the close similarity of structure of the quaternary cations of arsenic and nitrogen.

The antibody will also react with the compound in which the uncharged *tert*-butyl group replaces the trimethylammonium (Table 3.14). In order to solubilize the *tert*-butyl benzene group, it was coupled to H acid through the azo group. For comparison, the phenyltrimethylammonium group was also coupled to H acid through an azo group. The haptenic groups in these two substances are similar in size, shape, and electric polarizability; they differ significantly in that one haptenic group is electrically neutral while the other is positively charged. Accordingly, the van der Waals attraction and steric interaction of antibody with these two haptenic groups would be nearly the same, with the difference in values of K_{rel} to be attributed to the Coulombic attraction of the positively charged ammonium ion group for a complementary negative charge in the combining region of the antibody.

The ratio of K_{rel} values for H acid *p*-azophenyltrimethylammonium ion and H acid *p*-azo-*t*-butylbenzene is 8, corresponding to a value of ΔF_{rel} of -1150 cal/mole. This yields information about the equilibrium distance between the positive charge on the hapten and the negative charge in the antibody combining region. This distance is calculated in the manner used in Section 3.3g to calculate the distance of approach of the carboxylate to a positively charged group on anti-*p*-(*p*′-azophenylazo)benzoate antibody. The value obtained here for the distance between the positive charge on the trimethylammonium group and the negative charge on the antibody is 8 Å.

This distance is close to the shortest which is structurally possible. The positive charge of the phenyltrimethylammonium ion is considered to be at the center of the nitrogen atom and the radius of the ion to the surface of the methyl groups is 3.5 Å. The minimum distance from a negative charge to the surface of the antibody is the radius of an oxygen atom, 1.4 Å. Hence the minimum distance between charges, when the charged groups are in contact, is 4.9 Å. The fact that the value calculated from the hapten inhibition data is only 3.1 Å greater than this minimum value shows that the complementary negative charge is close to the surface of the antibody at the place where it fits around the trimethylammonium group. As will be shown later (Section 5.1), this charge is carried by a carboxylate ion side chain which constitutes the surface layer of the antibody at this location. The closest approach of the trimethylammonium ion group to the carboxylate ion group is 2 to 3 Å,

TABLE 3.13 Importance of the Nature of the Charged Group and of the Benzene Ring for Combination in the Anti-*p*-azophenyltrimethylammonium System[a]

Hapten		K_{rel}	ΔF_{rel} (cal)	Ion radius
Phenyltrimethylammonium	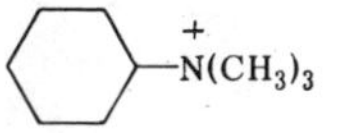 $C_6H_5\overset{+}{N}(CH_3)_3$	1.00	0	3.5 Å
Phenyltrimethylarsonium	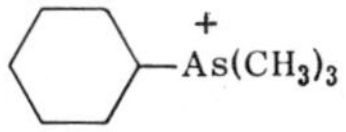 $C_6H_5\overset{+}{As}(CH_3)_3$	0.48	410	4.0 Å
Phenyltriethylammonium	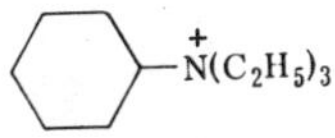 $C_6H_5\overset{+}{N}(C_2H_5)_3$	0.24	800	4.5 Å
p-Aminobenzyltrimethyl-ammonium	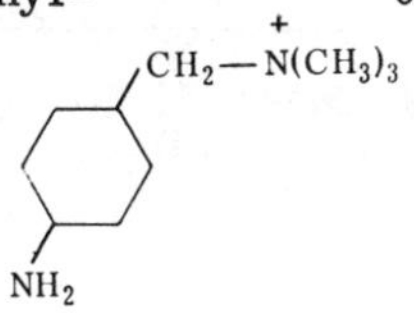 $NH_2C_6H_4CH_2-\overset{+}{N}(CH_3)_3$	0.63	260	
p-Acetaminobenzyltrimethyl-ammonium	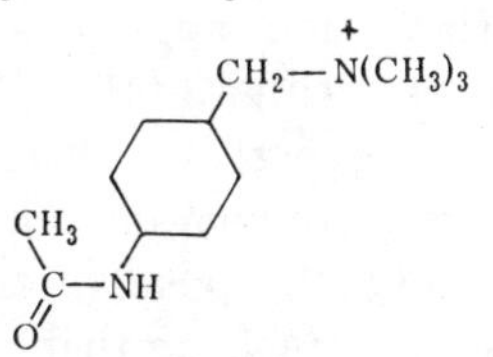 $CH_3C(=O)-NHC_6H_4CH_2-\overset{+}{N}(CH_3)_3$	0.70	190	
Tetramethylammonium	$CH_3\overset{+}{N}(CH_3)_3$	0.05	1700	
Tetraethylammonium	$C_2H_5\overset{+}{N}(C_2H_5)_3$	0.10	1300	
Trimethylammonium	$H\overset{+}{N}(CH_3)_3$	0.004	3100	
Triethylammonium	$H\overset{+}{N}(C_2H_5)_3$	0.010	2600	

[a]Data from Pressman *et al.* (1946).

TABLE 3.14 Contribution of the Positive Charge to Combination in the Anti-*p*-azophenyltrimethylammonium System[a]

Hapten[b]	Structure	K_{rel}	ΔF_{rel} (cal)
Phenyltrimethylammonium	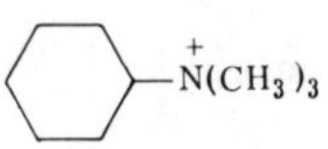 C_6H_5—$\overset{+}{N}(CH_3)_3$	1.00	0
"H-Acid"-*p*-azophenyltrimethylammonium	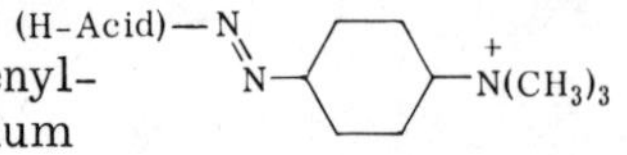 (H-Acid)—N=N—C_6H_4—$\overset{+}{N}(CH_3)_3$	5.2	−930
"H-Acid"-*p*-azo-*t*-butyl benzene	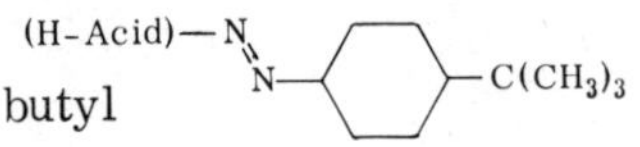 (H-Acid)—N=N—C_6H_4—$C(CH_3)_3$	0.68	220
"H-Acid"-azobenzene	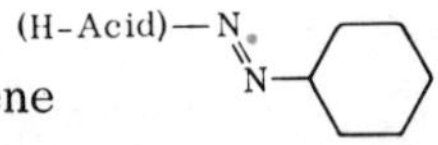 (H-Acid)—N=N—C_6H_5	0.06	1570

[a]Data from Pressman and Siegel (1953).

[b]"H-Acid" is [naphthalene structure bearing NH_2, OH, $^{-}O_3S$ and SO_3^{-} groups]

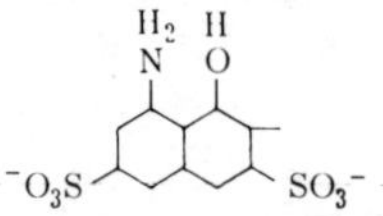

depending on whether the positive ion approaches the carboxylate "head on" (Fig. 3.11a) or from the side (Fig. 3.11b). When the approach is head on, the distance between the positive charge on the nitrogen and the negative charge distributed equally on both oxygens is 8 Å. When the approach is from the side, the positive charge is 7 Å from the charge of the nearer oxygen and 9.5 Å from that of the more distant.

A value can be calculated for the contribution of van der Waals or hydrophobic interaction to the free energy of combination due to the *tert*-butyl group (or trimethylammonium) by comparison of the binding of

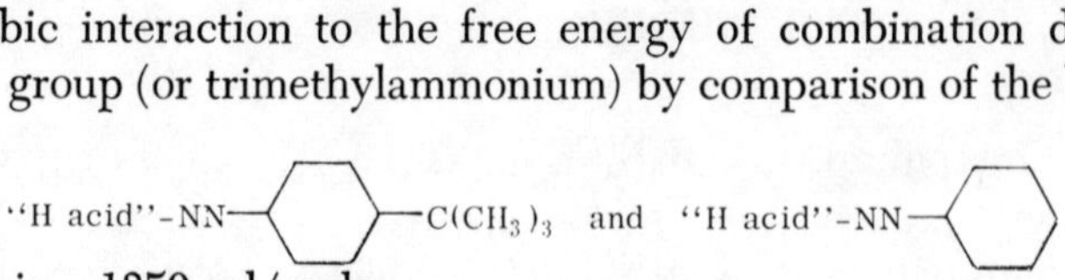

"H acid"-NN—C_6H_4—$C(CH_3)_3$ and "H acid"-NN—C_6H_5

The value is −1350 cal/mole.

Importance of the benzene ring. Unlike the systems involving the carboxylate ion, the benzene ring of trimethylphenylammonium can

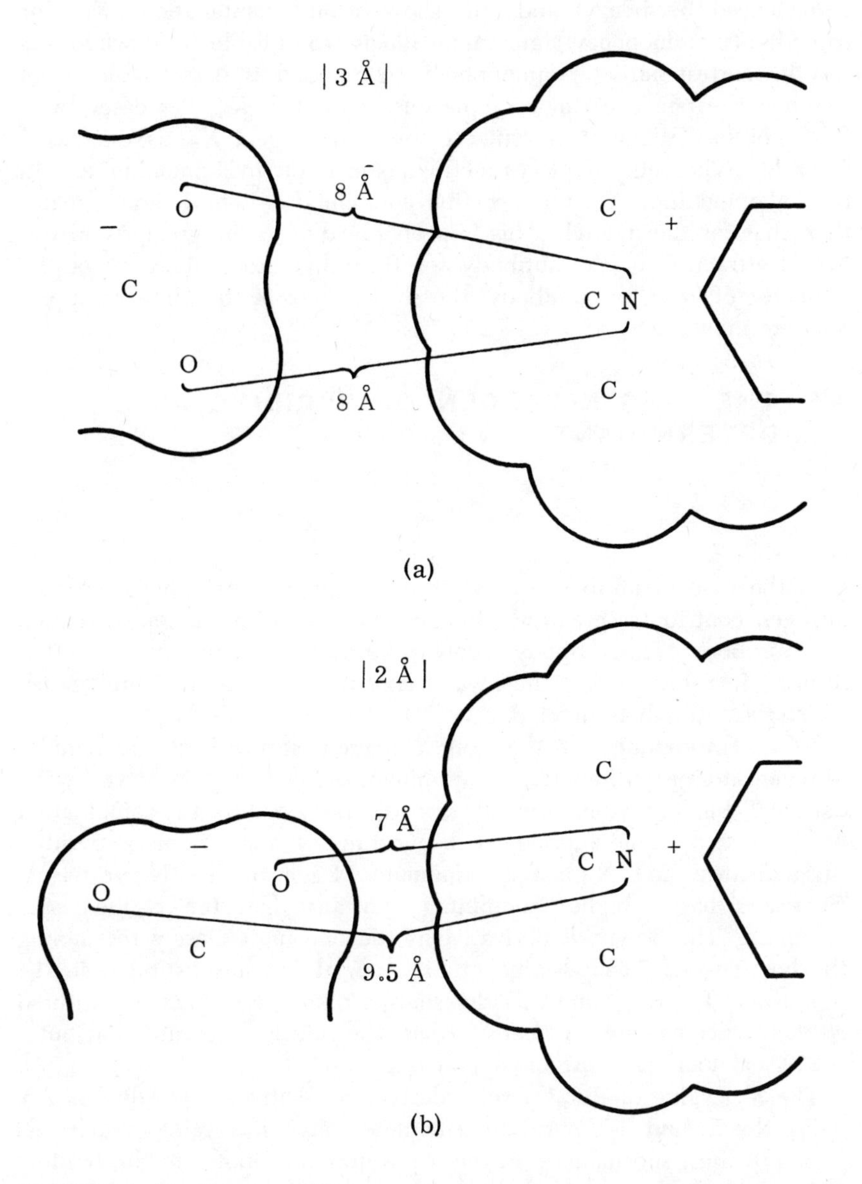

FIGURE 3.11 Apparent distance of approach of the trimethylammonium group to a carboxylate group. (a) Head on approach; (b) side approach. [From Pressman and Siegel (1953).]

be replaced by benzyl and still show strong combination. K_{rel} for trimethyl-(*p*-aminobenzyl)ammonium ion is 0.63 (Table 3.13) while K_{rel} for the corresponding *p*-aminophenyl compound is 0.93 (Table 3.12).

When the benzene ring is replaced by methyl, K_{rel} decreases by a factor of 20. When it is replaced by a hydrogen, K_{rel} is decreased 250-fold. When ethyl replaces methyl, as in tetraethylammonium and in triethylammonium, K_{rel} for the ethyl compound is 2 to 3 times greater than that for the methyl. This is probably due to the greater van der Waals attraction of the antibody for the ethyl group; because of the looseness of fit of the antibody, the steric effect of the larger group is not determinative.

3.6 THE RING NITROGEN OF PYRIDINE AS A DETERMINANT

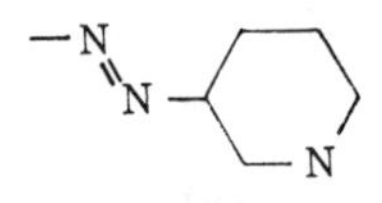

In the case of antibodies against the 3-azopyridine group, the ring nitrogen contributes greatly to the specificity of combination of hapten with antibody. The antibody seems to be directed against the hydrated form of the pyridine ring; thus, water contributes to the structure against which the antibody is directed.

3.6a Importance of the ring nitrogen atom. That the annular nitrogen atom is an important determinant of specificity is shown by the data in Table 3.15, where the values of K_{rel} are listed for the combination of anti-3-azopyridine antibody with pyridine, the three isomeric pyridylsuccinamates, and N-phenylsuccinamate. Each of the N-pyridylsuccinamates has a higher combining constant than the N-phenylsuccinamate. The 3-pyridyl derivative is the one most closely resembling the homologous 3-azopyridine group since it has a substituent in the 3 position. The K_{rel} value is 77 times larger than that of the unsubstituted N-phenylsuccinamate, indicating that the nitrogen atom contributes -2400 cal/mole to the ΔF of combination.

The K_{rel} value of the 3-pyridyl derivative relative to pyridine is 2.5, while the 2- and 4-N-pyridylsuccinamates have K_{rel} values much less than 1.0; thus, succinamate in the 3 position contributes to the binding more than does hydrogen, while in the other positions it interferes.

Further evidence of the specificity of the ring nitrogen is shown by the K_{rel} values of anti-3-azopyridine antibody with a number of pyridine derivatives bearing substituents in the 2, 3, and 4 positions (Table 3.16). Substitution in the 2 position or 4 position decreases the combining constant of pyridine in the case of each group tested (amino, methyl,

TABLE 3.15 Importance of the Annular Nitrogen of Pyridine for Combination in the Anti-3-azopyridine System[a]

Hapten[b]		K_{rel}	ΔF_{rel} (cal)
Pyridine	 (pyridine ring, N)	1.00	0
N-(Phenyl)succinamate	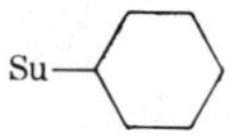 Su–(benzene ring)	0.032	1900
N-(3-Pyridyl)succinamate	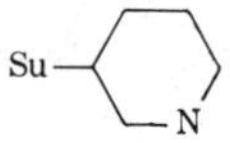 Su–(pyridine ring, 3-position)	2.50	−510
N-(2-Pyridyl)succinamate	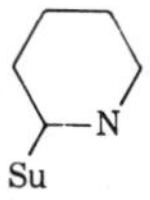 Su–(pyridine ring, 2-position)	0.065	1510
N-(4-Pyridyl)succinamate	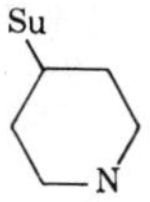 Su–(pyridine ring, 4-position)	0.10	1270

[a] Data from Nisonoff and Pressman (1957b).

[b] Su is $^{-}O(O=)C-CH_2-CH_2-C(=O)-N(H)-$

cyano, hydroxymethyl, succinamate, chloro, or bromo). Substitution of these various groups into the 3 position results in most instances in an increase in combining constant. Each substituent which was tested in all three positions exhibited its highest value of K_{rel} when present in the 3 position.

These results substantiate the belief that the ring nitrogen atom is an important determinant of specificity and is not antigenically equivalent to the CH group of benzene despite the similarity in size of the two groups and the nearly identical structures of pyridine and benzene. If the CH group and the N atom were equivalent, the position of a substituent relative to that of the nitrogen atom would not be significant, whereas in fact large differences obviously exist. The combining constant of 3-hydroxymethylpyridine, for example, is over 100 times greater than that of the corresponding 2-substituted derivative.

TABLE 3.16 Combination of Substituted Pyridines and Other Cyclic Nitrogen Compounds in the Anti-3-azopyridine System[a]

Hapten		K_{rel}	ΔF_{rel} (cal)
Pyridine		1.00	0
3-(*p*-Hydroxyphenylazo)pyridine	HO–	37	−2000
3-Aminopyridine	H_2N–	0.75	160
3-Methylpyridine	H_3C–	3.3	−660
3-Cyanopyridine	NC–	1.1	−50
3-Hydroxymethylpyridine	$HOCH_2$–	1.1	−50
3-Bromopyridine	Br–	2.4	−480
3-Acetylpyridine	$CH_3C(=O)$–	3.5	−690
Nicotinate	$^-O(O)C$–	0.12	1170
2-Aminopyridine	H_2N	0.17	980
2-Methylpyridine	H_3C	0.63	260
2-Cyano	NC	0.14	1090
2-Hydroxymethyl	$HOCH_2$	0.008	2760
2-Chloro	Cl	0.36	560
2-Bromo	Br	0.38	530

(continued)

TABLE 3.16 *(continued)*

Hapten		K_{rel}	ΔF_{rel} (cal)
4-Amino	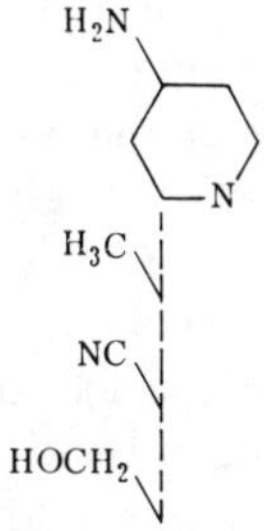 H_2N (4-position), piperidine-type ring with N	0.026	2020
4-Methyl	H_3C	0.41	490
4-Cyano	NC	0.14	1090
4-Hydroxymethyl	$HOCH_2$	0.072	1460
3,5-Dibromopyridine	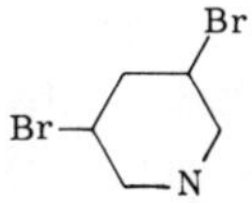 Br, Br, N	0.065	1510
Quinoline	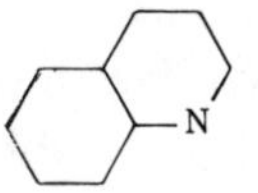 N	2.1	−410
Pyrrolidine	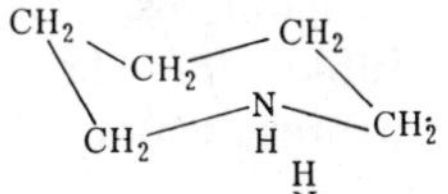 CH_2, CH_2, CH_2, CH_2, CH_2, N H	0.013	2400
Imidazole	 H N, N	0.027	2000

[a]Data from Nisonoff and Pressman (1957b).

3.6b Fit about the pyridine ring. The values of K_{rel} for the 2- and 4-substituted derivatives of pyridine are less than unity and show that there is a close fit of the antibody about both these positions of the pyridine ring. An indication that the fit of the antibody around either the 2 or 4 position is less than 2 Å is given by the fact that in neither position is an amino group accommodated. The ability of the antibody site to accommodate rather large substituents in the 3 position is readily attributable to the fact that this position corresponds to that occupied by the azo group in the immunizing antigen.

Of the haptens tested, 3-(4′-hydroxyphenylazo)pyridine has the highest combining constant (K_{rel}=37). The hydroxyphenylazo group thus contributes −2000 cal/mole to the free energy of interaction. This indicates that some of the specificity of the antibody was directed toward the azo group of the immunizing antigen and also, in all probability, toward the benzene ring of the tyrosine groups in the protein to which many of the azohaptenic groups must have been coupled in the immunizing antigen.

The only compound showing a distinctly unfavorable substitution effect in the 3 position is the 3-carboxypyridine (nicotinate), which has a K_{rel} value of 0.12. This suggests either that a negatively charged group is present near this part of the combining region of the antibody, or that hydration of the carboxylate prevents it from fitting the antibody.

The nitrogen atom in pyridine differs markedly from a CH group in benzene in its ability to form secondary bonds, because it possesses an unshared pair of electrons. Although the observed specificity for the nitrogen could be due to hydrogen bond formation between the antibody and the nitrogen atom, it appears that the nitrogen atom retains its water of hydration (attached to its unshared electron pair) during the process of antibody formation. The importance of this water as a structural feature is further indicated by the fact that the antibody site appears to have a large concavity in juxtaposition to the nitrogen atom which accommodates water (Fig. 3.12).

The properties of this concavity have been elucidated by a study of compounds in which the pyridine ring is replaced by a benzene with a substituent attached to the carbon atom in the same position as that occupied by the ring nitrogen atom of the pyridine. The compounds used were the ring substituted succinanilates. Their K_{rel} values (relative to succinanilate) are given in Table 3.17. The succinamate group serves the purpose of making these haptens water soluble at pH 8 and orienting the benzene ring in the antibody site. It occupies the attachment-homologous position.

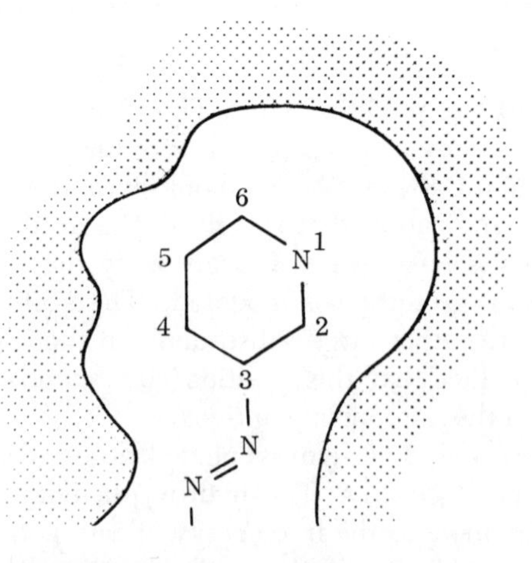

FIGURE 3.12 Sketch illustrating an antibody site directed against the hydrated 3-azopyridine group.

TABLE 3.17 **Effect of Substituents on the Benzene Ring of Phenylsuccinamates on Combination in the Anti-3-azopyridine System**[a, b]

Substituent	K_{rel} for compound with substituent in the indicated position (Su–⬡; ortho)	(meta)	(para)
CH_3	0.22	1.4	1.4
Cl	0.9	1.75	7.2
Br	0.94	2.3	8.1
I	0.81	14	22
NO_2	1.3	3.8	10
$CH_3C(=O)$	—	13	56
Ring N(pyridyl)(⟍N⟋)	2.0	78	3.2
	ΔF_{rel} (cal)		
CH_3	850	−180	−180
Cl	60	−310	−1090
Br	40	−470	−1160
I	120	−1470	−1720
NO_2	−160	−730	−1290
$CH_3C(=O)$	—	−1420	−2220
Ring N(pyridyl)(⟍N⟋)	−390	−2410	−630

[a] Data from Nisonoff and Pressman (1957b).

[b] Values of K_{rel} are relative to that for unsubstitued phenylsuccinamate (Su–⬡).

Su is $^{-}O(O=)C{-}CH_2{-}CH_2{-}C(=O){-}N(H){-}$

It is evident that substituents can readily be accommodated in the 3 position of succinanilate, since an increase in K_{rel} results from substitution of each group tested (methyl, chloro, bromo, iodo, nitro, or acetyl) in this position. Similarly, there appears to be a loose fit of anti-3-azopyridine antibody about the 4 position of succinanilate; each of the 4-substituted derivatives tested has a higher value of K_{rel} than the parent compound.

3.6c Interaction of various types of substituents with the antibody. Substituent groups tested in both the 3 and 4 positions show a somewhat greater enhancing effect on K_{rel} when present in the 4 position. For example, the K_{rel} values, relative to succinanilate, of the 3-acetyl and 4-acetyl derivatives are 13 and 56, respectively.

For halogens substituted in the 3 or 4 positions, the combining constants are in the order $Cl < Br < I$ which is also the order of increasing size and polarizability of the atom. Such increase of combining affinity with increasing size of halogens, when substituted in favorable positions, has been observed in other antibody systems. It can be attributed either to the greater polarizability of the larger halogen atoms and consequent increase in van der Waals attractive forces, or to the fact that a larger atom is capable of displacing more water from a nonpolar portion of the antibody surface.

The steric configuration of groups containing more than one atom, may be of importance in their interactions with antibody, so that the direct relationship of size to combining constant might not necessarily hold. Nevertheless, the correlation with size is good for those groups tested in addition to the halogens. The acetyl group, the largest of those investigated, produces by far the greatest increase in K_{rel} when substituted in the 4 position relative to the succinamate group, and produces a larger enhancing effect in the 3 position than does any other group except iodine. The nitro group, which is about as large as bromine, increases K_{rel} when in the 3 and 4 positions slightly more than does the bromine substituent. The methyl group produces a K_{rel} value somewhat lower than bromine although it is about equal in size. This may be ascribed to the fact that it is less polarizable than the bromine atom and hence capable of a smaller degree of van der Waals interaction with the antibody.

The somewhat greater enhancing effect of substitution in the 4 position than in the 3 position indicates that, although there is a space in the antibody site large enough to accommodate a substituent in either position, the space is so oriented that a substituent in the 3 position does not approach the antibody surface closely enough to interact effectively with it. When a substituent is in the 4 position, however, it does approach closely enough to give increased binding.

Substitution of a chloro, bromo, iodo, or nitro group for the hydrogen atom in the 2 position of succinanilate has little effect on K_{rel} (Table 3.17). The values, relative to that of unsubstituted succinanilate, vary between 0.80 and 1.3. However, the relative combining constant of the 2-methyl derivative is only 0.2. A simple interpretation of the results of substitution in the 2 position is that when combination takes place there is a small amount of steric interference, which is compensated for by van der Waals attractive forces in the case of the halogens and nitro group, but not in the case of the less polarizable methyl group.

The anti-3-azopyridine antibody fits closely about the 5 position of the pyridine group as shown by the low value (0.065) of K_{rel} for 3,5-dibromopyridine as compared with the value for the 3-bromopyridine ($K_{rel}=2.4$) or even the 2-bromopyridine (0.38) (Table 3.16). The bromine in the latter is accommodated by the antibody in the region directed against the azo group. The 5-bromine must interfere sterically to give the low value.

The antibody combines well with quinoline ($K_{rel}=2.1$; Table 3.16) and more strongly than with pyridine. This is due both to the greater polarizability of quinoline and to the fact that a large part of the benzene ring of quinoline occupies the space meta to the annular nitrogen atom. This region corresponds to the location of the azo group of the immunizing antigen and thus can be accommodated by the antibody.

The five-membered imidazole ring with its two nitrogen atoms combines very weakly with the antibody ($K_{rel}=0.027$) as does the saturated five-membered ring of pyrrolidine with its single nitrogen atom ($K_{rel}=$ 0.013).

3.7 ANTIBODY TO THE AZOBENZENE GROUP

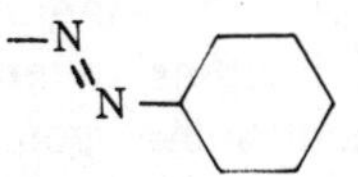

The azobenzene group is uncharged and the extent of fit of the anti-azobenzene antibody around the benzene ring has been determined with substituted succinanilates in the manner described for the anti-3-azopyridine system. The benzene ring is not hydrated and the group is identical with 3-azopyridine, except that a CH group replaces the ring nitrogen atom. The large succinamate group serves the dual purpose of solubilizing the haptens and orienting them with respect to the antibody site. It is assumed to occupy the azo-specific portion of the site. The data on combination of haptens with this antibody are shown in Table 3.18. Values of K_{rel} are relative to that of unsubstituted N-phenylsuccinamate (succinanilate).

The fit of anti-azobenzene antibody around the 3 and 4 positions of the benzene ring is loose enough to accommodate a chloro or iodo group in these positions. Indeed, with substitution by a chloro or iodo group in the 4 position, K_{rel} is greater than unity, indicating a close enough fit for these groups to contribute to the attraction. With a chloro or iodo group substitution in the 3 position, there is little effect on K_{rel}. In contrast, the pyridyl group is too large to be accommodated easily and interferes appreciably as shown by the low K_{rel} values for the N-2-, N-3-, and N-4-pyridylsuccinamates, which are 0.22, 0.018, and 0.019, respectively.

3.8 ANTIBODY TO THE *o*-, *m*-, AND *p*-AZOBENZENEARSONATES

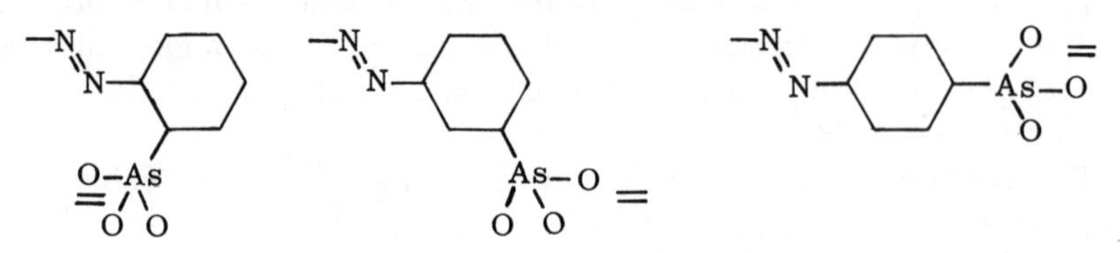

Antibodies against the benzenearsonate group seem to be a mixture of those directed against the singly ionized and the doubly ionized benzenearsonates. The dissociation constant for the second hydrogen of benzenearsonic acid is about 10^{-8}, so that both forms are present at physiological pH values. This complicating feature makes discussion of binding of various benzenearsonates difficult, since diverse substituents affect the dissociation constants differently, and for each compound the proportions of the two forms differ.

Nevertheless, there are many points of obvious similarity between these antibodies and the anti-*o*-azobenzoate, anti-*m*-azobenzoate, and anti-*p*-azobenzoate antibodies. For example, the binding of the ortho, meta, and para substituted haptens to antibody is greatest when the substituent is in the attachment-homologous position, that is, the position through which the benzenearsonate is attached to the protein in the immunizing antigens. In this position the substituent can be accommodated by the region of the combining site of the antibody directed against the azo group. The relevant features of this situation are shown in Fig. 3.13. Substituents in other positions generally give K_{rel} values of less than 1.00, indicating that the fit of antibody is rather close around the rest of the hapten and such substituents interfere sterically with the combination of hapten and antibody. A substituent in the position ortho to the arsonate group does not exert any tilt effect as it does in the case of the carboxylate, but exerts its steric effect directly on the antibody.

It is interesting that these antibodies can easily accommodate the very large *p*-hydroxyphenylazo group in positions other than the attachment-homologous position. Only the anti-*o*-azobenzenearsonate anti-

TABLE 3.18 Effect of Substituents on the Benzene Ring of Phenylsuccinamates on Combination in the Anti-*p*-azobenzene System[a, b]

Substituent	K_{rel} for compound with substituent in the indicated position (Su–ring; positions indicated by arrows)		
Cl	0.099	0.96	2.6
I	0.055	1.5	5.8
Ring N(⟍N⟋)	0.22	0.018	0.019
	ΔF_{rel} (cal)		
Cl	1280	20	−530
I	1610	−220	−970
Ring N(⟍N⟋)	840	2220	2190

[a] Data from Nisonoff and Pressman (1957b).

[b] Values for K_{rel} are relative to that for unsubstituted phenylsuccinamate (Su–⬡).

body shows a tight fit around the benzene ring and that is in the position para to the arsonate, so that *p*-(*p*′-hydroxyphenylazo)benzenearsonate has a value of $K_{rel}=0.007$. The next tightest fit is with anti-*p*-azobenzenearsonate antibody when the substituent is in the ortho position ($K_{rel}=0.14$). In all other combinations, K_{rel} is 0.4 or greater. These findings are summarized in Figure 3.14 in which K_{rel} is shown for the compound with the azo group in the indicated position. The results with the nitro, chloro, and methyl substituents are similar.

Of particular interest are values of K_{rel} which are greater than unity even for substituents in positions other than the attachment-homologous position. These situations indicate either a loose fit of antibody around the given position, or a strong enough attraction by the substituent to overcome any steric interference.

When the substituent is in the attachment-homologous position, K_{rel} is nearly always greater than unity. The *p*-hydroxyphenylazo and nitro

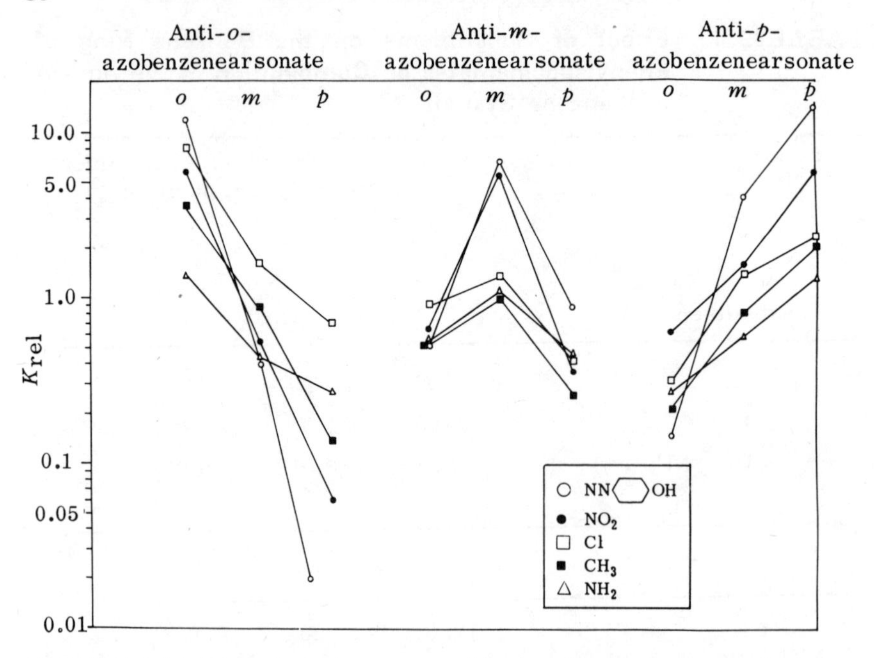

FIGURE 3.13 Effect of substituents on combination of benzenearsonate with anti-*o*-, -*m*-, and -*p*-azobenzenearsonate antibodies. [From Pressman (1957).]

substituents are particularly effective in producing high values of K_{rel}. The order $Cl > CH_3 > H$ holds for all three of these systems. In the case of anti-*p*-azobenzenearsonate antibody, studies with additional haptens have shown an order of $I > Br > Cl > CH_3 > H$ in accord with what has been found in several systems.

3.8a The charge specificity of the antibodies. The anti-azobenzenearsonate antibodies are very selective in their ability to bind various charged haptens as shown in Table 3.19. Replacing the arsonate

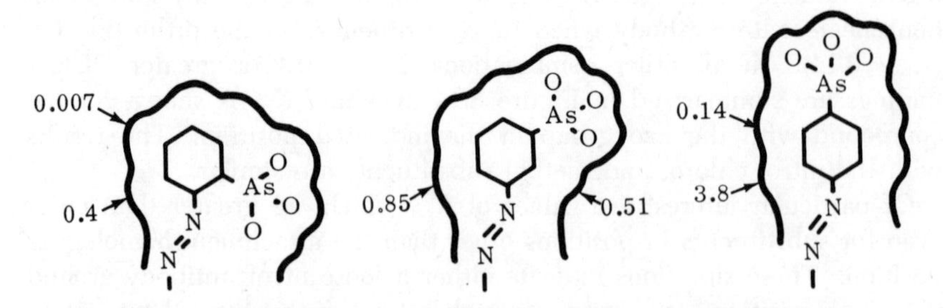

FIGURE 3.14 Effect (K_{rel}) of a *p'*-hydroxyazophenyl group in various positions of benzenearsonate on its combination with the anti-*o*-, -*m*-, and -*p*-azobenzenearsonate antibodies. Values given are for K_{rel} with the group in the indicated positions.

TABLE 3.19 Importance of the Nature of the Charged Group for Combination in the Anti-*o*-, -*m*-, and -*p*-azobenzenearsonate Systems[a]

Hapten		K_{rel} in the system: 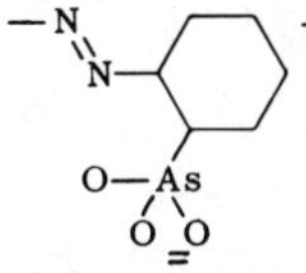 (ortho-arsonate)	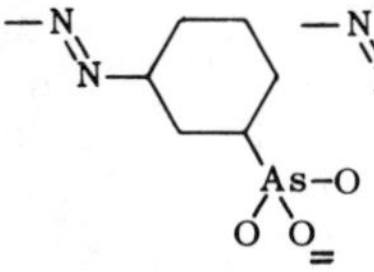 (meta-arsonate)	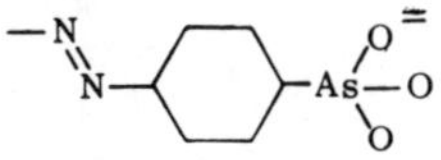 (para-arsonate)
Benzene-arsonate	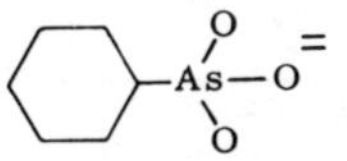 $C_6H_5{-}AsO_3^{=}$	1.0	1.0	1.0
Methylphenyl-arsinate	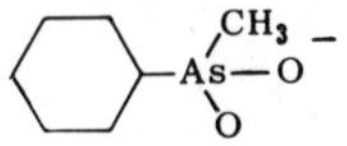 $C_6H_5{-}As(CH_3)O_2^{-}$	0.04	< 0.001	< 0.001
Benzene-phosphonate	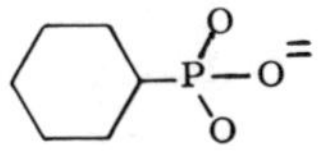 $C_6H_5{-}PO_3^{=}$	2.0	1.0	1.0
Benzene-sulfonate	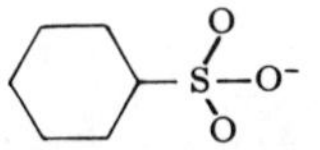 $C_6H_5{-}SO_3^{-}$	0.001	< 0.001	< 0.001

[a]Data from Pressman and Siegel (1953) and Pressman *et al.* (1945).

group by the sulfonate group decreases K_{rel} to less than 0.001. Replacing one of the oxygens of arsonate by a methyl to give methylphenylarsinate decreases K_{rel} to less than 0.01. However, the arsonate group can be very effectively replaced by phosphonate. Erlenmeyer and Berger (1932) first observed the cross reaction of antibody against the benzenearsonate group with the benzenephosphonate group. Indeed, in some cases, benzenephosphonate combines with the anti-azobenzenearsonate antibodies more strongly than does the homologous benzenearsonate. This may be due to the fact that 90% of benzenephosphonate exists in the doubly charged form at pH 8, while only 25% of benzenearsonate is in the doubly charged form.

3.8b The importance of the benzene ring next to the arsonate. When the benzene ring is replaced by a methyl group, K_{rel} approaches zero for combination of hapten with each of the anti-benzenearsonate antibodies (Table 3.20). Replacement of phenyl by a benzyl group also decreases the combining constant greatly. Benzylarsonate is somewhat more effective in combining than is methylarsonate, but much less effective than benzenearsonate itself. As in the anti-benzoate systems, the α-naphthylarsonate combines more strongly with anti-*o*-azobenzenearsonate antibodies than does the β-naphthylarsonate and the reverse is true for combination with the anti-*p*-azobenzenearsonate antibodies.

TABLE 3.20 Importance of the Benzene Ring for Combination in the Anti-*o*-, -*m*-, and -*p*-azobenzenearsonate Systems[a]

Hapten		K_{rel} in the system:		
		—N=N—(ring)—(o-)O—As(O)O=	—N=N—(ring)—(m-)As(O)O=	—N=N—(ring)—(p-)As(O)O=
Benzene-arsonate	(ring)—As(O)—O= (O)	1.0	1.0	1.0
Methyl-arsonate	CH_3—As(O)—O= (O)	<< 0.001	<< 0.001	<< 0.001
Benzyl-arsonate	(ring)—CH_2—As(O)—O= (O)	0.001	< 0.001	< 0.001
α-Naphthyl-arsonate	(naphthyl)—As(O)—O= (O)	2.2	0.46	0.52
β-Naphthyl-arsonate	(naphthyl)—As(O)—O= (O)	0.17	0.71	6.0

[a]Data from Pressman and Siegel (1953) and Pressman *et al.* (1945).

3.9 ANTIBODY TO THE *p*-(*p*′-AZOPHENYLAZO)-BENZENEARSONATE GROUP

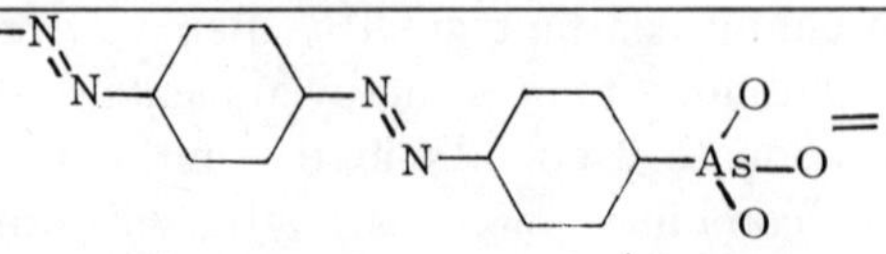

This antibody is directed against the azobenzenearsonate ion extended from the point of attachment to protein by an additional azophenyl group.

It bears the same relation to anti-*p*-azobenzenearsonate antibody that the anti-*p*-(*p'*-azophenylazo)benzoate antibody bears to anti-*p*-azobenzoate antibody. One striking property is that its binding to benzenearsonate is not decreased by the presence of a substituent in the ortho or meta positions. This has been observed for both the methyl and nitro groups (Table 3.21).

It appears that the antibody either fits loosely around the ortho or meta positions, or else fits along one side of the hapten so that large substituents on the other side do not interfere with the combination. This looseness of fit is also indicated by the large values of K_{rel} shown by α-naphthylarsonate ($K_{rel}=2.9$) and 1,4-aminonaphthylarsonate ($K_{rel}=3.2$) as compared to the values obtained for α-naphthyl derivatives with anti-*p*-azobenzenearsonate antibodies and with other systems. The α-naphthylarsonate combines almost as well as β-naphthylarsonate ($K_{rel}=3.9$). The effect of an amino group is peculiar when in the ortho or meta position because it decreases K_{rel} to below unity.

With these exceptions, the values of K_{rel} for the combination of various haptens with anti-*p*-azophenylazobenzenearsonate antibody show a dependence on the structure of the hapten similar to that found for anti-*p*-azobenzenearsonate antibody, although the *p*-(*p'*-hydroxyphenylazo) group is more important for combination with the former antibody. The values of K_{rel} for the para-substituted benzenearsonates depend on the substituent in the order given in Table 3.22. It is interesting that the order for decreasing K_{rel} values is $I>Br>Cl>CH_3>H$ in accord with other systems, and in order of decreasing van der Waals interaction.

The importance of the phenyl group is shown by the fact that methylarsonate has practically no inhibitory power.

3.10 ANTIBODY TO THE *p*-AZOBENZENEPHOSPHONATE GROUP

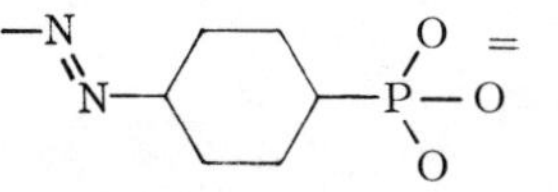

This antibody is directed against the benzenephosphonate group which is closely related to the benzenearsonate group; indeed, the antibody cross reacts extensively with the benzenearsonate group. It appears to be directed primarily against the doubly ionized form of the benzenephosphonate ion. The fit around the hapten group is apparently not close. The binding is not particularly affected, either by the presence of the ortho, meta, and para chloro substituents, or by the 3,5-dichloro substituent (Table 3.23).

The ortho chloro group reduces K_{rel} only to 0.76. Even the larger ortho methoxy group of *p*-nitro-*o*-methoxybenzenephosphonate reduces

TABLE 3.21 Effect of Ortho- and Meta-Substitution on Combination in the Anti-*p*-(*p'*-azophenylazo)benzenearsonate System[a]

Hapten	Structure	K_{rel}	ΔF_{rel} (cal)
Benzenearsonate	C_6H_5–$AsO_3^=$	1.0	0
o-Nitrobenzenearsonate	o-$NO_2C_6H_4$–$AsO_3^=$	1.8	−330
m-Nitrobenzenearsonate	m-$NO_2C_6H_4$–$AsO_3^=$	3.6	−710
o-Methylbenzenearsonate	o-$CH_3C_6H_4$–$AsO_3^=$	1.0	0
m-Methylbenzenearsonate	m-$CH_3C_6H_4$–$AsO_3^=$	1.1	−50
α-Naphthylarsonate	α-$C_{10}H_7$–$AsO_3^=$	2.9	−590
1,4-Aminonaphthylarsonate	H_2N–$C_{10}H_6$–$AsO_3^=$	3.9	−750
β-Naphthylarsonate	β-$C_{10}H_7$–$AsO_3^=$	3.2	−650

[a] Data from Pressman and Siegel (1953).

TABLE 3.22 Effect of Para Substituents on Combination in the Anti-*p*-(*p*′-azophenylazo)benzenearsonate System[a]

Hapten	K_{rel}	ΔF_{rel} (cal)
Benzenearsonate (H—C_6H_4—$AsO_3^{=}$)	1.0	0
p-(*p*′-Hydroxyphenylazo)-benzenearsonate (HO—C_6H_4—N=N—)	30	−1900
p-(*p*′-Aminophenylazo)-benzenearsonate (H_2N—C_6H_4—N=N—)	26	−1800
p-(*p*′-Aminobenzoyl)-benzenearsonate (NH_2—C_6H_4—C(=O)—)	7.0	−1080
p-(*p*′-Nitrobenzoyl)-benzenearsonate (NO_2—C_6H_4—C(=O)—)	6.1	−1000
p-Iodobenzenearsonate (I—)	6.8	−1060
p-Benzoylaminobenzenearsonate (C_6H_5—C(=O)—NH—)	4.8	−870
p-Nitro (O_2N—)	4.4	−820
p-Acetamino (H_3C—C(=O)—NH—)	3.3	−660
p-Bromobenzenearsonate (Br—)	3.1	−630
p-Chloro (Cl—)	2.9	−590
p-Methyl (H_3C—)	2.7	−550
p-Hydroxy (HO—)	1.2	−100
p-Amino (H_2N—)	1.0	0

(continued)

TABLE 3.22 *(continued)*

Hapten		K_{rel}	ΔF_{rel} (cal)
p-Carboxy	$^{-}O_2C-$	0.9	60

[a]Data from Pressman and Siegel (1953).

K_{rel} only to 0.71, as compared with K_{rel} for *p*-nitrobenzenephosphonate of 1.23. Although a meta chloro group gives a value for K_{rel} of 1.05, the larger nitro group does reduce binding, with $K_{rel}=0.66$. The smaller amino group in the meta position reduces the binding to about the same extent as does the nitro group. The *p*-(*p'*-hydroxyphenylazo) group increases the value of K_{rel} to 7.1 in accordance with similar findings in comparable hapten systems. Other para substituents, such as nitro and chloro, increase K_{rel} by a factor less than 2.

The effects of substituents on the combination of benzenearsonate with anti-benzenephosphonate antibody appear at first to differ from their effects on the combination of benzenephosphonate with the antibody when the relative binding constants are calculated on the basis of the total concentration of arsonate or phosphonate present (Table 3.24). However, when the constants are calculated on the basis of the concentration of the di-ionized form of the ions, it can be seen that the doubly charged benzenearsonates combine just as strongly as the corresponding doubly charged benzenephosphonates. Table 3.24 also lists the percent of each relevant hapten in the di-ionized form at pH 8.

3.10a Comparison of combining sites of anti-benzenephosphonate and anti-benzenearsonate antibodies. Since the arsonate group is about 0.4 Å larger than the phosphonate group it is not difficult to understand the combination of the smaller phosphonate ion with the anti-benzenearsonate combining site. The alternate fact that antibody formed in response to the smaller phosphonate ion can accommodate the larger arsonate group can be explained by the looser fit of anti-benzenephosphonate antibody about the hapten. This is shown by its ability to accommodate substituents in the ortho position. The cross reaction may also be due to a greater degree of hydration of the phosphonate ion, making both hydrated ions about the same size. Since phosphonate ion is smaller and has a greater charge density, it may well be more strongly hydrated. In addition, some of the difference in specificity observed for the two antibodies may be due to differences in the energies of hydra-

TABLE 3.23 Effect of Substituents on Combination in the Anti-*p*-azobenzenephosphonate System[a]

Hapten	K_{rel}	ΔF_{rel} (cal)
Benzenephosphonate	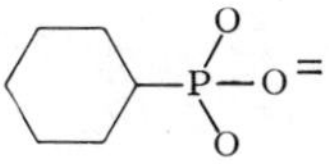 1.00	0
o-Chlorobenzenephosphonate	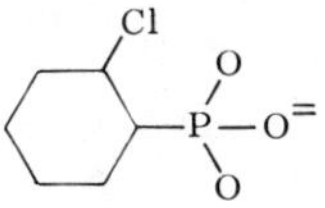 0.76	150
m-Chlorobenzenephosphonate	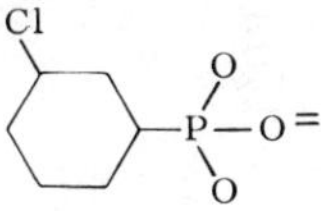 1.05	−30
p-Chlorobenzenephosphonate	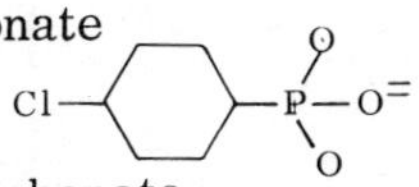 1.37	−170
3,5-Dichlorobenzenephosphonate	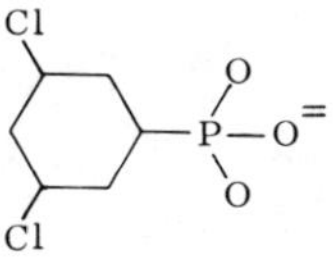 0.79	130
p-Nitrobenzenephosphonate	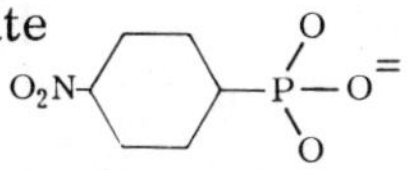 1.23	−110
2-Methoxy,4-nitrobenzenephosphonate	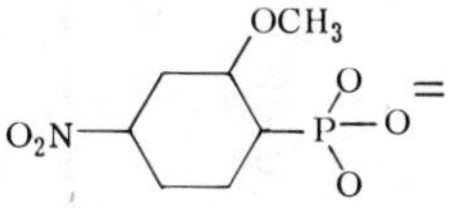 0.71	190
m-Nitrobenzenephosphonate	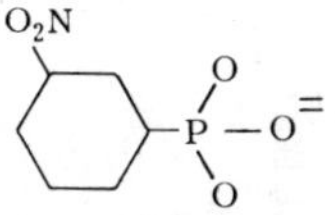 0.66	230

[a]Data from Kreiter and Pressman (1964).

TABLE 3.24 Dependence of Calculated K_{rel} Values on Ionic Species Present for Combination of Benzenephosphonates and Benzenearsonates with Anti-*p*-azobenzenephosphonate[a]

Hapten	K_{rel} calculated on the basis of:			
	Total hapten concentration		Di-ionized hapten concentration	
	Benzene-phosphonates	Benzene-arsonates	Benzene-phosphonates	Benzene-arsonates
Unsubstituted	1.00	0.31	1.00	1.15
m-Nitro	0.66	0.29	0.58	0.45
p-Nitro	1.23	0.69	1.09	1.00

	% Di-ionized hapten at pH 8	
	Benzenephosphonates	Benzenearsonates
Unsubstituted	90	25
m-Nitro	98	61
p-Nitro	98	61

[a]Data from Kreiter and Pressman (1964).

tion of benzenephosphonate and benzenearsonate ions or in the configurations of the hydrated ions.

The greater ability of the anti-benzenephosphonate antibody to accommodate ortho substituents is interesting in view of the fact that the combining site of each antibody (directed against the doubly charged ions) can accommodate either arsonate or phosphonate haptens equally well. This difference in specificity may be of fundamental significance in concepts of antibody site structure. It may be that the amino acid sequence of the primary peptide chain can fold in only certain ways, and that the only possible folding around the phosphonate ion yields a configuration which can accommodate the larger arsonate as well as the smaller phosphonate.

3.11 ANTIBODY TO THE 5-AZO-ISOPHTHALATE GROUP

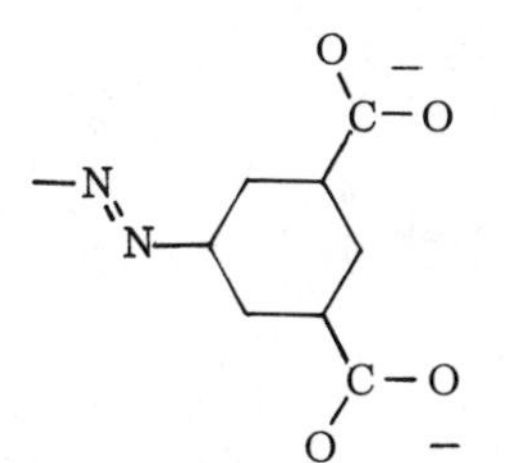

This antibody is of interest because it requires two carboxylate groups on the benzene ring in meta position to each other for good binding. Thus, it combines well with the isophthalate ion (Table 3.25) but not well with benzoate which has only a single carboxylate and gives a K_{rel} value of 0.007. This represents a contribution to ΔF of 2800 cal for the second carboxylate. Replacing one of the carboxylates of isophthalate with another negatively charged group, the sulfo group, to give *m*-sulfobenzoate, causes a drop in K_{rel} to 0.084, or a ΔF_{rel} of combination of 1400 cal. Replacing one of the carboxylates with a nitro, which has the same size and shape as the carboxylate, but has no charge, gives a K_{rel} of 0.014. Thus the structure required for good binding is not achieved by replacing one carboxylate with a hydrogen, a different negative charge, or an uncharged group of the same size and shape.

The binding constant is increased by the presence of a group in the attachment-homologous position (Table 3.26). The hapten most nearly related to the immunizing haptenic group, the 5-(*p*-hydroxyphenylazo)-isophthalate, has a K_{rel} value of 23 and the 5-carboxylate, 5-iodo, and 5-nitro isophthalates have K_{rel} values of 5.2, 5.3, and 1.8, respectively. However, as the iodo and nitro substituents are moved out of the 5 position into the 4 position, ortho to one of the carboxylates, the K_{rel} values drop to 0.45 and 0.16, respectively. When these groups are in the 2

TABLE 3.25 Importance of Two Carboxyl Groups for Combination in the Anti-isophthalate System[a]

Hapten	K_{rel}	ΔF_{rel} (cal)
Isophtalate	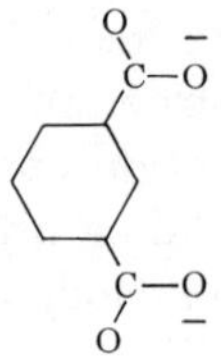 1.00	0
Benzoate	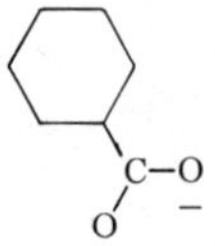 0.007	2800
m-Carboxybenzenesulfonate	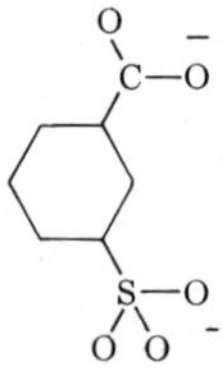 0.084	1400
m-Nitrobenzoate	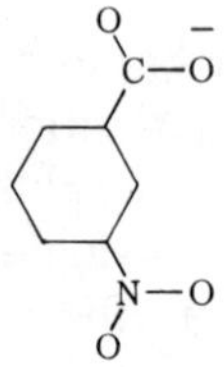 0.014	2300
p-Nitrobenzoate	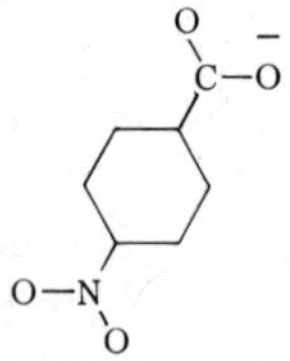 0.008	2600
o-Nitrobenzoate	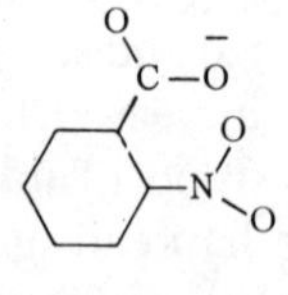 0.003	3200

[a]Data from Pressman and Siegel (unpublished).

TABLE 3.26 Effect of Substituents on Combination in the Anti-isophthalate System[a]

Hapten	K_{rel}	ΔF_{rel} (cal)
Isophthalate	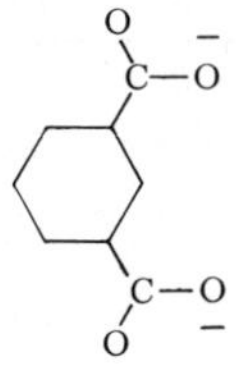 1.0	0
5-(*p*-Hydroxyphenylazo)-isophthalate	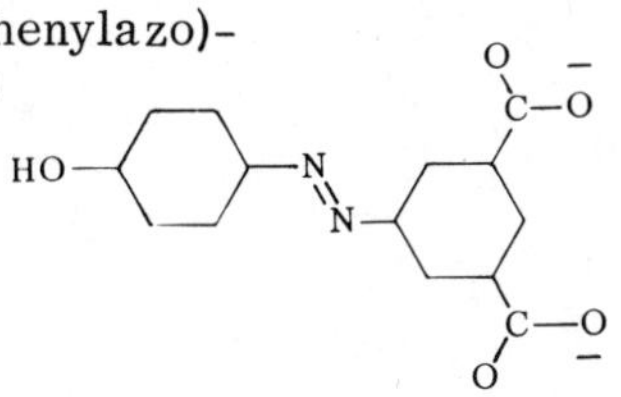 23	−1700
5-Nitroisophthalate	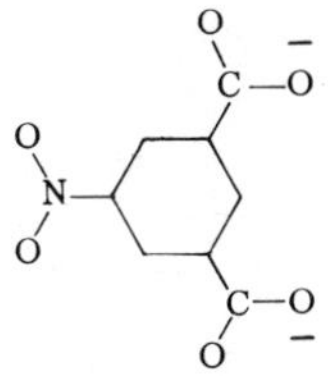 1.8	−300
4-Nitroisophthalate	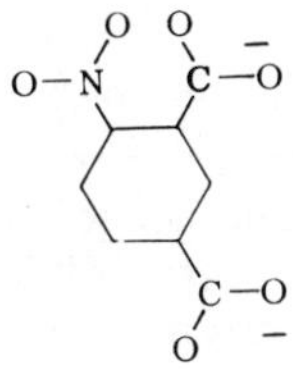 0.16	1000
2-Nitroisophthalate	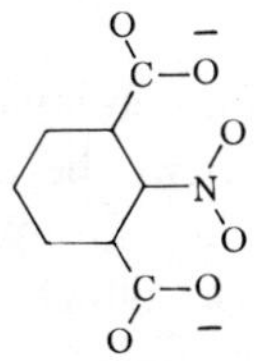 0.015	2300
5-Iodoisophthalate	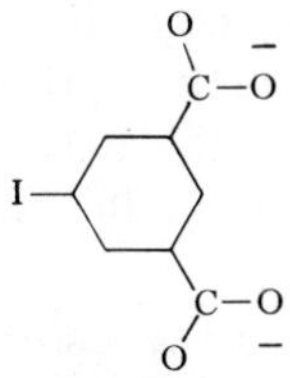 5.3	−900
4-Iodoisophthalate	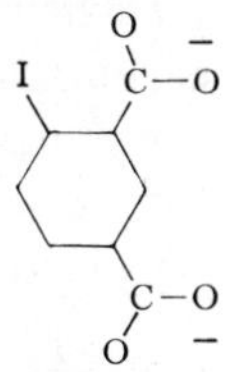 0.45	400

(continued)

TABLE 3.26 *(continued)*

Hapten	K_{rel}	ΔF_{rel} (cal)
2-Iodoisophthalate	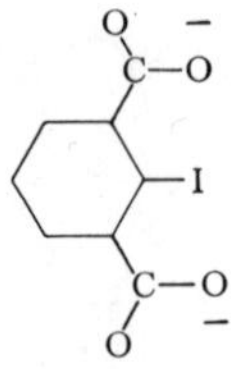 0.018	2200
Trimesate	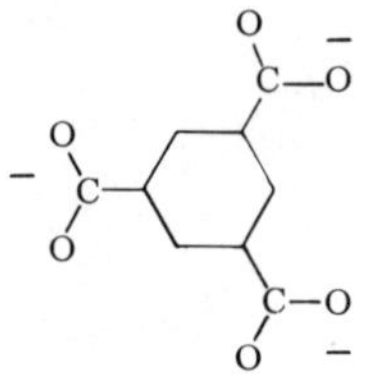 1.7[b]	−290[b]
Hemimellitate	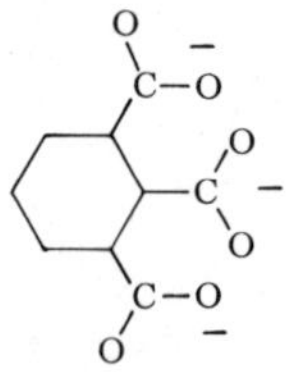 0.011	2500

[a]Data from Pressman and Siegel (unpublished).

[b]Values corrected by a factor of 3 for entropy effect since the trimesate can fit in 3 times the number of ways possible for isophthalate.

position, the K_{rel} values are much lower (0.018 and 0.015). The reduction in binding with substitution in the 4 and 2 positions is probably due largely to tilt of the carboxylate groups by a substituent ortho to them, in addition to the direct steric effect. The 2-substituent tilts both carboxylates and has the largest effect.

Although *m*-nitrobenzoate has a K_{rel} of only 0.014, there is evidence that the nitro group meta to the carboxylate participates in a positive manner to some extent, since the benzoates with the nitro in the ortho or para positions have even smaller values for K_{rel}, 0.003 and 0.008, respectively (Table 3.25).

3.11a The effectiveness of a residue larger than hydrogen. There is some gain in binding energy when a chlorine rather than a hydrogen occupies the position of a carboxylate against which the antibody is directed. This is shown by the *m*-(*p*′-hydroxyphenylazo)chlorobenzoate (Table 3.27). The unchlorinated azo compound has a K_{rel} value of 0.052. When the chlorine is in the 5 position K_{rel} is increased to 0.091. The

TABLE 3.27 Necessity for Two Carboxylates in the Correct Position for Combination in the Anti-isophthalate

Hapten	K_{rel}	ΔF_{rel} (cal)
Isophthalate	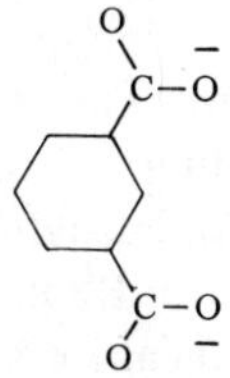 1.0	0
5-(*p*-Hydroxyphenylazo)-benzoate	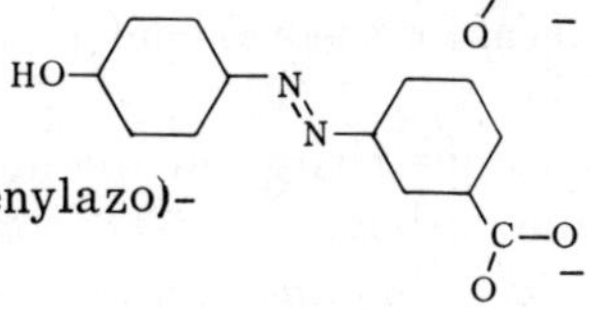 0.052	1650
-3- chlorobenzoate	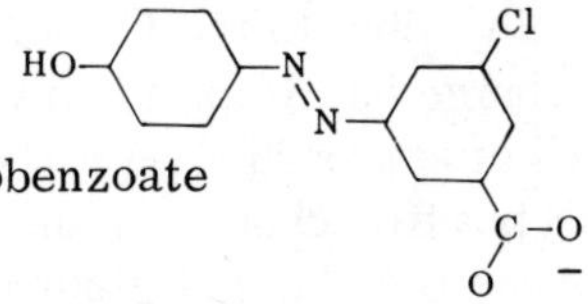 0.091	1300
-4-chlorobenzoate	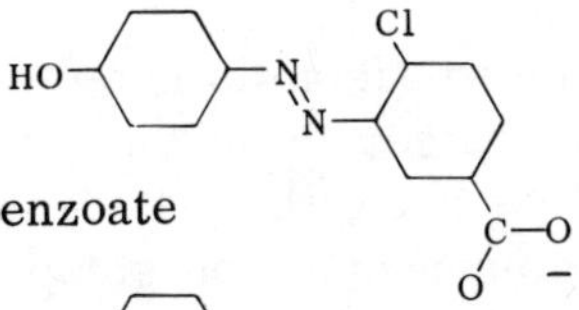 0.058	1600
-6-chlorobenzoate	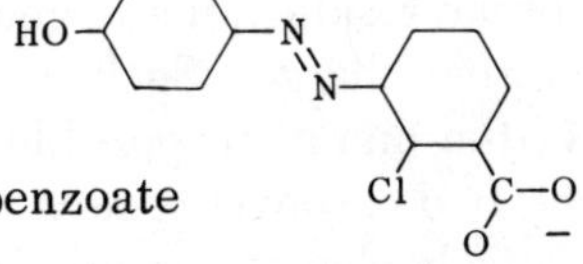 0.020	2200
Phthalate	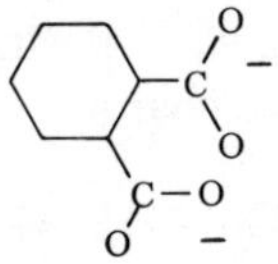 0.007	2700
Terephthalate	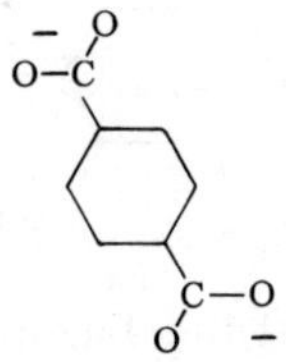 0.031	1900

[a]Data from Pressman and Siegel (unpublished).

values of K_{rel} are less when the chlorines are in other positions where they cannot be accommodated as well.

The requirement of carboxylates in the correct position is shown by comparison of phthalate, isophthalate, and terephthalate with the carboxylates in the ortho, meta, and para positions. It can be seen that only when the second carboxylate is in the meta position is there an appreciable degree of combination.

3.11b Charge interaction. The quantitative contribution of the second carboxyl to the binding is demonstrated by comparing the 5-azophthalate with the 3-azobenzoate as well as by comparing isophthalate with benzoate as above. Replacing one carboxyl by a hydrogen causes a ΔF_{rel} change of +3300 cal for the azo compound and +2800 cal for the unsubstituted phthalate.

This means that there is a positive charge in the antibody site close to the position occupied by the carboxylate. The contribution of the charge of the second carboxylate to binding can be obtained by use of the Schwartzenbach function for the effective dielectric constant (Section 3.3g), and is found to be essentially equal to the Coulombic energy of a positive charge and a negative charge 5.6 Å apart. This is 2.5 Å greater than the 3.1 Å minimum distance of approach for a carboxyl oxygen and an ammonium ion carrying the positive charge in the antibody. This same distance of approach between the charged groups was also found for the anti-*p*-azophenyltrimethylammonium system in which the positive charge is carried by the hapten.

The results obtained in this investigation do not answer the question of whether one or two positive charges are in the antibody combining region which is directed against the two carboxylate ion groups. It might well be expected that either an ammonium ion group on the antibody such as the ε-amino group of a lysine residue, or the guanidinium group of arginine would carry the positive charge. Such a group might be within (on the average) 2.6 Å of the minimum possible distance of approach of 3.0 Å from each of the two carboxyl groups. However, there might instead be present two positively charged groups, on opposite sides of the haptenic group, with each positive charge being approximately 5.6 Å from the nearest negative charge.

3.12 ANTIBODIES TO THE 4-AZOPHTHALATE ION

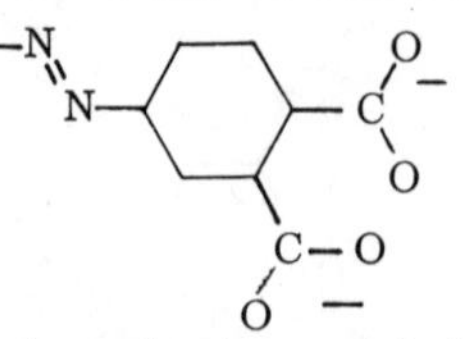

Studies with antibody against the 4-azophthalate ion have shown that in this system, as in the anti-isophthalate system, the two carboxyl groups are important for specificity. These studies have also shown that there is a rather loose fit of antibody around the rest of the phthalate group as compared with anti-isophthalate antibody.

3.12a The effect of substituents on the benzene ring on the interaction of phthalate ion with antibody. The introduction of a nitro group onto the phthalate ion in the 4′ position increases the combining constant by only 3% (Table 3.28). This effect is very small compared to

TABLE 3.28 Effect of Substituents on Combination in the Anti-phthalate System[a]

Hapten	K_{rel}	ΔF_{rel} (cal)
Phthalate	1.0	0
4-Nitrophthalate	1.03	−20
3-Nitrophthalate	0.65	230
Tetrachlorophthalate	0.62	270
Tetrabromophthalate	0.81	120
Tetraiodophthalate	0.35	590

[a] Data from Pressman and Siegel (1953).

the effect of a nitro group in the position occupied by the azo group for most other systems studied. The small effect with anti-phthalate antibody indicates a loose fit of the antibody around the side of the phthalate ion opposite to the charged groups. Even the substitution of a nitro group in the 3 position results in a combining constant only slightly lower than that of the unsubstituted ion ($K_{rel}=0.65$). This indicates some looseness of fit of antibody also around the position adjacent to at least one of the carboxylate groups of the phthalate ion. The nature of the fit is further borne out by the fact that the replacement of the four hydrogen atoms of the ring by four chlorine atoms, giving the tetrachlorophthalate ion, results in a K_{rel} value of 0.62. It might be expected that the steric effect of forcing four large chlorine atoms into the region of the antibody fitted to the ring hydrogen atoms would greatly decrease the combination of the hapten with antibody. Instead, the greater van der Waals attraction possessed by the chlorine atoms in comparison to the replaced hydrogen atoms is more important than the steric effect. In the case of the tetrabromophthalate ion, K_{rel} is 0.81; thus, the increased van der Waals attractive force is still somewhat more effective in counterbalancing the steric effect of the larger bromine atoms. The very large size of the iodine atoms in the tetraiodophthalate ion ($K_{rel}=0.35$) results in a steric effect which overcomes the greater van der Waals attraction of these more polarizable atoms. The relative sizes of the tetrachloro-, tetrabromo-, and tetraiodophthalate ions can be seen from Fig. 3.15. An increase in diameter of the hapten by 2.0 Å (from the phthalate ion to the tetraiodo-

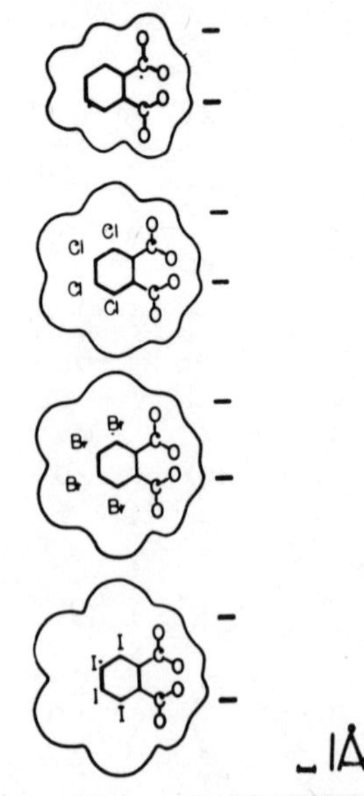

FIGURE 3.15 Relative sizes of the tetrahalo substituted phthalate ions.

phthalate ion) causes K_{rel} in this system to decrease to one third its value, whereas the same K_{rel} decrease in the *p*-azobenzoate system is caused by an increase in diameter of only 0.8 Å (due to the introduction of a single bromine atom in the 3 position of benzoic acid). These numbers may serve to represent the average closeness of fit of the antibody to the haptenic group in the two systems.

3.12b The effect of charge on the combination of antibody and hapten (Table 3.29). The antibody to the phthalate ion combines only slightly with the singly charged benzoate ion, or with the *o*-nitrobenzoate ion, which has essentially the same steric configuration and size as the phthalate ion but with only one charge. However, it combines moderately well with the *o*-sulfobenzoate ion ($K_{rel}=0.26$). In the anti-*p*-azobenzoate system, the sulfonate cannot replace carboxylate but in this system there appears to be a reduced specificity for the structure of the second charged group, a sulfonate ion group being less effective than the carboxylate ion group by only 750 cal.

The reason for the effectiveness of the sulfonate group in the anti-phthalate system is probably that the carboxylates in phthalate are tilted out of the plane of the benzene ring, because they do not have enough room to assume the coplanar configuration exhibited by the carboxylate and benzene ring in benzoate (see Fig. 3.16). The antibody is directed against this thicker structure and thus can accommodate the sulfonate somewhat better. Antibody formed against the coplanar carboxylate of benzoate cannot accommodate the sulfonate.

3.12c Importance of the benzene ring. Maleate, fumarate, and succinate ions are similar to the phthalate ion in that they are composed of two carboxylate ion groups separated by two carbon atoms, although they do not have a benzene ring. Fumarate ion does not combine with the antibody, since the carboxylate ion groups in it are in the trans configuration. Succinate ion does not combine for the same reason. However, the carboxylates of maleate ion are in a configuration similar to that of the phthalate ion. The maleate ion combines measurably with antibody (Table 3.29), but less strongly than does the phthalate ion because it has smaller van der Waals and hydrophobic interactions, due to the lack of the benzene ring.

The benzene ring can be replaced effectively by the naphthalene ring, since the 1,8-naphthalate ion combines appreciably with anti-phthalate antibody, giving $K_{rel}=0.22$. The fit of this hapten into the antibody site is poor, however, for naphthalene is much larger than benzene; furthermore, the carboxylate groups do not occupy the same relative positions in the naphthalate ion as they do when they are ortho to each other on the benzene ring. The effective diameter of the combining region of the antibody must be at least 1.5 Å greater than the diameter of the homologous haptenic group (the diameter of 1,8-naphthalate ion parallel to a line

TABLE 3.29 Importance of Carboxyl Groups and the Benzene Ring for Combination in the Anti-phthalate System[a]

Hapten	K_{rel}	ΔF_{rel} (cal)
Phthalate	1.0	0
o-Carboxybenzenesulfonate	0.26	750
Benzoate	0.01	2600
o-Nitrobenzoate	0.01	2600
α-Carboxynaphthoate	0.22	850
Maleate	< 0.005	> 3000

[a] Data from Pressman and Siegel (1953) and Pressman and Pauling (1949).

connecting the two carboxyl groups is 8.8 Å, and that of the phthalate ion is 7.3 Å).

When the benzene ring is replaced by pyridine to give pyridine-2,3-dicarboxylate ion, which differs from the phthalate ion in that a nitrogen atom takes the place of one of the CH groups in the benzene ring adjacent to a carboxylate ion, K_{rel} drops to the value 0.36. A further drop, to 0.05, is shown by pyrazine-2,3-dicarboxylate ion, in which there is a similar

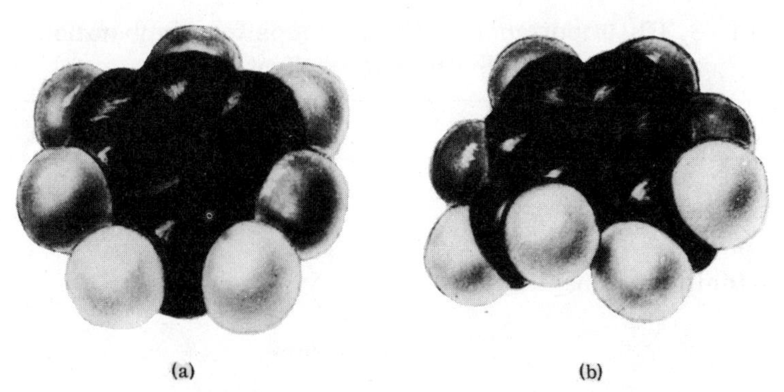

FIGURE 3.16 Tilt of carboxylates out of the plane of the benzene ring in *o*-phthalate. (a) Benzoate with carboxylate in plane of benzene ring; (b) *o*-phthalate with carboxylates tilted.

second nitrogen atom. These decreases are comparable to that observed with anti-*p*-azobenzoate antibody when the benzene ring of benzoate is replaced by pyridine to give the *o*-carboxypyridine. The decrease is due to the water of hydration attached to the ring nitrogen (see Chapter 7).

3.13 ANTIBODY TO THE AZO-3,5-DINITRO-BENZENE GROUP

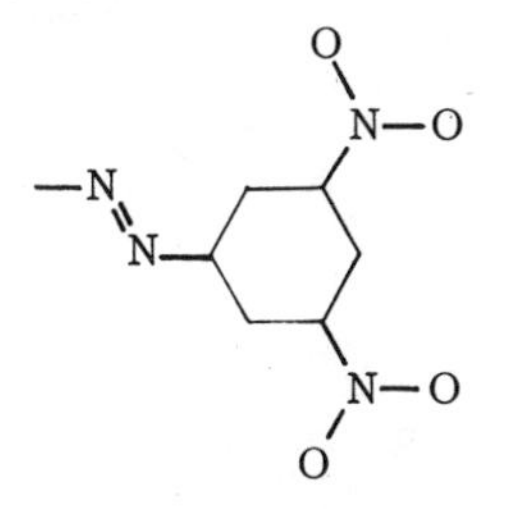

Antibody directed against this hapten has specificity directed against both uncharged nitro groups. As in the cases of anti-isophthalate and anti-phthalate antibodies, where both carboxylates are important, both nitro groups are important for combination here. The contribution of each to the free energy of combination with anti-3,5-dinitro antibody is shown by comparing the free energies of combination of the antibody with 3,5-dinitrosuccinanilate, 3-nitrosuccinanilate, and succinanilate. The loss of one nitro group results in an increase in ΔF_{rel} of 2800 cal/mole (Table 3.30). Loss of the second nitro group causes a further increase of 1700 cal/mole. The total contribution of both nitro groups is thus 4500 cal/mole.

The group in the attachment-homologous position is very important. Replacement of a succinamate group by a carboxylate group in this position decreases K_{rel} to 0.03. This may be due to a negative charge in this

TABLE 3.30 Importance of Nitro Groups for Combination in the Anti-3,5-dinitrobenzene System[a, b]

Hapten		K_{rel}	ΔF_{rel} (cal)
3,5-Dinitrosuccinanilate	Su–C_6H_3(–NO_2)$_2$ (3,5)	1.00	0
3-Nitrosuccinanilate	Su–C_6H_4–NO_2 (3)	0.006	2800
Succinanilate	Su–C_6H_5	0.0003	4500
3,5-Dinitrobenzoate	$^-$O–C(=O)–C_6H_3(–NO_2)$_2$ (3,5)	0.030	1900
3-Nitrobenzoate	$^-$O–C(=O)–C_6H_4–NO_2 (3)	0.001	3800
Benzoate	$^-$O–C(=O)–C_6H_5	< 0.0005	> 4200
3-Nitro-5-carboxysuccinanilate	Su–C_6H_3(–COO^-)(–NO_2) (3,5)	0.003	3200

(continued)

TABLE 3.30 *(continued)*

Hapten	K_{rel}	ΔF_{rel} (cal)
3,5-Dicarboxysuccinanilate	$<$ 0.0005	$>$ 4200

[a]Data from Nisonoff *et al.* (1959a).

[b]Su is $^{-}O_2C-CH_2-CH_2-C(=O)-NH-$

particular region of antibody. The 3,5-dinitrobenzoate has its nitro groups in the correct positions. Removing one of these increases the free energy change of the reaction by 1900 cal. Removing the second to give benzoate ion decreases combination still further. When a carboxylate replaces one of the nitro groups in the 3,5-dinitrophenylsuccinamate, combination is greatly decreased ($K_{rel}=0.003$). Replacing the second by a carboxylate drops the constant still further. This is in accord with the previously observed phenomenon that a carboxylate is ineffective in replacing a nitro group (Section 3.4a). This is further evidence that the nitro group combines with a nonpolar region of the antibody molecule whereas the carboxylate may not be able to do so because of its charge and probable large degree of hydration.

The situation is similar to that of antibody against the 2,4-dinitrobenzene group, in that good combination is obtained only with haptens containing the 2,4-dinitro group; removing one of the nitro groups results in a large decrease in combining constant, as discussed in the following section.

3.14 ANTIBODY TO THE 2,4-DINITROPHENYL GROUP

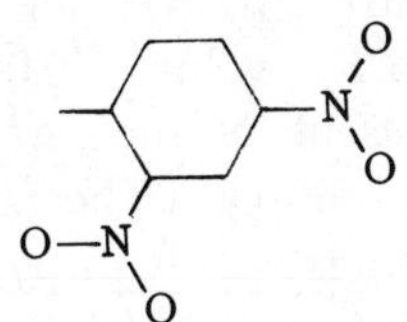

The antibodies formed against the 2,4-dinitrophenyl group have been studied by Eisen and his collaborators (Eisen, 1962; Eisen, 1966; Carsten and Eisen, 1955; Eisen and Siskind, 1964). The immunogen is formed by the reaction of dinitrofluorobenzene or dinitrobenzenesulfonate with protein. These antibodies are of particular interest because these investigators have shown that it is possible to obtain sera containing antibodies with extremely large differences in their combining constant with the same hapten. These differences seem to depend in part on the amount of antigen injected and in part on the time after initial immunization. Thus when the protein antigen, coupled with 40 to 50 dinitrophenyl groups per protein molecule, is injected in large amount (100–250 mg), the antibody formed combines with ε-2,4-dinitrophenyl-L-lysine with a relatively low average binding constant ($K'_H \approx 10^5$). The value of K'_H remains in this range for at least 2 months after initial immunization (Eisen and Siskind, 1964). On the other hand, when a small amount (5 mg) of the same antigen is injected, antibodies formed within 2 weeks after the injection have K'_H values of 10^5 to 10^6; after an additional 3 to 6 weeks, the antibodies formed have much larger K'_H values of 10^7 to 10^8. It is quite possible that many of the other systems described in this book also would show similar differences in binding properties if investigated under the correct conditions.

The properties of antibody with a high binding constant cannot be investigated readily by the methods of hapten inhibition of precipitation or by dialysis equilibrium, but can be determined by fluorescence quenching (Section 2.3). K_{rel} values can be obtained directly from ratios of measured K'_H values.

The data for the K_{rel} values for anti-2,4-dinitrophenyl antibody of high binding constant are given in Table 3.31 with *m*-dinitrobenzene as the reference compound.

When the hydrogen in the attachment-homologous position of *m*-dinitrobenzene is replaced by an amino group, K_{rel} is 3.7; when it is replaced by a methyl, K_{rel} is 2.2; when it is replaced by the phenolic OH, which is ionized under these conditions, K_{rel} drops to 0.45.

The requirement of both nitro groups for good combination of hapten with antibody is shown by the low K_{rel} values of 0.012 and 0.010 for *p*-mononitroaniline and *o*-mononitroaniline, respectively. This result is in accord with the previously mentioned fact that, for anti-3,5-dinitro antibody, removing one nitro group from the 3,5-dinitrosuccinanilate reference hapten produces a K_{rel} value of 0.006, corresponding to a ΔF_{rel} value of 2800 cal. In the present instance, ΔF_{rel} for the equivalent loss of a nitro group is also about 2800 cal. The fact that the coupling of the dinitrophenyl group to protein is mainly through the lysine ε-amino groups to give ε-DNP-L-lysyl groups is reflected in the large value of K_{rel}, 38, for ε-DNP-L-lysine. For ε-DNP-D-lysine, the somewhat smaller value of K_{rel}, 20, is in accord with the fact that the lysine in the protein antigen is in

TABLE 3.31 Binding of Various Haptens in the Anti-2,4-dinitrophenyl System[a]

Hapten	Structure	K_{rel}	ΔF_{rel} (cal)
m-Dinitrobenzene	1,3-$(O_2N)_2C_6H_4$	1.00	0
2,4-Dinitroaniline	H_2N—	3.7	−800
2,4-Dinitrotoluene	H_3C—	2.2	−480
2,4-Dinitrophenol	^-O—	0.45	500
p-Nitroaniline	$H_2N-C_6H_4-NO_2$	0.012	2700
o-Nitroaniline	$H_2N-C_6H_4-NO_2$ (ortho)	0.01	2800
ε-DNP-L-lysine	$^-OOC-CH(NH_2)-CH_2-CH_2-CH_2-CH_2-NH-$	38	−2200
ε-DNP-D-lysine	$^-OOC-CH(NH_2)-CH_2-CH_2-CH_2-CH_2-NH-$	20	−1800
ε-DNP-aminocaproate	$^-OOC-CH_2-CH_2-CH_2-CH_2-CH_2-NH-$	47	−2350

(continued)

TABLE 3.31 *(continued)*

Hapten	K_{rel}	ΔF_{rel} (cal)
δ-DNP-L-ornithine $^{-}O_2C{-}CH(NH_2){-}CH_2{-}CH_2{-}CH_2{-}NH{-}$	14.3	−1600
γ-DNP-aminobutyrate $^{-}O_2C{-}CH_2{-}CH_2{-}CH_2{-}NH{-}$	33	−2100
β-DNP-alanine $^{-}O_2C{-}CH_2{-}CH_2{-}NH{-}$	31	−2100
α-DNP-L-alanine $^{-}O_2C{-}CH(CH_3){-}NH{-}$	14.7	−1650
α-DNP-L-norleucine $CH_3{-}CH_2{-}CH_2{-}CH_2{-}CH(CO_2^{-}){-}NH{-}$	9	−1330
DNP-glycine $^{-}O_2C{-}CH_2{-}NH{-}$	7.7	−1230
α-DNP-L-phenylalanine $C_6H_{11}{-}CH_2{-}CH(CO_2^{-}){-}NH{-}$	5	−970

[a] Data from Eisen and Siskind (1964).

the L configuration. δ-DNP-L-ornithine, with a chain one carbon shorter than ε-DNP-L-lysine, has a K_{rel} value of 14.3. In fact, it appears that any hydrocarbon chain attached to the DNP group, as in ε-DNP-aminocaproate, γ-DNP-aminobutyrate, or even β-DNP-alanine, produces a K_{rel} value much greater than 1.0. Thus it would seem that the antibody site which is binding the dinitrophenyl derivatives fits closely around the van der Waals outline of the ε-DNP-amino hydrocarbon chain.

In connection with the α-DNP-amino acids, the L-alanine derivative is bound somewhat more tightly than are the L-norleucine or the L-phenylalanine derivatives. This finding suggests that the butyl and phenyl residues, as well as the α-carboxyl group, interfere sterically with the binding. In comparing DNP-glycine with α-DNP-alanine, the lower K_{rel} value of the former indicates that the methyl group of the latter contributes somewhat to its combination with the antibody.

With respect to the anti-2,4-dinitrophenyl antibody of high binding constant for ϵ-DNP-L-lysine ($\Delta F \cong 10.1$ kcal/mole), there is a large difference between its ability to bind ϵ-DNP-L-lysine and its ability to bind 2,4-dinitroaniline (Table 3.32). In contrast, the anti-dinitrophenyl antibody with a low binding constant for ϵ-DNP-L-lysine ($\Delta F \cong 7.6$ kcal/mole) binds these two haptens with almost the same strength. The binding force involved appears to be largely that of nonpolar interaction or van der Waals interaction.

TABLE 3.32 Differences in Hapten Combining Properties of Anti-2,4-dinitrophenyl Antibodies of High and Low Combining Constant[a]

Hapten	K_{rel} of "high constant" antibody	K_{rel} of "low constant" antibody
ϵ-DNP-L-lysine	1.0	1.0
2,4-Dinitroaniline	0.1	0.5

[a] Data from Eisen and Siskind (1964).

3.15 ANTIBODY TO THE AZO-3-NITRO-5-CARBOXYBENZENE GROUP

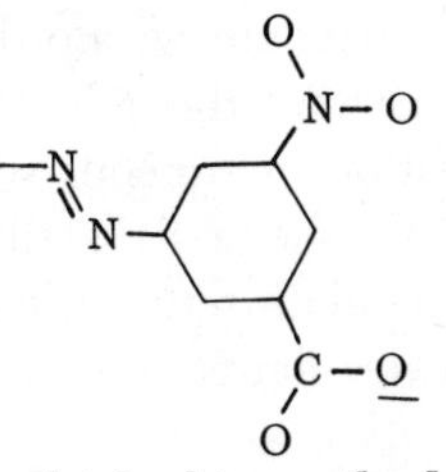

The structure against which this antibody is directed is intermediate between the structures in the anti-3,5-dinitrobenzene and the anti-isophthalate systems. Whereas anti-3,5-dinitro antibody requires two nitro groups, and the anti-isophthalate antibody two carboxylate groups, for good combination, this antibody requires both a carboxylate and a nitro group. As shown in Table 3.33, removing the carboxylate group drops K_{rel} to a value of 0.0013, while removing the nitro group drops K_{rel} to 0.0005. Removing both groups drops the K_{rel} to 0.0001. Replacing the carboxyl with the nitro to give the 3,5-dinitrosuccinanilate gives a K_{rel} value of 0.013, and replacing the nitro of the homologous hapten by a carboxylate group to give the 3,5-dicarboxysuccinanilate gives a very low value of K_{rel} (0.0001).

Apparently a nitro group can replace a carboxylate more effectively than vice versa. As suggested previously, this may mean either that a carboxylate is larger in size, due perhaps to hydration, so that it does not fit as well; or that there is a negative charge close to the region directed against the nitro group of the injected hapten, so that repulsion occurs when a carboxylate is presented.

The group which is in the attachment-homologous region plays an important role, as shown in Table 3.33. The groups are in the following order: Su, 1.0 > NO_2, 0.65 > CO_2^-, 0.24 > H, 0.13. The observed constants for 3,5-dinitrobenzoate and 5-nitroisophthalate were divided by two to give the values listed to take care of a symmetry factor, because there are twice the number of ways these haptens can combine as can the reference 3-nitro-5-carboxysuccinanilate. This antibody can tolerate the presence of a carboxylate group in the attachment-homologous position much better than can the anti-3,5-dinitro antibody.

3.16 ANTIBODY TO THE *p*-AZOSUCCINANILATE ION GROUP

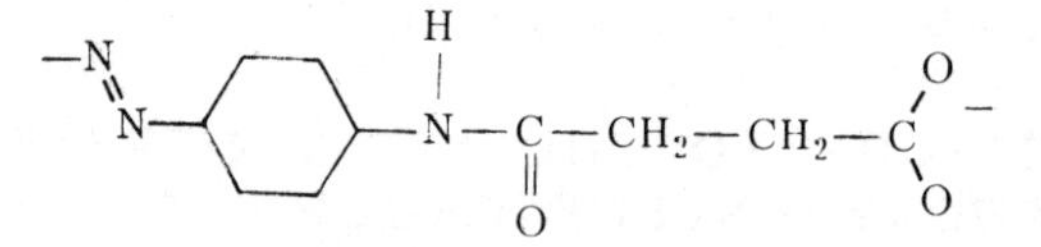

Antibody to the *p*-azosuccinanilate group is of particular interest because it has yielded evidence that the side chain of the succinanilate group exists in a cis configuration in aqueous solution. Landsteiner and van der Scheer (1934) originally showed that the maleate ion combines more strongly with anti-succinanilate serum than does fumarate ion, and that citraconate (methyl maleate) ion combines more strongly than does mesaconate (methyl fumarate) ion.

Quantitative determinations using various pools of antibody give values of K_{rel} from 0.1 to 0.25 for maleanilate, while K_{rel} for fumaranilate is 0.01 (Table 3.34). Thus, it appears that the antibody is complementary to a cis configuration (Fig. 3.17a) similar to that of maleanilate ion

TABLE 3.33 Importance of Both a Nitro and Carboxylate Group for Combination in the Anti-3-nitro-5-carboxybenzene System[a]

Hapten[b]	K_{rel}	ΔF_{rel} (cal)
3-Nitro-5-carboxysuccinanilate	1.0	0
3-Nitrosuccinanilate	0.0013	3700
3-Carboxysuccinanilate	0.0005	4700
Succinanilate	0.0001	5100
3,5-Dinitrosuccinanilate	0.013	2400
3,5-Dicarboxysuccinanilate	0.0001	5100
3,5-Dinitrobenzoate	0.65[c]	240
5-Nitroisophthalate	0.24[c]	800

(continued)

TABLE 3.33 *(continued)*

Hapten[b]		K_{rel}	ΔF_{rel} (cal)
m-Nitrobenzoate	(structure: benzene ring with $-COO^-$ and $-NO_2$ in meta positions)	0.13	1130

[a] Data from Pressman and Nisonoff (unpublished).

[b] Su is $^{-}O(O)C—CH_2—CH_2—C(=O)—N(H)—$

[c] Corrected for symmetry (see text).

(Fig. 3.17b), rather than to an extended configuration shown in Fig. 3.17c which is similar to that of fumaranilate (Fig. 3.17d).

It is likely that the cis configuration indicated for this haptenic group has a hydrogen bond between the amide nitrogen atom and one of the oxygen atoms of the carboxylate group, and that it is largely the energy of this hydrogen bond which stabilizes the cis configuration. The ring closed by the bond probably is not coplanar; the two methylene groups probably assume the staggered rather than the eclipsed orientation, that is, the groups attached to the two ethane carbons lie between each other rather than opposite one another (Fig. 3.18).

3.16a Structural features affecting interaction with antibody. The negatively charged carboxylate group is of considerable importance in the reaction of haptens with anti-succinanilate antibody. Other important structural features are the arrangement about the two carbons of the ethane part of the molecule, the relative distance between the carboxylate and carbonyl group, the carbonyl group, the NH group, and the benzene ring.

3.16b Arrangement about the ethane grouping. As shown in Table 3.34, when the ethane group is altered there is a change in combining power. Replacing one of the hydrogens with hydroxyl on each carbon to give tartranilic acid greatly reduces combining strength. This sizeable effect may be due to the OH groups alone, but is more probably due to the fact that they are hydrated, giving a larger steric effect. Similarly, replacing one CH_2 group by NH to give hydantoate increases ΔF_{rel} by 1300 cal ($K_{rel}=0.1$). Here the large effect of the NH group, which by

TABLE 3.34 Effect of Changes in Structure of the Ethane Part of Succinanilate on Combination in the Anti-*p*-azo-succinanilate System[a]

Hapten	Structure	K_{rel}	ΔF_{rel} (cal)
Succinanilate	$C_6H_5-NH-C(=O)-CH_2-CH_2-COO^-$	1.00	0
Tartranilate	$-C(=O)-CH(OH)-CH(OH)-COO^-$	<< 0.01	>> 2600
Hydantoate	$-C(=O)-NH-CH_2-COO^-$	0.10	1300
Fumaranilate	$-C(=O)-CH=CH-COO^-$ (trans)	0.01	2600
Maleanilate	$-C(=O)-CH=CH-COO^-$ (cis)	0.11 to 0.25	770 to 1200

[a] Data from Pressman and Siegel (1953) and Pressman *et al.* (1948).

itself is no greater in size than the CH_2 group, probably is also due to hydration which increases its effective size and causes steric interference. When the $-CH_2-CH_2-$ group is replaced by the trans ethylene group to give fumaranilate there is essentially no combination; when it is replaced by the cis ethylene group to give the maleanilate, K_{rel} is 0.1 to 0.25 depending on the serum used. This strong interaction with maleanilate ion is evidence that the antibody is directed against a cis configuration.

3.16c The importance of correct distance between the carbonyl and carboxylate groups. The data in Table 3.35 show the importance of maintaining the correct distance between the carbonyl and carboxylate groups. Shortening this distance by one methylene group, from succinanilate to malonanilate, reduces K_{rel} by a factor of 30. Increasing

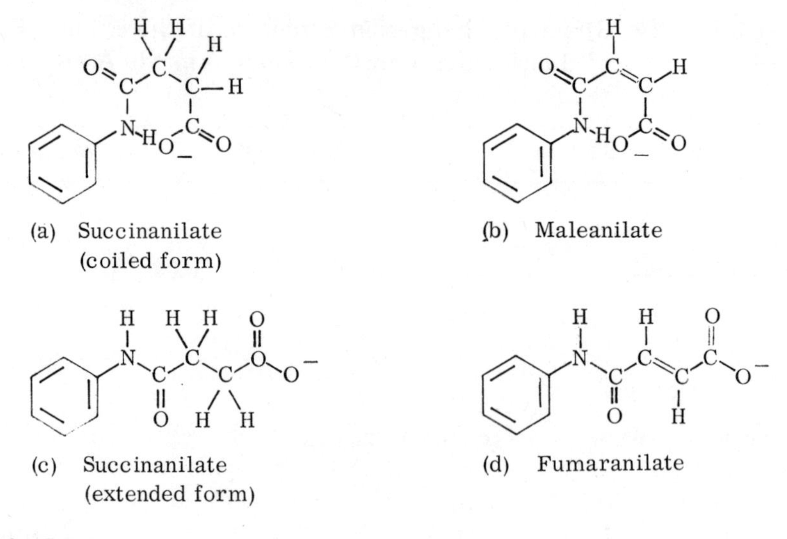

FIGURE 3.17 Coiled and extended forms of the succinanilate ions.

the distance by one methylene group, to give glutaranilate, also reduces K_{rel} by a factor of 30. A similar effect is shown in that β-benzoylpropionate has a K_{rel} value of 0.70 whereas that of benzoylbutyrate is only 0.05.

3.16d The importance of the carbonyl group. The carbonyl group probably acts as a proton acceptor in the formation of a hydrogen bond with the antibody. It may also be a factor in the cyclization which gives the cis configuration for substances like β-benzoylpropionate (see

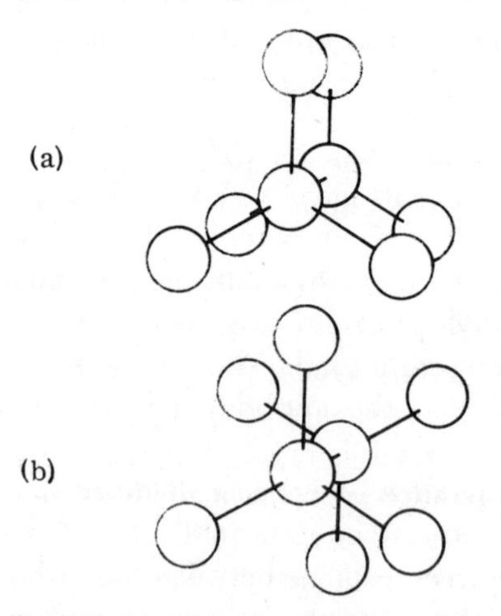

FIGURE 3.18 (a) Eclipsed and (b) staggered orientations about a carbon-carbon single bond.

TABLE 3.35 Importance of Correct Distance between Carbonyl and Carboxyl Groups for Combination in the Anti-*p*-azosuccinanilate System[a]

Hapten	Structure	K_{rel}	ΔF_{rel} (cal)
Succinanilate	$C_6H_5-NH-CO-CH_2-CH_2-COO^-$	1.00	0
Malonanilate	$-CO-CH_2-COO^-$	0.03	1900
Glutaranilate	$-CO-CH_2-CH_2-CH_2-COO^-$	0.03	1900
β-Benzoyl-propionate	$C_6H_5-CO-CH_2-CH_2-COO^-$	0.70	200
γ-Benzoyl-butyrate	$-CO-CH_2-CH_2-CH_2-COO^-$	0.05	1700

[a]Data from Pressman *et al.* (1948).

Section 3.16i). In Table 3.36, the contribution of the carbonyl group is demonstrated by comparing the values of K_{rel} for succinanilate ion ($K_{rel}=1.00$) and for the γ-anilinobutyrate ion ($K_{rel}=0.01$) in which the carbonyl is replaced by a methylene. A similar comparison of the same replacement may be made with β-benzoylpropionate ion ($K_{rel}=0.70$) and γ-phenylbutyrate ion ($K_{rel}=0.01$). In addition, levulinate ion, which has a methyl group in place of the phenylamino, has a K_{rel} of 0.07, whereas $K_{rel}=0.01$ when the carbonyl of this ion is replaced by methylene to give valerate ion.

These data, as well as those in Table 3.35, further demonstrate that the NH group is not particularly important, inasmuch as the benzoylpropionate ion shows a relatively large combining constant ($K_{rel}=0.20$–0.70 for different preparations). Indeed, when the phenylamino group is replaced by a methyl group, as in levulinate, combining activity is still observed.

3.16e The importance of the benzene ring. In Table 3.37 are listed data for compounds in which the benzene ring of succinanilate has been replaced by hydrogen, methyl, isopropyl or cyclohexyl. All

TABLE 3.36 Importance of the Carbonyl Group for Combination in the Anti-*p*-azosuccinanilate System[a]

Hapten		K_{rel}	ΔF_{rel} (cal)
Succinanilate	C_6H_5–NH–C(=O)–CH_2–CH_2–COO^-	1.00	0
γ-Anilinobutyrate	–CH_2–CH_2–CH_2–COO^-	0.01	2600
β-Benzoyl-propionate	C_6H_5–C(=O)–CH_2–CH_2–COO^-	0.70	200
γ-Phenylbutyrate	–CH_2–CH_2–CH_2–COO^-	0.01	1300
Levulinate	CH_3–C(=O)–CH_2–CH_2–COO^-	0.07	1500
Valerate	CH_3–CH_2–CH_2–CH_2–COO^-	< 0.01	> 2600

[a]Data from Pressman *et al.* (1948).

these replacements result in a decrease in combining activity. Replacing the phenyl by a hydrogen causes a 25-fold decrease in K_{rel} and shows the very important van der Waals or hydrophobic interactions of antibody with the benzene ring. A methyl group or isopropyl group is not especially effective in replacing the benzene ring. A cyclohexyl group is somewhat more effective ($K_{rel}=0.15$); the smaller value than with a benzene ring is probably due to the smaller van der Waals attraction of the cyclohexyl, which in turn results from its smaller polarizability and greater thickness. When the benzene ring is displaced from its homologous position by a methylene group, as in N-benzylsuccinamate, K_{rel} is 0.18.

3.16f Stereospecificity of antibody sites. An interesting phenomenon occurs when one of the hydrogens of the benzyl group is replaced by a methyl to give the α-methylbenzylsuccinamate. The α-methyl-

TABLE 3.37 Importance of the Benzene Ring for Combination in the Anti-*p*-azosuccinanilate System[a]

Hapten		K_{rel}	ΔF_{rel} (cal)
Succinanilate	$C_6H_5-NH-CO-CH_2-CH_2-COO^-$	1.00	0
Succinamate	$H-$	0.04	1800
N-Methyl-succinamate	H_3C-	0.05	1700
N-Isopropyl-succinamate	$(CH_3)_2CH-$	0.06	1600
N-Cyclohexyl-succinamate	$C_6H_{11}-$ (cyclohexyl: CH_2 ring $-CH-$)	0.15	1100
N-Benzyl-succinamate	$C_6H_5-CH_2-$	0.18	950
D-α-Methylbenzyl-succinamate	$C_6H_5-CH(CH_3)-$	0.10	1300
L-α-Methylbenzyl-succinamate	$C_6H_5-CH(CH_3)-$	0.16	1000
Dimethylsuccinamate	$(CH_3)_2N-$	0.34	600
N,N-Pentamethylene-succinamate	$CH_2(CH_2-CH_2)_2N-$	0.16	1000
Diethyl-succinamate	$(C_2H_5)_2N-$	0.12	1200

[a]Data from Pressman *et al.* (1948).

phenyl group exists in D and L forms. Reaction with these compounds demonstrates a stereospecificity of the antibody directed against the optically inactive succinanilate ion. It combines more strongly with one form than with the other (Table 3.37). Different preparations of antiserum give different relative abilities to combine with the D and L forms, but any particular pool of antiserum can differentiate between the two forms. This indicates a lack of symmetry of the antibody around the succinanilate group. This is to be expected, because the antibody site is composed of amino acid residues which, owing to their space-consuming nature, are unable to mold themselves symmetrically around the determinant.

3.16g Contribution of the NH group. When the amide hydrogen of succinanilate ion is replaced by a methyl, there is a decrease in combining power which is probably due to a steric effect but may be due to a decrease in capability to form a hydrogen bond between the carboxylate and the NH. When both the hydrogen and phenyl are replaced by methyls to give the dimethylsuccinamate, the value for K_{rel} is 0.34. This indicates that the antibody can still accommodate the disubstituted nitrogen unless one group is a large phenyl. The K_{rel} values of 0.16 and 0.12 for the N,N-pentamethylenesuccinamate and the diethylsuccinamate, respectively, give a measure of the hydrophobic interaction of these groups with the antibody directed against the benzene ring.

3.16h Closeness of fit about the benzene ring. The effects of various groups in the para position of the benzene ring of the succinanilate ion are shown in Table 3.38. The values of K_{rel} are in the order

$$NO_2 > HOC_6H_4NN > Br > \text{hydrogen} \approx NH_2$$

The nitro group (as observed in other systems) confers an equal or greater combining power on the ion than does the homologous azo group. The increase in combining constants over that of the unsubstituted benzene ring indicates that the antibody site extends beyond the benzene ring and is directed partially against the azo grouping.

In agreement with the other systems studied, moving a group from the attachment-homologous position (the para position) to the ortho and meta positions causes a decrease in combining power. It appears, however, that the fit is not very close around the benzene ring, inasmuch as bromine can be accommodated in the meta position and produces a K_{rel} value greater than 1.0. The β-naphthyl group is accommodated much more readily than the α-naphthyl group because it is a 3,4-disubstituted benzene, whereas the α-naphthyl is a 2,3-substituted benzene ring and gives a greater degree of interference.

Of the ions shown in Table 3.39, both maleate and citraconate show

TABLE 3.38 Closeness of Fit Around the Benzene Ring of Anti-*p*-azosuccinanilate Antibodies[a]

Hapten	K_{rel}	ΔF_{rel} (cal)
Succinanilate	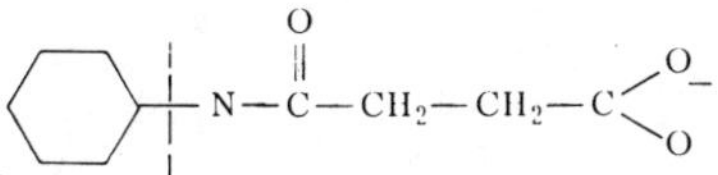 1.00	0
p-Nitrosuccinanilate	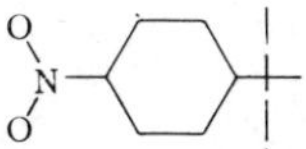 4.1	−800
p-(*p*′-Hydroxphenylazo)-succinanilate	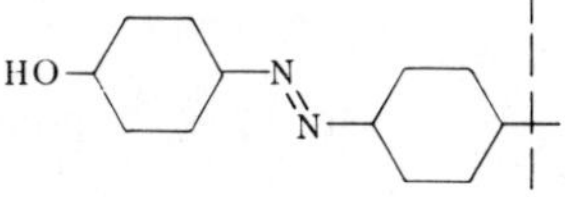 3.9	−750
p-Bromosuccinanilate	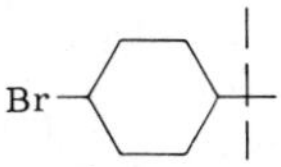 2.2	−450
p-Aminosuccinanilate	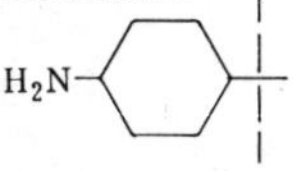 0.95	25
m-Bromosuccinanilate	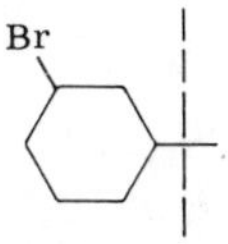 1.8	−300
o-Bromosuccinanilate	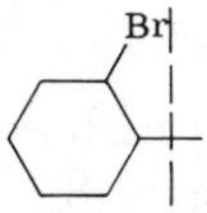 0.40	500
α-Naphthyl-succinamate	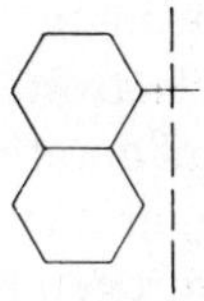 0.32	650
β-Naphthylsuccinamate	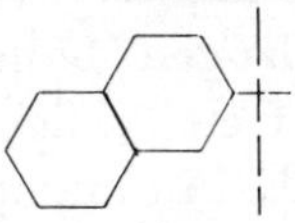 2.2	−450

[a]Data from Pressman *et al.* (1948).

TABLE 3.39 Combination of Cis and Trans Configurations in the Anti-*p*-azosuccinanilate System[a]

Hapten		K_{rel}	ΔF_{rel} (cal)
Succinanilate	$C_6H_5\text{—NH—C(=O)—CH}_2\text{—CH}_2\text{—COO}^-$	1.00	0
Succinate	$^-OOC\text{—CH}_2\text{—CH}_2\text{—COO}^-$	0.01	2600
Maleate	$^-OOC\text{—CH=CH—COO}^-$ (cis; H, H on same side)	0.03	2000
Citraconate	$^-OOC\text{—C(CH}_3\text{)=CH—COO}^-$ (cis; CH_3, H on same side)	0.02	2200
Fumarate	$^-OOC\text{—CH=CH—COO}^-$ (trans)	0.00	> 4000
Mesaconate	$^-OOC\text{—C(CH}_3\text{)=CH—COO}^-$ (trans)	0.00	> 4000

[a]Data from Pressman *et al.* (1948).

some combination. Both of these have two carboxylate groups on the same side of the ethylene bond and show appreciably greater combination than do the trans forms, fumarate and mesaconate. Succinate probably exists as an extended molecule, due to the electrostatic repulsion of the two carboxylate groups, although this cis configuration is one of several readily accessible configurations. A cis configuration is easily formed in those molecules which can stabilize it with hydrogen bonds; succinanilate, succinamate, and N-methylsuccinamate are examples.

3.16i Cis configuration without hydrogen bond stabilization. There is also evidence for predominance of cis configurations in some molecules with no stabilizing hydrogen bonds. An example is β-benzoylpropionate (Table 3.35). The predominance of the cis configuration for this ion in solution is indicated, since the large K_{rel} value of 0.70 would require the cis configuration. A reasonable explanation in this case is that the configuration is stabilized by the electrostatic attraction between the negative charge of the carboxylate ion and a positive charge on the benzene ring and on the carbonyl carbon atom. The resonance structures can place a significant amount of positive charge on either (Fig. 3.19).* The corresponding negative charge is on the carbonyl oxygen atom. In substances like levulinate an attraction exists between the carboxylate negative charge and the positive side of the carbonyl dipole. In N,N-dimethylsuccinamate ion, the positive charge can move from the carbon of the carbonyl dipole to the nitrogen by resonance. Thus, in all these molecules there is the possibility of a cis configuration stabilized by a dipole elsewhere in the molecule.

3.17 ANTIBODIES TO THE *p*-AZOMALEANILATE AND *p*-AZOFUMARANILATE ION GROUPS

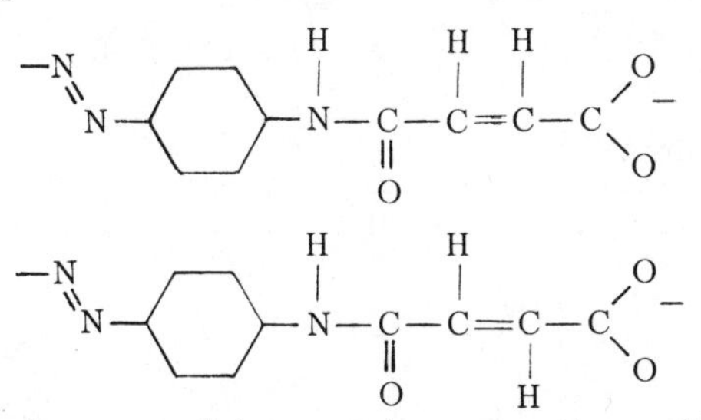

These antibodies are of interest in connection with the observation that antibodies to the related succinanilate ion specifically reflect the cis configuration of that ion in aqueous solution. The maleanilate ion must exist in a cis configuration, whereas the fumaranilate ion must exist in an extended configuration. The antibodies under consideration are directed against each of these structures.

3.17a The maleanilate system (Table 3.40). The anti-maleanilate antibody fits very closely about the *cis*-maleanilate ion, and therefore does not combine with the *trans*-fumaranilate ion. Neither does it combine well with the succinanilate ion, as shown by the ΔF_{rel} value of 2300 cal for the binding. The latter fact suggests that the antibody fits so closely around the flat maleanilate group that it cannot accommodate the thicker methylene groups of the succinanilate ion, in spite of the fact that succinanilate ion can exist in a cis configuration. Of all nonhomologous substances tested, however, succinanilate combines to the greatest extent. Phenylhydantoate and benzoylpropionate, with structures somewhat further removed from that of maleanilate, combine less well, with ΔF_{rel} values of 3000 and 3200 cal, respectively. In phenyl-

* See p. 132 for Fig. 3.19.

TABLE 3.40 Combination of Various Haptens with Antibody in the Anti-maleanilate System[a]

Hapten	Structure	K_{rel}	ΔF_{rel} (cal)
Maleanilate	$C_6H_5-NH-C(=O)-CH=CH-COO^-$ (cis: H, H on same side)	1.00	0
Fumaranilate	$C_6H_5-NH-C(=O)-CH=CH-COO^-$ (trans: H, H on opposite sides)	0.00	> 4000
Succinanilate	$C_6H_5-NH-C(=O)-CH_2-CH_2-COO^-$	0.016	2300
Phenylhydantoate	$C_6H_5-NH-C(=O)-NH-CH_2-COO^-$	0.004	3000
β-Benzoylpropionate	$C_6H_5-C(=O)-CH_2-CH_2-COO^-$	0.003	3200
Maleate	$^-OOC-CH=CH-COO^-$ (cis)	0.00	> 4000
Fumarate	$^-OOC-CH=CH-COO^-$ (trans)	0.00	> 4000
Succinate	$^-OOC-CH_2-CH_2-COO^-$	0.00	> 4000
p-Nitro-maleanilate	$O_2N-C_6H_4-NH-C(=O)-CH=CH-COO^-$ (cis)	9.7	−1300
p-Nitro-succinanilate	$O_2N-C_6H_4-NH-C(=O)-CH_2-CH_2-COO^-$	0.068	1500

[a] Data from Siegel and Pressman (1954).

hydantoate a methylene of succinanilate is replaced by an NH group; in benzoylpropionate the amido NH group is deleted.

The rest of the structural changes other than substitution on the benzene ring result in changes in ΔF_{rel} of more than 3200 cal, which is the largest ΔF_{rel} that has been measured with accuracy in this system. The anilino grouping

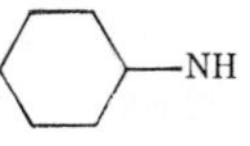

is seen to be very important for combination since its replacement in maleanilate by a negative oxygen to give maleate ion, essentially eliminates measurable combination. Succinate does not combine measurably either.

Substitution of a nitro group in the para position on the benzene ring increases the combination with both maleanilate and succinanilate. The ΔF_{rel} values are more negative by 1300 and 800 cal, respectively. This is due to the greater van der Waals interaction (compared to hydrogen atom) of the nitro group with the antibody region complementary to the azo group of the immunizing antigen.

3.17b The fumaranilate system (Table 3.41). In this system also, any change in hapten structure other than a substitution in the benzene ring greatly decreases the combining power. As is to be expected, this antibody does not react with the maleanilate ion. However, it does react to an appreciable extent with succinanilate ion ($K_{rel}=0.14$) which can also exist in a trans configuration in aqueous solution to some extent. Since the larger methylene groups of the succinanilate ion can be accommodated, this antibody apparently does not fit as closely around the side chain as does the antibody against maleanilate. Changes other than this saturation of the double bond to form succinanilate ion decrease the combining power still further.

Other substances related to the saturated succinanilate structure such as phenylhydantoate and benzoylpropionate, which exist in the coiled configuration, have also been shown to exist in an extended configuration since they combine with anti-fumaranilate antibody. Replacing a methylene group of succinanilate by NH (in phenylhydantoate) decreases combination by increasing ΔF_{rel} by 800 cal. Deleting the NH group of succinanilate to give benzoylpropionate increases ΔF_{rel} by 1200 cal. Placing a methyl group on the anilino NH (N-methylsuccinanilate) increases ΔF_{rel} by 1600 cal. Replacing the anilino group by an oxygen to give fumarate ion increases ΔF_{rel} by at least 3200 cal. The importance of the carbonyl group is also shown by the fact that γ-phenylbutyrate ion ($\Delta F_{rel}=3200$ cal) combines to a lesser extent than does the β-benzoylpropionate ion ($\Delta F_{rel}=2300$ cal).

The significance for combination of the benzene-carboxyl distance is

TABLE 3.41 Combination of Various Haptens with Antibody in the Anti-fumaranilate System[a]

Hapten	Structure	K_{rel}	ΔF_{rel} (cal)
Fumaranilate	$C_6H_5-NH-CO-CH=CH-COO^-$ (trans)	1.00	0
Maleanilate	$C_6H_5-NH-CO-CH=CH-COO^-$ (cis)	0.00	> 4000
Succinanilate	$C_6H_5-NH-CO-CH_2-CH_2-COO^-$	0.14	1100
Phenylhydantoate	$C_6H_5-NH-CO-NH-CH_2-COO^-$	0.030	1900
β-Benzylpropionate	$C_6H_5-CO-CH_2-CH_2-COO^-$	0.016	2300
N-Methyl-succinanilate	$C_6H_5-N(CH_3)-CO-CH_2-CH_2-COO^-$	0.007	2700
Fumarate	$^-OOC-CH=CH-COO^-$	< 0.003	> 3200
γ-Phenylbutyrate	$C_6H_5-CH_2-CH_2-CH_2-COO^-$	0.003	3200
δ-Phenylvalerate	$C_6H_5-CH_2-CH_2-CH_2-CH_2-COO^-$	0.008	2700
p-Nitrofumaranilate	$O_2N-C_6H_4-NH-CO-CH=CH-COO^-$	16.0	− 1600
p-Acetaminofumaranilate	$CH_3-CO-NH-C_6H_4-NH-CO-CH=CH-COO^-$	6.0	−1000
p-Nitrosuccinanilate	$O_2N-C_6H_4-NH-CO-CH_2-CH_2-COO^-$	1.3	−100

[a] Data from Siegel and Pressman (1954).

reflected in the stronger (by 500 cal) combination of phenylvalerate than phenylbutyrate, which is one carbon short of the distance between the groups in the homologous hapten.

The effect of substitution in the benzene ring in the para position (the attachment-homologous position) is to increase the combining power. This is exemplified by the presence of a nitro group in this position which decreases the relative free energy by 1600 cal in the case of *p*-nitrofumaranilate ion, and 1200 cal in the case of *p*-nitrosuccinanilate. The acetamino group has a similar effect (1000 cal) in the fumaranilate system.

The results of these experiments show that succinanilate, N-methylsuccinanilate, benzoylpropionate, and phenylhydantoate ion can exist in aqueous solution in the trans configuration (or readily assume that configuration) as well as the cis configuration which is responsible for their combination with antibodies to succinanilate ion.

3.18 ANTIBODY TO THE *p*-AZO-N-METHYL-SUCCINANILATE ION

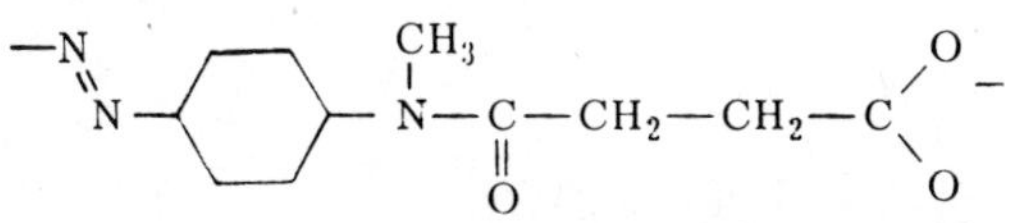

The profound effect that can be displayed by a single methyl group attached to a nitrogen atom makes this antibody interesting (see Table 3.42). The antibody combines very poorly with succinanilate ($K_{rel}=0.005$). Since it also combines poorly with both the *trans*-N-methylfumaranilate and the *cis*-N-methylmaleanilate ions ($K_{rel}=0.017$ and 0.022, respectively), information is not available about the possibility that a coiled N-methylsuccinanilate structure is the one against which the antibody is directed. The benzene ring appears important because its replacement by a methyl or hydrogen to give the N,N-dimethylsuccinamate or N-methylsuccinamate decreases the combination greatly ($K_{rel}=0.022$ and 0.001, respectively).

The data of Table 3.42 indicate that the configurations of the succinanilate and the N-methylsuccinanilate differ greatly. Replacement of the hydrogen by the methyl must have an effect that goes beyond the larger van der Waals or hydrophobic interactions of the methyl group. Apparently the N-methylsuccinanilate can assume a configuration which is different from that of the succinanilate ion.

The fit around the benzene ring is close enough so that the para nitro group when present in succinanilate, fumaranilate, and maleanilate increases the energy of binding from 400 to 800 cal for each compound (Table 3.43).

TABLE 3.42 Combination of Various Haptens with Antibody in the Anti-N-methylsuccinanilate System[a]

Hapten	Structure	K_{rel}	ΔF_{rel} (cal)
N-Methyl-succinanilate 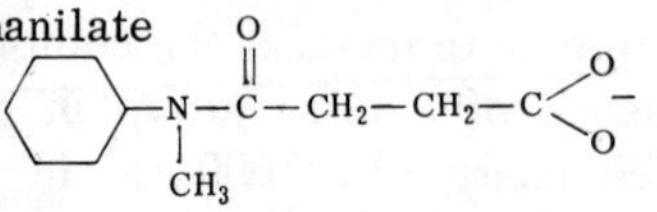	$C_6H_5-N(CH_3)-C(=O)-CH_2-CH_2-COO^-$	1.00	0
N-Methyl-maleanilate 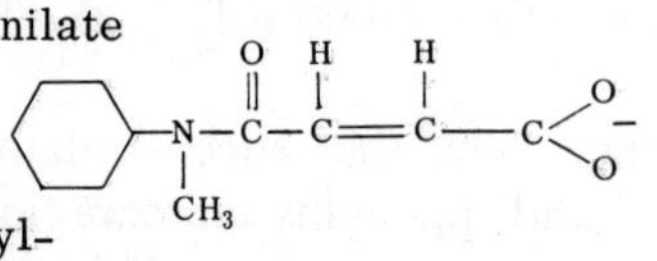	$C_6H_5-N(CH_3)-C(=O)-CH=CH-COO^-$ (cis)	0.022	2100
N-Methyl-fumaranilate 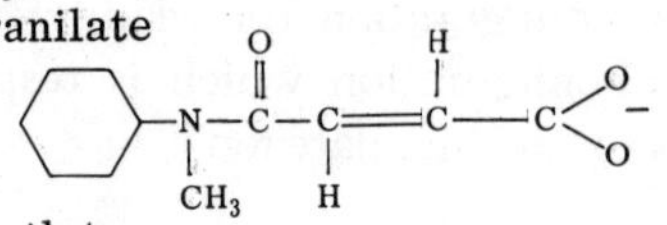	$C_6H_5-N(CH_3)-C(=O)-CH=CH-COO^-$ (trans)	0.017	2300
Succinanilate 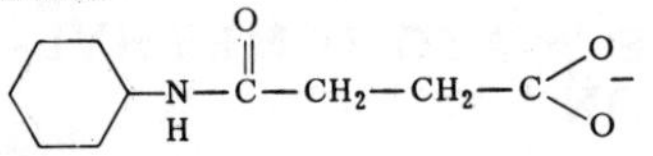	$C_6H_5-NH-C(=O)-CH_2-CH_2-COO^-$	0.005	3000
N,N-Dimethyl-succinamate 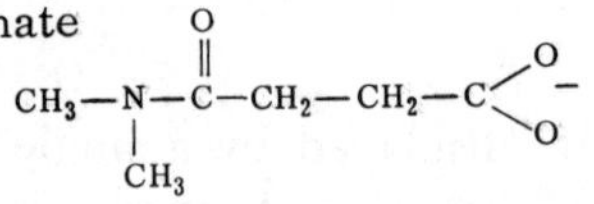	$CH_3-N(CH_3)-C(=O)-CH_2-CH_2-COO^-$	0.022	2100
N-Methyl-succinamate 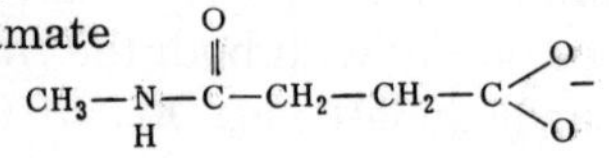	$CH_3-NH-C(=O)-CH_2-CH_2-COO^-$	0.001	3800
β-Benzoylpropionate	$C_6H_5-C(=O)-CH_2-CH_2-COO^-$	0.025	2000
γ-Benzoylbutyrate	$C_6H_5-C(=O)-CH_2-CH_2-CH_2-COO^-$	0.009	2600
γ-Anilinobutyrate	$C_6H_5-NH-CH_2-CH_2-CH_2-COO^-$	< 0.001	> 3800
Levulinate 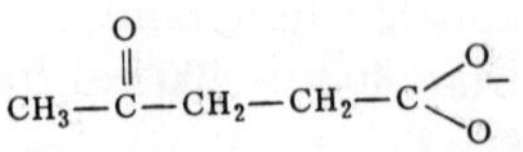	$CH_3-C(=O)-CH_2-CH_2-COO^-$	0.006	2900

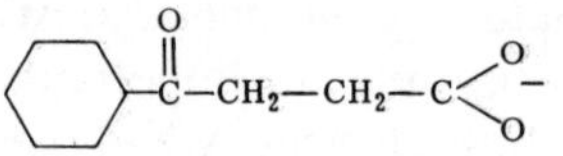

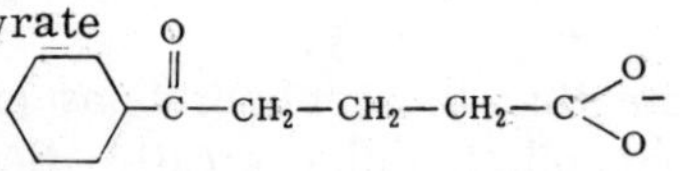

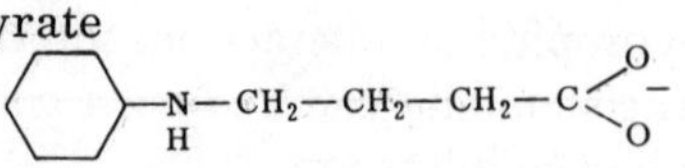

[a] Data from Siegel and Pressman (unpublished).

TABLE 3.43 Closeness of Fit Around the Benzene Ring for Combination in the Anti-N-methylsuccinanilate System[a]

Hapten	K_{rel}	ΔF_{rel} (cal)
N-Methyl-succinanilate $C_6H_5-N(CH_3)-C(=O)-CH_2-CH_2-COO^-$	1.00	0
Succinanilate $C_6H_5-NH-C(=O)-CH_2-CH_2-COO^-$	0.005	3000
p-Nitro-succinanilate $O_2N-C_6H_4-NH-C(=O)-CH_2-CH_2-COO^-$	0.019	2200
Maleanilate $C_6H_5-NH-C(=O)-CH=CH-COO^-$	0.008	2700
p-Nitro-maleanilate $O_2N-C_6H_4-NH-C(=O)-CH=CH-COO^-$	0.014	2300
Fumaranilate $C_6H_5-NH-C(=O)-CH=CH-COO^-$	0.001	3800
p-Nitro-fumaranilate $O_2N-C_6H_4-NH-C(=O)-CH=CH-COO^-$	0.002	3400

[a] Data from Siegel and Pressman (unpublished).

Replacing the methylanilino group by phenyl to give β-benzoylpropionate reduces K_{rel} to 0.025. γ-Benzoylbutyrate, γ-anilinobutyrate, and levulinate have low values of K_{rel}. At the high hapten concentrations used in the inhibition of precipitation by these compounds, they exhibit some combination, probably due to a common feature such as the carboxylate group.

3.19 ANTIBODIES TO *p*-AZO-β-BENZOYLPROPIONATE ION

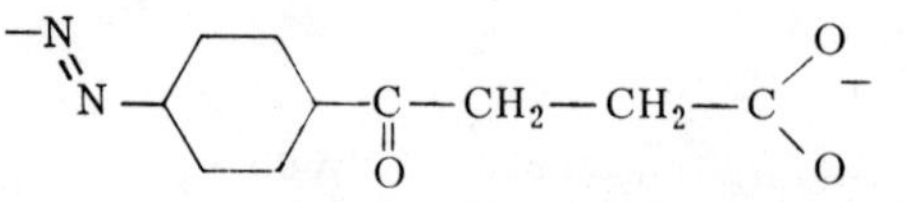

This antibody is of interest in connection with the configuration of the propionate side chain against which it is directed. It is evident that the antibody fits closely about the hapten since all the changes made in structure of that ion (that is, replacement of the phenyl, carbonyl, or methylene groups by other groups) decrease the strength of combination with the antibody appreciably, as shown by the values of ΔF_{rel} for the modified structures, which are all over 1000 cal (Table 3.44).

When the benzene group of benzoylpropionate ion is replaced by the methyl, anilino, or methylanilino groups (leaving the $COCH_2CH_2COO^-$ residue intact) as in the levulinate, succinanilate, and N-methylsuccinanilate ion, K_{rel} is decreased and ΔF_{rel} is increased (group A in Table 3.44). The increase of 1200 cal in ΔF_{rel} which results from the replacement of the benzene by methyl to give levulinate ion is probably due largely to the difference between the phenyl and methyl groups in their van der Waals or hydrophobic attraction for antibody. Replacement of the benzene by an anilino group has a greater effect, increasing ΔF_{rel} by 1800 cal. This appears to be a steric effect, due to displacement of the phenyl group from the position next to the carbonyl group. Replacing the NH of succinanilate by a N—CH_3 group decreases ΔF_{rel}, possibly because the branched structure is more equivalent to the structure of the original benzene group. Another possibility is that the coiled configurations for the NH and NCH_3 compounds are different, and the configuration of the N-methyl compound is closer to that of the benzoylpropionate.

The replacement of a methylene group in the $COCH_2CH_2COO^-$ residue by an NH group to give hippurate increases ΔF_{rel} by 1400 cal (group B in Table 3.44). This decrease of combining power is very large considering that NH and CH_2 are about the same size. It appears that the NH group is hydrated in aqueous solution, the resultant increase in size

TABLE 3.44 Combination of Various Haptens with Antibody in the Anti-β-benzoylpropionate System[a]

Hapten	Structure	K_{rel}	ΔF_{rel} (cal)
Group A			
β-Benzoylpropionate	$C_6H_5-CO-CH_2-CH_2-COO^-$	1.00	0
Levulinate	$CH_3-CO-CH_2-CH_2-COO^-$	0.12	1200
Succinanilate	$C_6H_5-NH-CO-CH_2-CH_2-COO^-$	0.04	1800
N-Methyl-succinanilate	$C_6H_5-N(CH_3)-CO-CH_2-CH_2-COO^-$	0.15	1000
Group B			
Hippurate	$C_6H_5-CO-NH-CH_2-COO^-$	0.08	1400
β-Benzoylacrylate	$C_6H_5-CO-CH=CH-COO^-$	0.04	1800
Group C			
Succinanilate	$C_6H_5-NH-CO-CH_2-CH_2-COO^-$	0.04	1800
Maleanilate	$C_6H_5-NH-CO-CH=CH-COO^-$ (cis)	0.04	1800
Fumaranilate	$C_6H_5-NH-CO-CH=CH-COO^-$ (trans)	0.005	2900
Group D			
γ-Phenylbutyrate	$C_6H_5-CH_2-CH_2-CH_2-COO^-$	0.02	2200
γ-Benzoylbutyrate	$C_6H_5-CO-CH_2-CH_2-CH_2-COO^-$	0.04	1800
Valerate	$CH_3-CH_2-CH_2-CH_2-COO^-$	<0.005	> 2900

[a]Data from Pressman and Siegel (1953b).

causing more steric interference in the combination of the hapten with antibody than that which could be caused by van der Waals interaction or a change in bond angle. Evidence for the hydration of the NH group has already been brought out in the cases of similar compounds interacting with antibodies to the succinanilate ion group (Section 3.16b), and also in connection with the interaction of annular nitrogen compounds with antibenzoate antibodies (Section 3.2e).

The replacement of the CH_2—CH_2 group by CH=CH to give β-benzoylacrylate ion increases ΔF_{rel} by 1800 cal. An effect of this size shows that benzoylacrylate does not fit the antibody well. This would support the belief that β-benzoylacrylate probably exists in the extended trans configuration while the antibody region appears to be complementary to a cis configuration.

The similar change of saturation to unsaturation, in going from succinanilate to maleanilate (group C in Table 3.44) involves no change in ΔF_{rel}, but the change to the trans isomer, fumaranilate, causes an increase in ΔF_{rel} of 1100 cal. These data are in accord with the previous observation that succinanilate can exist in the cis configuration in aqueous solution—a configuration closer to the cis configuration of maleanilate than to the trans configuration of fumaranilate. Moreover, these data also indicate that the anti-benzoylpropionate antibody is more nearly complementary to a cis or coiled configuration of the $COCH_2CH_2COO^-$ grouping than to the trans. On the basis of this argument, it is believed that part of the β-benzoylpropionate ion must be in a cis configuration during the period of antibody formation. Such a cis configuration would be stabilized by the resonance structures shown in Fig. 3.19.

The replacement of the carbonyl group by a methylene group to give phenylbutyrate increases ΔF_{rel} by 2200 cal, indicating that the carbonyl group is very important for the combination of hapten with this antibody. It either functions as a proton acceptor in forming a hydrogen bond or as a factor in stabilizing cyclization. The relative positions of the carbonyl group and the carboxylate group is critical, since moving the benzoyl group one methylene group further from the carboxylate group

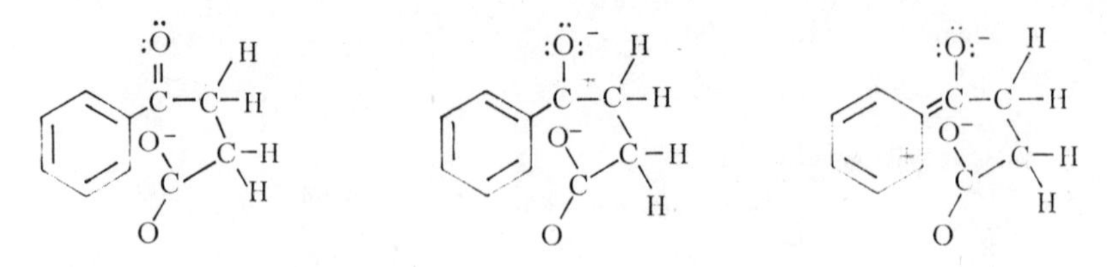

FIGURE 3.19 Resonance forms stabilizing the coiled form of β-benzoylpropionate.

(as in benzoylbutyrate) decreases ΔF_{rel} by 1800 cal (group D in Table 3.44).

The importance of the van der Waals interaction of the benzene ring is indicated by a comparison of antibody combination with phenylbutyrate in which the phenyl and carboxylate are the correct distance apart, and with valerate, in which the phenyl is replaced by methyl (group D in Table 3.44). ΔF_{rel} for the combination with the aliphatic compound is at least 700 cal greater.

3.20 ANTIBODIES TO THE *p*-AZOHIPPURATE GROUP

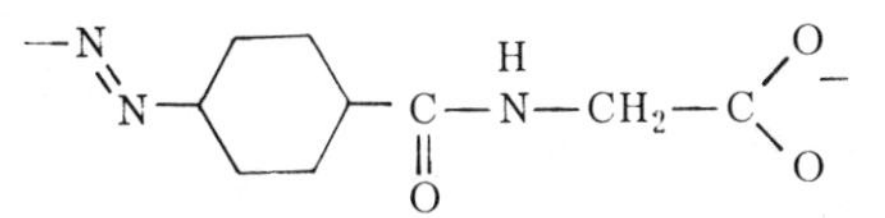

The observation has been made with other antibodies that replacement of a methylene group in a hapten by the amido NH group reduces combination with antibody which has been prepared against the substance containing the methylene group. Thus, phenylhydantoate ion does not combine as well as does succinanilate with antibody prepared against the latter ion (Table 3.40); also hippurate does not combine as well as benzoylpropionate with antibody prepared against benzoylpropionate (Table 3.44). The differences in combining strength are greater than would be expected from the differences in van der Waals interaction or from the difference in size of the CH_2 and NH groups. They have therefore been attributed to hydration of the NH group which would increase its size and provide steric hindrance to the combination. Antibodies against the *p*-azohippurate ion were first studied by van der Scheer and Landsteiner (1935), who determined the antibody reactions with the *p*-nitrobenzoyl derivatives of several amino acids and peptides.

The fit of antibody around the glycine residue of hippurate is very close. The replacement by a methyl group of a hydrogen on the carbon atom α to the carboxylate ion (as in N-benzoylalanate) causes a large decrease in K_{rel} to 0.016 [2300 cal increase in ΔF_{rel} (group A in Table 3.45)]. Increasing the size of the substituent to ethyl, propyl, butyl, or benzyl, as in α-N-benzoylaminobutyrate, α-N-benzoylaminovalerate, α-N-benzoylaminocaproate, and N-benzoylphenylalanate, increases ΔF_{rel} still further.

Replacement of the NH group of hippurate by a methylene group to give β-benzoylpropionate ion also results in a decrease in combining ability ($K_{rel}=0.14$) (group B in Table 3.45). The corresponding increase in the free energy of combination, 1100 cal, is of the same magnitude as the reverse change from methylene to NH observed with anti-benzoyl-

TABLE 3.45 Combination of Various Haptens with Antibody in the Anti-*p*-azohippurate System[a]

Hapten	Structure	K_{rel}	ΔF_{rel} (cal)
	GROUP A		
Hippurate	$C_6H_5-CO-NH-CH_2-COO^-$	1.00	0
N-Benzoylalanate	$C_6H_5-CO-NH-CH(CH_3)-COO^-$	0.016	2300
α-N-Benzoylamino-butyrate	$C_6H_5-CO-NH-CH(C_2H_5)-COO^-$	0.006	2800
α-N-Benzoylamino-valerate	$C_6H_5-CO-NH-CH(C_3H_7)-COO^-$	< 0.006	> 2800
α-N-Benzoylamino-caproate	$C_6H_5-CO-NH-CH(C_4H_9)-COO^-$	< 0.006	> 2800
N-Benzoyl-phenylalanate	$C_6H_5-CO-NH-CH(CH_2C_6H_5)-COO^-$	0.007	2700
	GROUP B		
β-Benzoyl-propionate	$C_6H_5-CO-CH_2-CH_2-COO^-$	0.14	1100
Phenylhydantoate	$C_6H_5-NH-CO-NH-CH_2-COO^-$	0.085	1400
Succinanilate	$C_6H_5-NH-CO-CH_2-CH_2-COO^-$	0.030	1900
N-Acetylglycinate	$CH_3-CO-NH-CH_2-COO^-$	0.012	2400
Levulinate	$CH_3-CO-CH_2-CH_2-COO^-$	0.004	3100

(continued)

TABLE 3.45 *(continued)*

Hapten		K_{rel}	ΔF_{rel} (cal)
Benzenesulfonyl-glycinate	$C_6H_5-SO_2-NH-CH_2-COO^-$	0.013	2400
GROUP C			
Hippurate	$C_6H_5-CO-NH-CH_2-COO^-$	1.00	0
β-Benzoyl-propionate	$C_6H_5-CO-CH_2-CH_2-COO^-$	0.14	1100
γ-Benzoyl-butyrate	$C_6H_5-CO-CH_2-CH_2-CH_2-COO^-$	0.024	2100
γ-Phenyl-butyrate	$C_6H_5-CH_2-CH_2-CH_2-COO^-$	0.0085	2600
GROUP D			
Hippurate	$C_6H_5-CO-NH-CH_2-COO^-$	1.00	0
Phenylhydantoate	$C_6H_5-NH-CO-NH-CH_2-COO^-$	0.085	1400
β-Benzoyl-propionate	$C_6H_5-CO-CH_2-CH_2-COO^-$	0.14	1100
Succinanilate	$C_6H_5-NH-CO-CH_2-CH_2-COO^-$	0.03	1900
p-Nitro-hippurate	$O_2N-C_6H_4-CO-NH-CH_2-COO^-$	1.4	−200
Malonanilate	$C_6H_5-NH-CO-CH_2-COO^-$	0.25	760

[a] Data from Siegel and Pressman (1953)

propionate antibody. It is a larger change than occurs upon the substitution of methylene for NH in going from phenylhydantoate to succinanilate or from N-acetylglycinate to levulinate, 500 to 700 cal, respectively. These lower values probably reflect the decreased combining power already characteristic of the two molecules containing anilino or methyl groups rather than the benzene ring. The greater combining power of the compounds containing the NH group may be due to hydration of this group, making it quite different sterically from the CH_2 group. It is also possible that the antibody has a proton donor or acceptor group in the region where it can complex with the NH group, thereby increasing the strength of combination.

When a carbonyl group is replaced by a sulfonyl group, as in benzenesulfonylglycinate, the ΔF_{rel} value is 2400 cal (group B in Table 3.45). This probably means that the fit of antibody around the carbonyl group is too close to accommodate the larger sulfonyl group. Displacement of the carbonyl group one carbon atom from its homologous position (γ-benzoylbutyrate) still gives measurable binding, $K_{rel}=0.024$ (group C in Table 3.45). Although ΔF_{rel} is increased by 1000 cal over that of the β-benzoylpropionate, it is interesting that γ-benzoylbutyrate still combines more strongly (500 cal) than does γ-phenylbutyrate, which lacks the carbonyl group but has the same distance between the benzene and carboxylate as the homologous hippurate ion. The loss of hydrogen bonding properties caused by the removal of the carbonyl oxygen is thus more important than increasing the distance between the benzoyl and carboxylate group.

The replacement of the benzene group by an anilino group increases the free energy of combination by 1400 cal in going from hippurate to phenylhydantoate, or by 800 cal in going from β-benzoylpropionate to succinanilate (group D in Table 3.45). (It is consistently observed that a structural variation applied to the homologous ion has a greater effect than the same variation applied to an ion which differs slightly. In the above case the β-benzoylpropionate differs from the ion against which the antiserum was prepared by the substitution of a methylene for the amido NH group.) This increase in energy of combination is presumably due to the increase in the benzene-carboxylate distance; if the antibody fits closely around both the benzene ring and the carboxylate of the immunizing hapten, alteration of this distance will result in weaker combination.

The importance of the van der Waals or hydrophobic contributions of the benzene ring is indicated by the fact that its replacement by a methyl group (acetylglycinate) increases ΔF_{rel} by 2400 cal (group B in Table 3.45).

The substitution of a nitro group into the benzene ring in the para

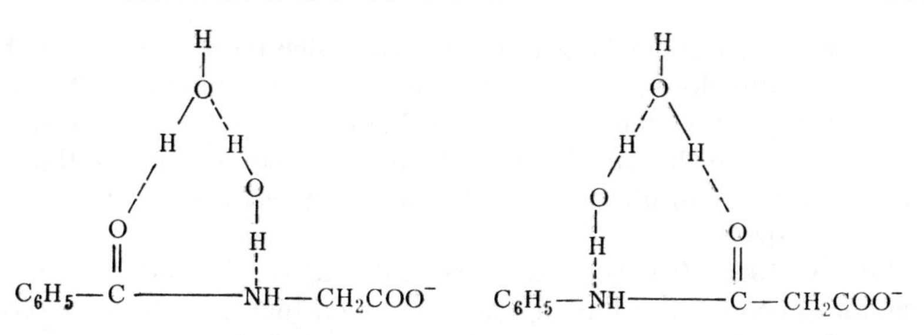

FIGURE 3.20 Apparent equivalence of hydrated forms of hippurate and malonanilate.

position (the attachment-homologous position) produces a ΔF_{rel} value of -200 cal. This is due to the greater van der Waals interaction of the antibody with the para nitro group than with the hydrogen of the unsubstituted compound. The relatively small value of 200 cal indicates, however, a relatively loose fit of antibody around the azo group and benzene ring of the injected hapten.

It is interesting that malonanilate ion, the compound which is structurally like hippurate except that the NH and carbonyl groups are interchanged, has a relatively high combining constant, within 760 cal of that of hippurate itself. This may well be due to hydration of both the NH and carbonyl groups. The compound with the hydrated NH and carbonyl groups reversed (Fig. 3.20) appears structurally and configurationally quite like the original hydrated hippurate as far as the antihippurate antibody is concerned.

3.21 ANTIBODIES TO THE D- AND L-PHENYL-(*p*-AZOBENZOYLAMINO)ACETATE GROUP

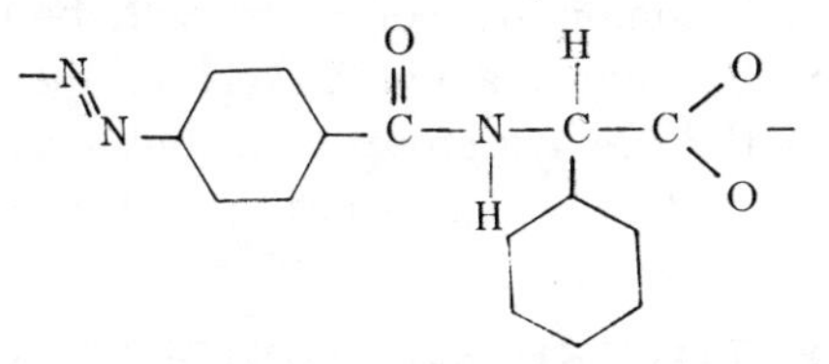

This group exists in two optically active forms differing in the arrangement of the four groups around the α carbon of the acetate. Landsteiner and van der Scheer (1928) first studied the antibodies to each form qualitatively. They found that the antibody against the D form of the hapten combines well with D form but poorly with the L form, and vice versa. These observations emphasize the great effect of steric configuration in these antibody-hapten combinations.

It is much easier for antibody to an L configuration to accept a somewhat larger or smaller group of an L configuration than to combine with the antipode—the D configuration. A good analogy is the fit of gloves. It is possible to put a left-handed glove on a left hand even though the glove is somewhat smaller or larger than the correct size. On the other hand it is very difficult to put a left-handed glove, even though it is of the correct size.

Karush (1956) has studied these antibodies quantitatively by the method of competitive binding and has found that the D form of phenyl (*p*-nitrobenzoylamino)acetate combines over 100 times better with the antibody to the D form than does the L form; similarly, the L form combines 100 times more effectively with the anti-L antibody than does the D form, as shown in Table 3.46.

Removal of the nitro group from the para position decreases the binding constants of the L and D forms in their respective systems by a factor of 2. The removal of the *p*-nitrobenzoylamino group, leaving phenylacetate, reduces the combining constant by a factor of about 100, whereas removing just the phenyl group, leaving the benzoylamino group attached, causes a much greater loss of combining strength and drops the constant by a factor of over 1000. This represents an increase in ΔF_{rel} of 4000 cal which is also the ΔF increase observed when a molecule of benzene is transferred from liquid benzene to water. Since in the latter case benzene is transferred from a hydrophobic medium to an aqueous medium, it would appear that the phenyl group of the hapten is transferred into a hydrophobic region when it combines with antibody.

The effect of the two different steric arrangements of an optically active substance is quite apparent with the homologous D and L haptens. On the other hand, each of the two optically inactive haptens, phenylacetate and benzoylaminoacetate, which do not exist in the D and L forms, show the same relative combining constants with both antisera. The benzoylamino group contributes about 2 kcal to the free energy of combination, whereas the phenyl group contributes over 4 kcal. This energy can be due either to van der Waals or hydrophobic interaction.

3.22 ANTIBODY TO THE *p*-AZOPHENYL-β-LACTOSIDE GROUP

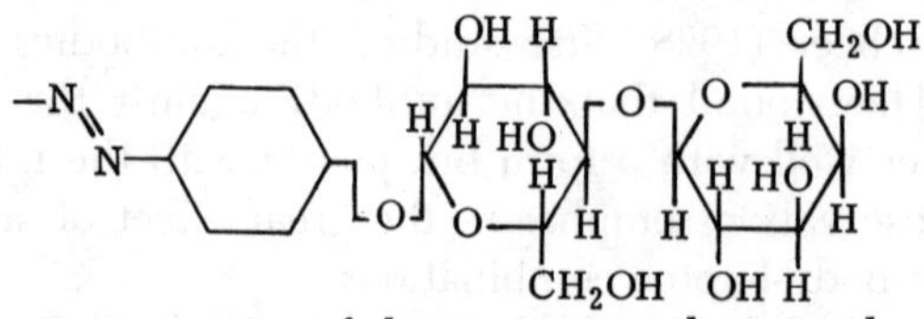

A very important group of haptens are the simple carbohydrates. Avery and Goebel (1929) converted simple sugars such as glucose and

TABLE 3.46 Combination of Optical Isomers with Antibodies in the Anti-D- and Anti-L-phenyl (*p*-azobenzoylamino) acetate Systems[a]

Hapten	Structure	Anti-D- K_{rel}	Anti-L- K_{rel}
D-Phenyl-(*p*-nitrobenzoylamino)acetate	$O_2N-C_6H_4-CO-NH-CH(C_6H_5)-COO^-$	1.00	0.0090
L-Phenyl-(*p*-nitrobenzoylamino)acetate	$O_2N-C_6H_4-CO-NH-CH(C_6H_5)-COO^-$	0.006	1.00
D-Phenyl-(*p*-benzoylamino)acetate	$C_6H_5-CO-NH-CH(C_6H_5)-COO^-$	0.45	
L-Phenyl-(*p*-benzoylamino)acetate	$C_6H_5-CO-NH-CH(C_6H_5)-COO^-$		0.61
Phenylacetate	$C_6H_5-CH_2-COO^-$	0.03	0.01
Benzoylglycine	$C_6H_5-CO-NH-CH_2-COO^-$	0.0006	0.00064

[a] Data from Karush (1956).

galactose into the *p*-aminophenyl-β-glycosides. These were then diazotized and coupled to protein for use as antigens. The antibodies which were formed showed structural specificity with respect to the various carbohydrates used. Some of these antibodies were of particular interest in view of their reactions with many of the naturally occurring poly-

TABLE 3.47 Combination of Haptens with Antibody in the Anti-*p*-azophenyllactoside System[a]

Hapten	K_{rel}	ΔF_{rel} (cal)
Lactose (64% β)	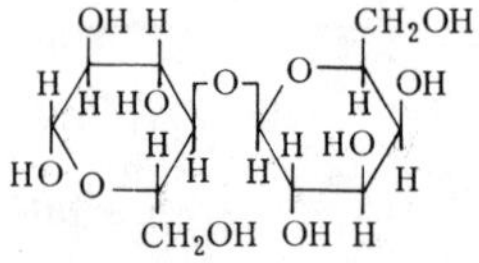 1.00	0
Methyl-β-lactoside	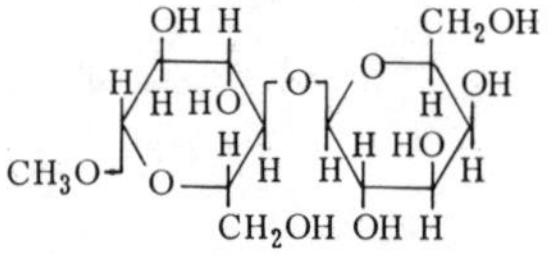 1.9	−360
Methyl-β-D-glucoside	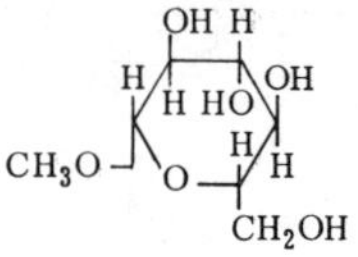 0.0005	4900
Methyl-β-D-galactoside	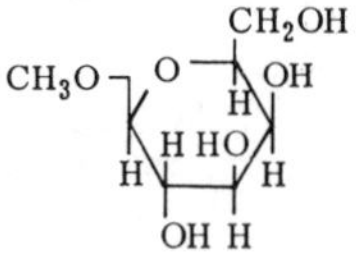 0.007	3000
Cellobiose (66% β)	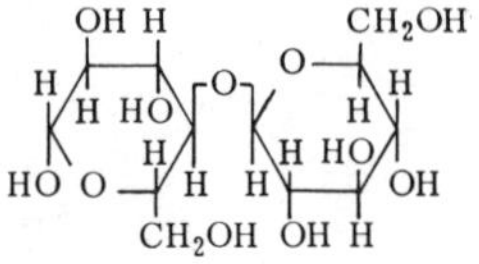 0.0025	3600
Methyl-α-D-galactoside	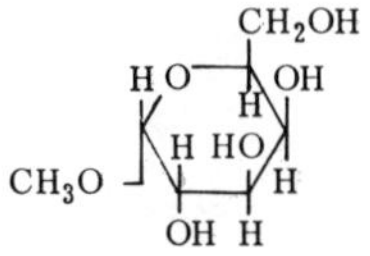 0.0012	4000
p-Nitrophenyl-β-lactoside	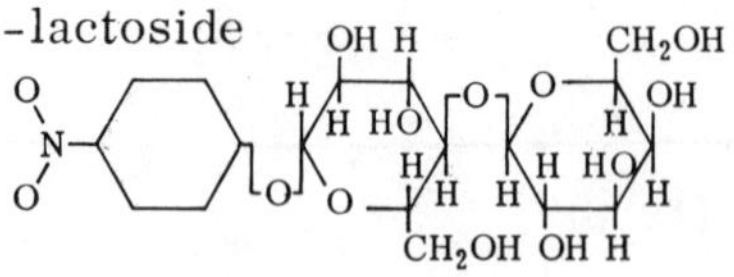 6.0	−1100

[a]Data from Karush (1957).

saccharides, such as those that occur in bacterial cell walls and capsules. However this earlier work gave no quantitative information on specificity of the antibodies.

Quantitative information on the binding of antibody against the *p*-azophenyl-β-lactoside group with various sugars and sugar derivatives has been obtained by Karush (1957) by the method of competitive dialysis equilibrium. Lactose is composed of two sugars, glucose and galactose, so that the immunizing hapten then has an azophenyl group, a β-glucoside group, and a β-galactoside group.

The great importance of the configuration of the terminal galactoside residue is shown by a comparison (Table 3.47) of the ΔF_{rel} values for lactose and cellobiose, whose structures differ only in the configuration of the hydrogen and hydroxyl groups around the terminal carbon atom of the ring. Lactose combines much more strongly than cellobiose (ΔF_{rel} for cellobiose $= 3600$ cal).

Replacing the glucose residue of lactose by a methyl to give methyl β-D-galactoside results in a 3000 cal increase in ΔF_{rel}. This large decrease in affinity gives some measure of the contribution of the penultimate glucose residue to combination. Methyl-β-D-glucoside combines less strongly than methyl β-D-galactoside, with a difference in ΔF of 1900 cal. Since the exact orientation of the methyl glucoside in the antibody site is uncertain, this value is due to a lesser combination of the glucoside either with the region of the site directed against the galactoside residue or the region directed against the penultimate glucoside residue of lactose.

A change in orientation about the middle ether linkage in going from the α-galactoside to the β-galactoside changes ΔF_{rel} by only 1000 cal.

The contribution to combination of a *p*-nitrophenyl group, in the position equivalent to the *p*-azophenyl group of the homologous structure, is indicated by the ΔF_{rel} value of -1100 cal for *p*-nitrophenyl-β-lactoside.

3.23 ANTIBODIES TO OTHER HAPTENIC STRUCTURES

Many other anti-hapten systems have been studied and have yielded interesting and important information. Some of the more recent studies were carried out in a manner quantitative enough to yield accurate values for K_{rel}. These systems are listed in Appendix III.

Some systems listed are of particular biological interest, such as those involving antibodies against coupled carbohydrates, steroids, purines, pyrimidines, and nucleotides. Drugs which are sensitizing agents, such as penicillin, have given good information on the specificity of antibodies against them.

3.24 SUMMARY

From the information in this chapter we know that specificity of interaction of a hapten with antibody depends on the groups present in the hapten and their arrangement in the molecule. Groups which have been discussed as being important determinants are the following: carboxylate, nitro, benzene, ring nitrogen and amido nitrogen, water of hydration, carbonyl, arsonate, phosphonate, trimethylammonium, *cis*- and *trans*-ethylene, and methyl. Each one of these groups has been shown to be important when the antibody was directed against it.

The importance of charge interaction has been demonstrated in systems involving a carboxylate group, an arsonate group, or a trimethylammonium group. The antibody site appears to contain a group of opposite charge. A further specificity in charge interaction, which has appeared in various systems studied, is that antibody to the negatively charged group usually does not accommodate other negatively charged groups particularly well. With antibody to the positive trimethylammonium group, however, a lesser degree of specificity is observed, since ions as large as 1 Å greater in radius than the homologous trimethylammonium group can be accommodated.

A benzene ring is a large structural feature which contributes much van der Waals and hydrophobic interaction energy. It is very important in some systems and less so in others. The effect of replacing the benzene ring by the methyl group or the benzyl group is summarized in Table 3.48. It can be seen that in most systems these groups cannot effectively replace the benzene ring.

Antibodies against some haptens appear to fit more closely around the benzene ring than do antibodies against other haptens. This is shown in Table 3.49, in which the combinations of unsubstituted haptens are compared with those of the *p*-methyl, *m*-methyl, and *o*-methyl substituted groups and with those of the α-naphthyl and β-naphthyl compounds. Antibodies to the *p*-azophenyltrimethylammonium group and the *p*-(*p*′-azophenylazo)benzenearsonate group seem to fit less closely around the haptens than do the antibodies against the *p*-azobenzenearsonate group, since the former antibodies can accommodate substituents in the ortho and meta positions, and indeed combine very well with the α-naphthyl derivative in which one side of the benzene ring is completely blocked. The other antibodies do not accommodate the α-naphthyl ring and show low values of K_{rel} with the α-naphthyl derivatives.

Another general rule is that a hapten with a substituent in the attachment-homologous position shows a greater combining power than does a hapten with the substituent in a position other than the attachment-homologous one. In the other positions the substituent usually interferes

TABLE 3.48 Van der Waals Attraction Due to Benzene Ring

System	K_{rel} of hapten		
	⬡–	H_3C	⬡CH_2–
–NN–⬡–AsO_3H^-	1.00	0	0
⬡–AsO_3H^- (–NN in meta position)	1.00	0	0
⬡–AsO_3H^- (–NN in ortho position)	1.00	0	0
–NN–⬡–NN–⬡–AsO_3H^-	1.00	0	0.05
–NN–⬡–CO_2^-	1.00	0	0
–NN–⬡–NN–⬡–CO_2^-	1.00	0	0
–NN–⬡–$C(=O)CH_2CH_2CO_2^-$	1.00	0.12	
–NN–⬡–$C(=O)NHCH_2CO_2^-$	1.00	0.01	
–NN–⬡–$NHC(=O)CH_2CH_2CO_2^-$	1.00	0.05	0.18
–NN–⬡–$N(CH_3)_3^+$	1.00	0.10	(0.5)

TABLE 3.49 Closeness of Fit in Various Para Systems

System*	K_{rel} of the following hapten where the asterisk represents $N(CH_3)_3^+$, AsO_3H^- or COO^- homologous for the system studied					
	(benzene ring, *)	(ring, *, CH_3)	(ring, *, CH_3)	(ring, *, CH_3)	(naphthalene, *)	(naphthalene, *)
NN-C₆H₄-$N(CH_3)_3^+$	1.0	1.45	0.86	1.05	2.0	
NN-C₆H₄-NN-C₆H₄-AsO_3H^-	1.0	2.7	1.1	1.0	2.9	3.9
NN-C₆H₄-AsO_3H^-	1.0	1.9	0.78	0.21	0.52	6.0
NN-C₆H₄-NN-C₆H₄-COO^-	1.0	1.8	0.21	0.03	0.03	1.98
NN-C₆H₄-COO^-	1.0	3.0	0.66	0.08	0.18	10

sterically and reduces the extent of combination. In some systems, however, the fit is loose enough to accommodate such a substituent sufficiently well so that its greater van der Waals or hydrophobic interaction becomes effective and gives a K_{rel} value greater than 1.0.

When a substituent is present in the attachment-homologous position the binding constant relative to the unsubstituted hapten is usually greater than 1.0; the antibody fits closely enough so that hydrophobic and van der Waals forces can be effective. This is found to be true for the substituents methyl, chloro, bromo, and iodo, which fall in this order of increasing effectiveness in raising K_{rel},—also the order of increasing van der Waals attraction. The rule is demonstrated by Fig. 3.21, in which the order is shown for several systems.

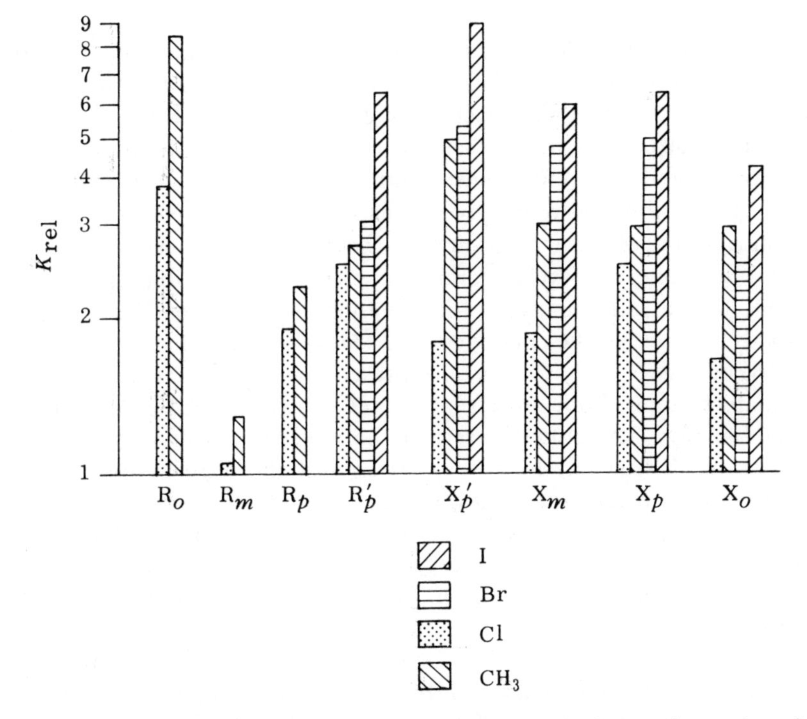

FIGURE 3.21 Effects of van der Waals of substituents in the attachment homologous position. Note the regularity of the order I > Br > Cl > CH_3 in each of the several systems as they effect K_{rel} values. The abbreviations for the systems are:

R_o, anti-*o*-azobenzenearsonate;
R_m, anti-*m*-azobenzenearsonate;
R_p, anti-*p*-azobenzenearsonate;
R'_p, anti-*p*-(*p'*-azophenylazo)benzenearsonate;
X'_p, anti-*p*-(*p'*-azophenylazo)benzoate;
X_o, anti-*o*-azobenzoate;
X_m, anti-*m*-azobenzoate;
X_p, anti-*p*-azobenzoate.

The Limited Strength of Combination of Antibody with Hapten. The evidence so far obtained indicates that anti-hapten antibodies fall into two groups with respect to their average strength of binding of the homologous hapten. Antibodies in the first group have several specificities (Table 3.50) and show a standard free energy of combination of −6 to −7 kcal/mole. Those of the second group, represented primarily by some antibodies to 2,4-dinitrobenzene, show an average free energy of combination of about −11 kcal. Other anti-2,4-dinitrobenzene antibodies are in the former group. It appears that antibodies are formed with the ability to combine with the homologous hapten with a certain limited strength of combination. Deletion of any strong determinant increases the free energy of combination by 2 kcal or more, and decreases K_{rel} by a factor of 30 or more, so that the reaction is greatly weakened. On this basis, if a certain structural feature contributes a great deal to combination, other parts of the structure must contribute less. Systems involving the carboxylate and nitro groups give perhaps the best evidence of the limit of contribution of various groups to the total energy of combination. Thus, when one carboxylate group is present it contributes a certain amount to the free energy of the combination upon reaction with the antibody, the rest of the energy coming from the remaining hapten structure. When two carboxylates are present, as in the isophthalate or phthalate systems, both are essential and contribute to the free energy of combination. Therefore the rest of the molecule must contribute less.

The same is true for the antibodies against the nitro group. When a single group is present, it makes a large contribution. When two groups are present, each seems to make a large contribution. An example of the importance of two determinant groups is best shown in the anti-3-carboxy-5-nitrobenzene system, in which removal of either the nitro group or the carboxylate from the hapten increases ΔF_{rel} by over 2 kcal.

The systems studied have demonstrated that immunological specificity depends on very fine details of molecular structure. Small structural differences between given substances markedly affect their degrees of reaction with antibody.

TABLE 3.50 Some Observed Binding Constants

The following antibodies have been measured in their combination with homologous haptens, and all have values of K'_H in the range 0.05×10^5 to 10×10^5. The antibodies are heterogeneous, so that within each antibody preparation individual antibody molecules show a wide range of constants. Indeed, only 75% of the antibodies may fall within a 2000-fold range from 0.025 to 40 times K'_H depending on the values of the heterogeneity index a. (See Table I-1 of Appendix I.)

Antibody system	Range of values of:		Index	References
	$K'_H \times 10^{-5}$ (liters/mole)	$-\Delta F$ (kcal/mole)	a	
Anti-*p*-azobenzoate	0.05–0.8[a]	4.7–6.3	0.5–1.0	1, 2
Anti-*p*-azophenyltrimethyl-ammonium	4–11[a]	7.1–7.8	0.6–1.0	3, 4, 5
Anti-3-azopyridine	0.4–1.6[b]	5.9–6.7	0.6–0.8	4, 5
Anti-*p*-azobenzenearsonate	1–10[a]	6.4–7.7	0.5–0.9	4, 5, 6
Anti-D-phenyl(*p*-azobenzoylamino)-acetate	4.4–6.7[c]	7.3–7.5	ca. 0.7	7
Anti-*p*-azophenyl-β-lactoside	3–4.5[c]	7.0–7.3	ca. 0.8	8
Anti-dinitrophenyl	0.4–8.7[d]	5.9–7.6	0.4–0.9	9

Note: Combining constants were measured with the following analogues: [a]*p*-iodo; [b]3-iodo; [c]*p*-dimethylaminophenylazo; [d]ϵ-DNP lysine.

References: (1) Nisonoff and Pressman (1958a); (2) Kitagawa *et al.* (1966); (3) Grossberg and Pressman (1960); (4) Grossberg *et al.* (1962a); (5) Grossberg *et al.* (1963); (6) Kreiter and Pressman (1964a,b); (7) Karush (1956); (8) Karush (1957); (9) Eisen and Siskind (1964).

4

HETEROGENEITY OF ANTIBODY

Antibody preparations are often heterogeneous with respect to the properties of their binding sites. The analysis of the structural basis of such heterogeneity for certain systems is discussed in this chapter. Studies are described which involve fractionation of a heterogeneous population of antibodies into subpopulations whose characteristics are different. These differences allow definition of some of the factors that are involved in antibody heterogeneity.

4.1 BASIS OF HETEROGENEITY

Antibody activity is found in several of the different classes of immunoglobulins (IgG, IgA, and IgM),[1] so that antibodies are of different protein types. Antibody molecules thus differ in molecular weight and electrophoretic mobility, and they might therefore be expected to show differences in their binding sites. However, even antibodies of a single immunoglobulin class, and against a single determinant, show differences in binding sites. The heterogeneity which will be discussed here is that of the combining site of antibody preparations which are of the 6S γ_1- and γ_2-globulin class (IgG).

This heterogeneity appears to arise from the fact that antibodies against a given antigenic group may be directed against different parts of it. This can occur in several ways. First, in the case of anti-hapten antibody, the haptenic determinant can be coupled to a variety of different regions

[1] See Bull. Wld. Hlth. Org. **30**, 447–450 (1964).

on the protein antigen; this can affect the kind of antibody formed since a portion of the antibody site may be directed against at least part of the protein component. Second, the hapten may assume various orientations with respect to the protein, such as projecting from or lying on the surface with either an edge or a face exposed, as described in Section 1.9. These different orientations of the hapten would give rise to different kinds of combining regions of the antibodies directed against them. These combining regions would necessarily be different structurally, although they may have certain features and amino acid residues in common.

Even in the case of antibodies directed against the same part of the antigenic (haptenic) group, there may be heterogeneity with respect to binding constant and with respect to amino acid composition of the site.

Anti-protein antibody sites formed in response to a protein antigen are heterogeneous for additional reasons. Some antibodies are directed against one part of the protein molecule, whereas some are directed against other parts (see Fig. 1.4). This has been shown for several proteins. For example, when bovine serum albumin molecule is digested into smaller component pieces and these are separated (Lapresle *et al.*, 1959), some of the antibodies formed against the intact molecule react with one piece and other antibodies react with other pieces.

Heterogeneity of anti-hapten antibody binding sites results in a distribution of combining constants for the binding of hapten with antibody. This is apparent in determinations of nearly all such interactions, whether measured by equilibrium dialysis or by inhibition of precipitation. The observed reactions do not follow the equilibrium laws for homogeneous populations. Thus, in inhibition of precipitation, if the antibodies showed a single combining constant with the antigen, and another single combining constant with a particular hapten, a plot of the amount of precipitate obtained with increasing concentration of hapten would be expected to follow a straight line; the amount of precipitate obtained would be inversely proportional to the amount of hapten added (Fig. II-4, Appendix II). In the actual situation, however, the plot is not a straight line, owing to the heterogeneity of the combining constants as discussed in Appendix II. The heterogeneity is a property of the antibody, because nonlinear inhibition curves are obtained when synthetic substances which have two identical antigenic sites are used as precipitating antigens. Figure 4.1 shows such a substance.

Also, in the measurement of binding by equilibrium dialysis, the extent of curvature of a plot of the reciprocal of the bound concentration against the reciprocal of the free hapten concentration indicates the degree of heterogeneity. A straight line is obtained with a homogeneous system, as is discussed in Appendix I.

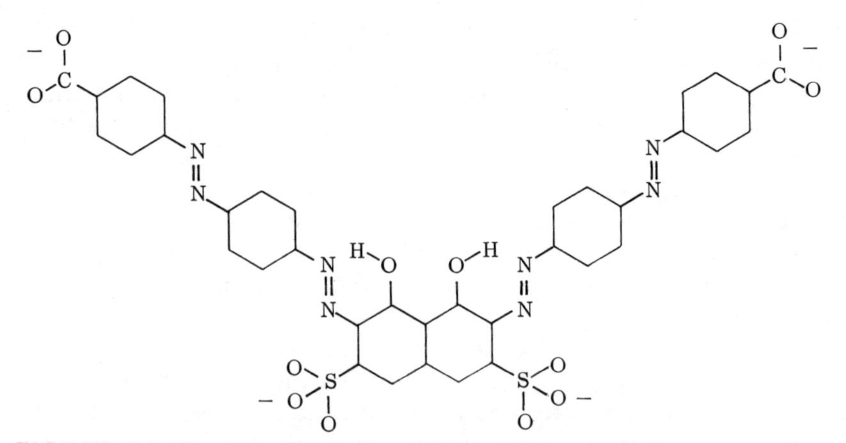

FIGURE 4.1 Bivalent dihaptenic simple substance capable of precipitating with anti-*p*-azobenzoate antibodies.

4.2 FRACTIONATION OF HETEROGENEOUS ANTIBODIES—THE ANTI-GIL SYSTEM

Heterogeneous anti-hapten antibodies, formed in response to a given haptenic determinant group, can be separated into fractions with immunochemically different binding properties, that is, different specificities. It can then be shown that the antibodies are directed against different parts of the haptenic group. Such separation and characterization of antibodies has been performed with antibodies directed against the azoisophthaloyl-glycine-D,L-leucine group (the GIL group) (Kreiter and Pressman, 1964c). The GIL group (Fig. 4.2) is an isophthalic acid residue

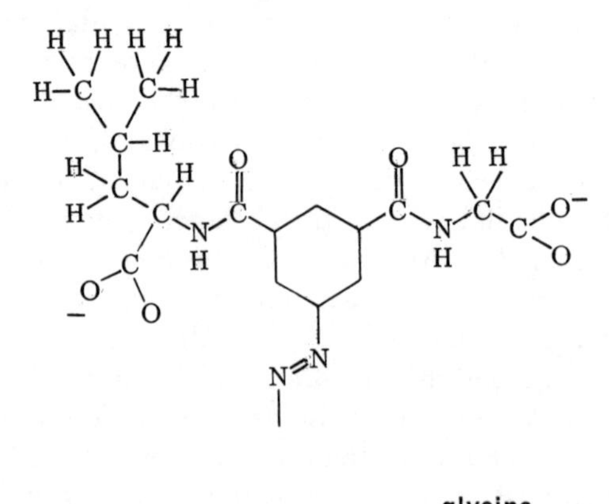

FIGURE 4.2 The GIL group—azoisophthaloyl ⟨ glycine / leucine

with glycine coupled through its amino group to one carboxyl, and with leucine coupled through its amino group to the other carboxyl. The diamide is coupled to protein through an azo group in the 5 position of the isophthaloyl ring to form the immunizing antigen.

Originally, Landsteiner and van der Scheer (1938), who first studied these antibodies, showed that the antiserum gave a precipitate with GIL-antigens (containing the GIL group), G-antigens (containing the *m*-azobenzoylglycine group), and L-antigens (containing the *m*-azobenzoylleucine group). When anti-GIL serum was treated with a solid adsorbent made by coupling diazotized *p*-aminobenzoylglycine to the insoluble stromata of erythrocytes, the ability to precipitate with a G-antigen was lost. However the remaining antibodies still precipitated with the L-antigen and with the GIL-antigen. Similarly, when the antibody was treated instead with a solid adsorbent containing the *p*-azobenzoylleucine groups, the antibodies precipitating with L-antigen were removed and the remaining antibodies gave a precipitate with G- or GIL-antigens. After treatment of the antiserum with both G-antigen and L-antigen, Landsteiner and van der Scheer found that the antibodies which remained were precipitable only by the GIL-antigen. Extensive adsorption with either the G- or L-antigens removed even these antibodies.

Better information about these antibodies has since been obtained by Kreiter and Pressman (1964c). Fractions of antibody were obtained by adsorbing anti-GIL serum on a column of an immunoadsorbent made by coupling GIL with cellulose, washing the column free of nonantibody protein, and eluting with the three haptens in succession at 5×10^{-3} *M*, *m*-nitrobenzoylleucine (L-hapten), *m*-nitrobenzoylglycine (G-hapten), and isophthaloyl-glycine-D,L-leucine (GIL-hapten) (Fig. 4.2). The eluted antibodies so obtained by the stepwise procedure were designated L fraction, G fraction, and GIL fractions as shown in Fig. 4.3. It can be seen that a larger amount of antibody was eluted by the L-hapten than by the G-hapten. The order of treatment was not the determining factor in the amount eluted, however, because in either order the larger amount was still eluted with the L-hapten.

The antibodies so separated were analyzed for their strength of binding by dialysis equilibrium with the G-azohapten, L-azohapten, and GIL-azohapten, as shown in Table 4.1. Results showed that the G fraction from anti-GIL serum bound the G-azohapten with approximately the same binding constant as was found for antibody in whole anti-GIL-γ-globulin. The G fraction did not bind the L-azohapten. The L fraction bound the L-azohapten but not the G-azohapten, and the binding constant with L-azohapten again was approximately that of the antibody in the whole γ-globulin. Although the antibodies in the G and L fractions combined with the G- and L-haptens, respectively, there was also an addi-

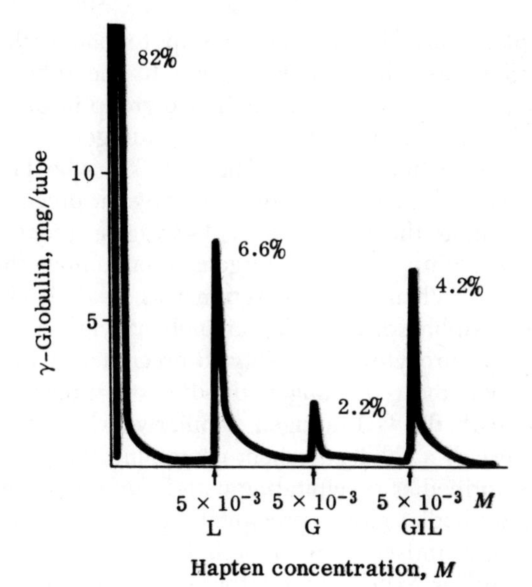

FIGURE 4.3 Fractionation of anti-GIL antibody. Elution from GIL-solid adsorbent by L-, G-, and GIL-haptens. [From Kreiter and Pressman (1964c).]

tional contribution by the structure of the rest of the GIL-hapten. Thus, the antibodies in both the G and L fractions combined even more strongly with the GIL-azohapten with a change in $-\Delta F$ value from 6.9 to 7.3 kcal and from 6.5 to 7.4 kcal, respectively, when the second amino acid residue was present in the azohapten.

The effect is illustrated in Fig. 4.4, which shows the van der Waals outline of one form of the GIL-hapten. (The molecule is depicted with the carboxylates extended in opposite directions.) The figure also shows the types of antibody which can be formed, according to which part

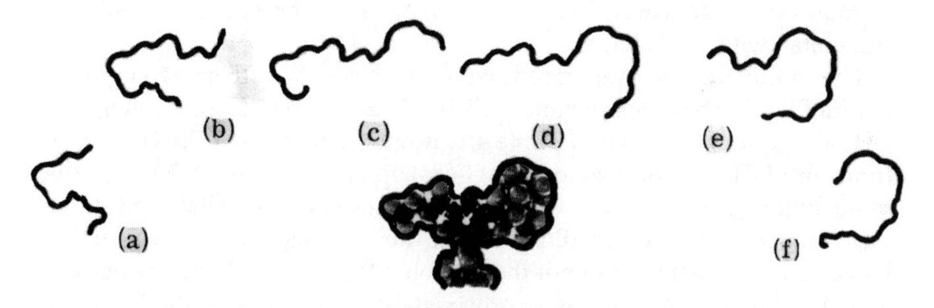

FIGURE 4.4 Outlines of GIL group against which different antibodies appear to be directed. [From Kreiter and Pressman (1964c).]

TABLE 4.1 Properties of Fractions of Anti-GIL, Anti-G, and Anti-L Antibodies Determined with G-, L-, and GIL-Azohaptens[a, b]

Antibody fraction	G-azohapten		L-azohapten		GIL-azohapten	
	$K'_H \times 10^{-4}$ (liter/mole)	ΔF_H (cal)	$K'_H \times 10^{-4}$ (liter/mole)	ΔF_H (cal)	$K'_H \times 10^{-4}$ (liter/mole)	ΔF_H (cal)
Whole γ-globulin of anti-GIL serum	31	−6950	9.5	−6300	17	−6650
G fraction of anti-GIL serum	27	−6900	~0		59	−7300
L fraction of anti-GIL serum	~ 0		12	−6450	69	−7400
GIL fraction of anti-GIL serum	6	−6150	6	−6150	106	−7650
G fraction of anti-G serum	78	−7450	~ 0		65	−7350
L fraction of anti-L serum	~ 0		46	−7200	54	−7250

[a] Data from Kreiter and Pressman (1964b).
[b] G-azohapten is the G group coupled to phenol.
L-azohapten is the L group coupled to phenol.
GIL-azohapten is the GIL group coupled to phenol.

of the GIL-hapten the combining site is directed against, starting with antibody directed largely against the G part (Fig. 4.4a,b) and progressing through intermediate forms directed against portions of both the G and the L group (Fig. 4.4c,d) to antibody directed largely against the L part (Fig. 4.4e,f). The extreme cases, in which antibody directed against the glycine or the leucine would not show an increased combination with the GIL-azohapten, have not been observed.

The fact that the G fraction and L fraction combined more with the GIL-azohapten than with the G- or the L-azohaptens indicates that about 400 and 950 cal, respectively, were the energy contributions due to combination of these fractions with the second residue. The antibodies in these fractions appear to have been directed against the parts of the hapten depicted in Fig. 4.4b,e.

The properties of the GIL fraction (eluted with the GIL-hapten) differed from those of the G and L fractions. The GIL fraction bound both the G- and L-azohaptens, but bound the GIL-hapten more strongly with an additional ΔF decrease of 1500 cal. Moreover, it combined with GIL-azohapten even more strongly than did the G and the L fractions by about 300 cal. Although the antibodies contained in the GIL fraction combined with the individual G- and L-azohaptens, they appeared to be those directed more against the central part of the azohapten (Fig. 4.4c,d). The proportion of the combining energy supplied by the second residue was larger for this fraction than for the other fraction.

For comparison, anti-G antibodies prepared against just the *m*-azobenzoylglycine, and anti-L antibodies prepared against the *m*-azobenzoylleucine, were similarly purified by adsorption and elution. The antibody eluted by the G-azohapten from anti-G serum bound the G-azohapten but not the L-azohapten. Antibody eluted from the anti-L serum bound the L-azohapten but not the G-azohapten. Both anti-L and anti-G antibodies bound the GIL-azohapten but there was little difference between the binding strength with GIL-azohapten and with the G- or L-azohapten.

Although these antibodies exhibit preferential reactivity for one amino acid residue or the other, as do those isolated from anti-GIL serum, they differ significantly in specificity from the anti-GIL antibodies. The antibody combining sites of these anti-L and anti-G antibodies do not encompass enough of the benzene ring of the immunizing hapten to be affected by the presence of a second amino acid residue.

4.3 PROPERTIES OF ANTI-p-AZOBENZENEARSONATE ANTIBODIES (ANTI-R_p) FRACTIONATED BY STEPWISE ELUTION WITH INCREASING CONCENTRATION OF HAPTEN

When antibodies against a hapten are adsorbed on a column of a specific solid adsorbent containing coupled hapten, they can be fractionated by elution with solutions of hapten in increasing concentrations (Lerman, 1953); hapten in low concentration elutes only a small amount, and a higher concentration of hapten then elutes more antibody.

Typical stepwise patterns for the elution of anti-p-azobenzenearsonate antibody with benzenearsonate are shown in Fig. 4.5 (Kreiter and Pressman, 1964b). The pattern is reproducible and characteristic for each pool of antiserum. It reflects the distribution of antibodies with different combining properties in that pool. The differences in the patterns for three different pools are apparent in Fig. 4.5. Moreover, the fractions eluted at different hapten concentrations have different binding properties and show different elution patterns when rechromatographed (Fig. 4.6). When the individual fractions were refractioned, each was still heterogeneous but required concentrations of hapten for elution comparable to those initially required.

The combining constants with p-(p'-hydroxyphenylazo)benzenearsonate of each of the several different antibody fractions separated by elution were different, as shown by dialysis equilibrium measurements (Table 4.2). The combining constants with respect to p-(p′-hydroxyphenylazo)-benzenearsonate decrease as the concentration of benzenearsonate required for elution increases. The combining constant for the original γ-globulin fraction of anti-R_p serum is intermediate. Of interest is the fact that the 10-fold difference in values for the binding constants of the first and last fractions is considerably less than the 10,000-fold difference in the concentrations of the eluting hapten.

The binding of p-iodobenzenearsonate is different from the binding of the azohapten. In contrast to the 10–12-fold difference in values of binding constants obtained with the azohapten, the difference in binding constants of p-iodobenzenearsonate with the 10^{-5} M and 10^{-1} M elution fractions is less than a factor of two.

The fractionation procedure described here separates the antibody molecules on the basis of variation in the ratios of their binding constants with the immunoadsorbent to their binding constants with the eluting hapten. Antibodies are eluted in the order of increasing ratios of K_{ad}/K_H, where K_{ad} is the binding constant of the antibody with adsorbent and K_H

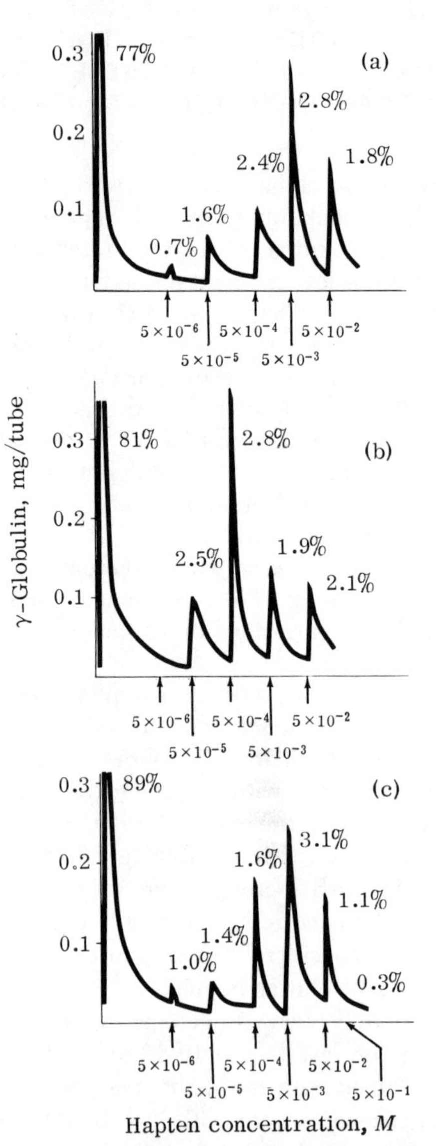

FIGURE 4.5 Elution patterns of anti-R_p γ-globulin from R_p-solid adsorbent by *p*-nitrobenzenearsonate. Note the difference in patterns for 3 different pools of antiserum (a), (b), and (c). [From Kreiter and Pressman (1964b).]

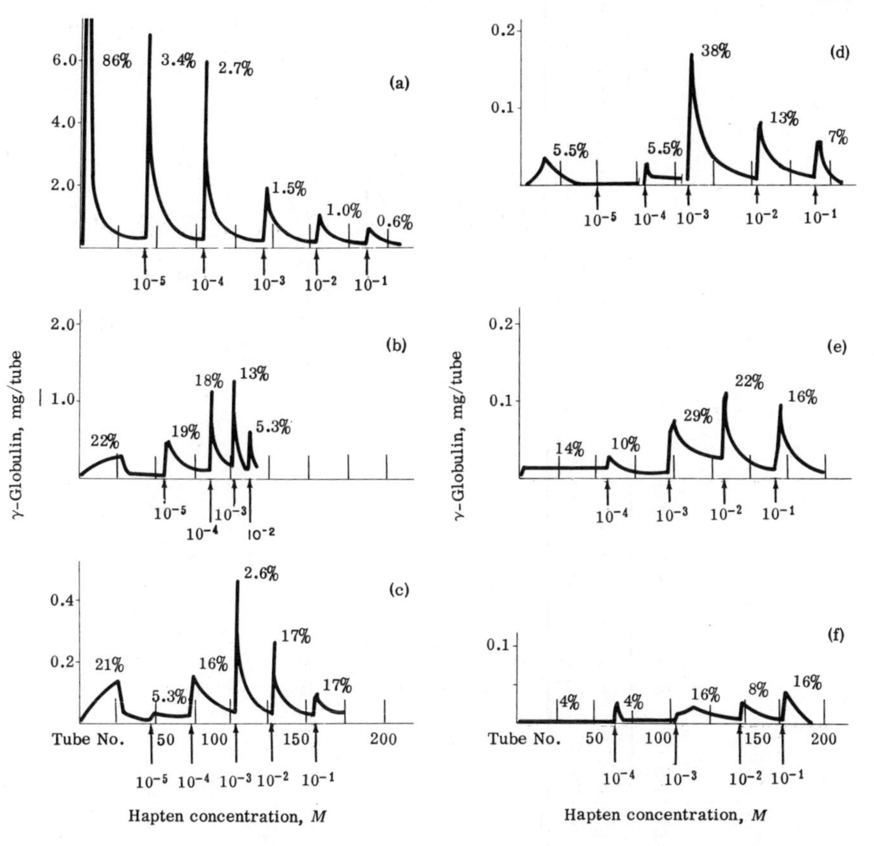

FIGURE 4.6 Refractionation of anti-R_p antibody fractions obtained by stepwise elution with benzenearsonate. (a) Whole γ-globulin; (b) 10^{-5} *M* fraction; (c) 10^{-4} *M* fraction; (d) 10^{-3} *M* fraction; (e) 10^{-2} *M* fraction, (f) 10^{-1} *M* fraction. [From Kreiter and Pressman (1964b).]

is the binding constant of the antibody with hapten. Thus, antibody bound relatively more strongly by hapten comes off early; antibody bound relatively more strongly by adsorbent comes off later; and antibody bound weakly by both adsorbent and hapten is eluted along with antibody bound strongly by both if the ratio K_{ad}/K_H is the same for the two cases. In the system studied it appears that the ratios of the binding constants with immunoadsorbent and with benzenearsonate differ by a factor of approximately 10^4, since the antibody in the last fraction requires a 10,000-fold higher concentration of benzenearsonate to remove it from the immunoadsorbent than does the antibody in the first fraction. As noted above the antibody eluted by benzenearsonate

TABLE 4.2 Binding Properties of Fractions of Anti-R_p Antibodies[a]

Concentration of benzenearsonate eluting solution	Binding of *p*-(*p*′-hydroxyphenylazo)-benzenearsonate $K'_H \times 10^{-6}$ (liter/mole)	Binding of *p*-iodobenzenearsonate $K'_H \times 10^{-6}$ (liter/mole)
10^{-5} *M*	12.0	1.1
10^{-4} *M*	5.5	—
10^{-3} *M*	2.4	—
10^{-2} *M*	2.2	—
10^{-1} *M*	0.9	0.75
Whole anti-R_p γ-globulin	4.2	—

[a]Data from Kreiter and Pressman (1964a).

at a concentration of 10^{-5} M and that eluted by 10^{-1} M benzenearsonate bind *p*-iodobenzenearsonate almost equally well, and it is probable that the various fractions bind the similar benzenearsonate equally well. The heterogeneity is thus apparently due to different degrees of complementariness of the antibody sites toward the azo group and the second benzene ring of the azohapten.

4.4 HETEROGENEITY IN THE ANTI-*p*-AZOBENZOATE (ANTI-X_p) SYSTEM

The anti-*p*-azobenzoate system has been studied by stepwise elution using either increasing concentrations of one hapten or several different haptens. The absorbent, X_p-RSA-PAS, which has been used, consists of *p*-azobenzoate groups (X_p groups) coupled to protein (rabbit serum albumin), which is coupled to diazotized polyaminostyrene.

In such studies (Kitagawa *et al.*, 1965a,b) the antibody is trace-labeled with radioactive iodine, making it possible to follow very minute amounts of the protein. Moreover, the use of two different iodine labels facilitates the assay of two different preparations of antibody, or antibody and nonantibody protein, on the same column simultaneously, thereby obtaining a precise comparison of the elution patterns of two proteins. A pattern for elution of antibody is shown in Fig. 4.7. The antibodies

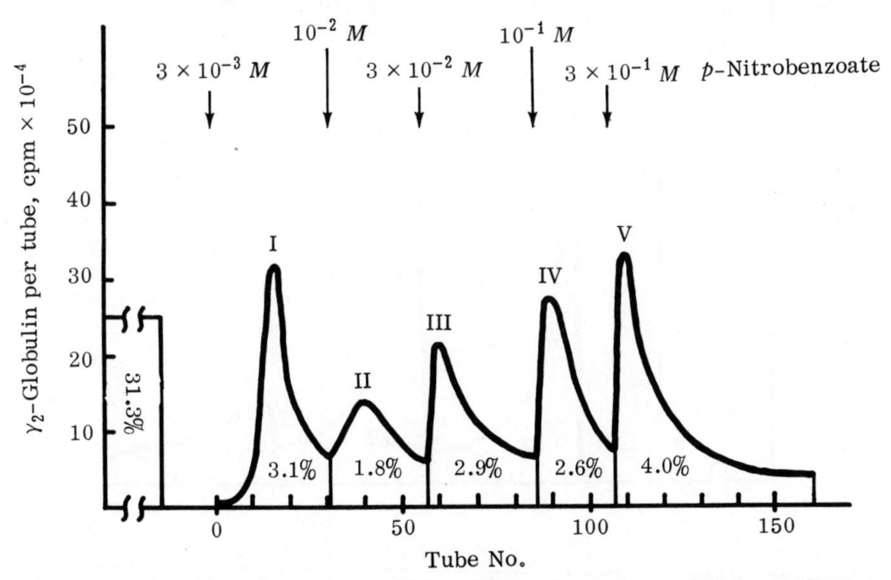

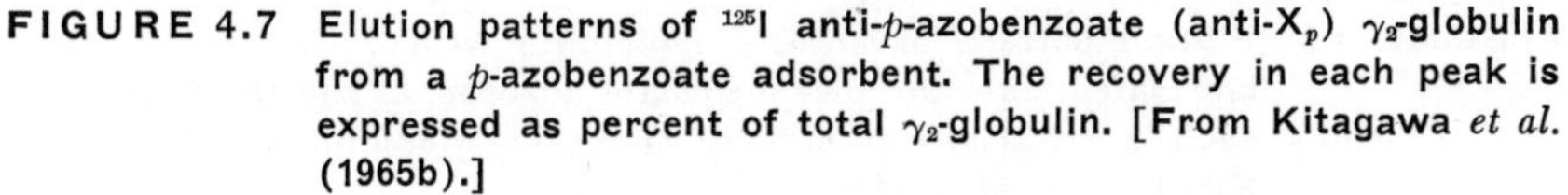

FIGURE 4.7 Elution patterns of ^{125}I anti-*p*-azobenzoate (anti-X_p) γ_2-globulin from a *p*-azobenzoate adsorbent. The recovery in each peak is expressed as percent of total γ_2-globulin. [From Kitagawa *et al.* (1965b).]

obtained in various fractions differ in their binding properties as shown by rechromatography. When fractions such as those eluted by 3×10^{-3} *M*, 3×10^{-2} *M*, and 3×10^{-1} *M* *p*-nitrobenzoate are refractionated by the same program of elution, the curves obtained reflect the original concentration requirements for elution.

Elution with various substituted benzoates indicates further heterogeneity of the antibodies. For example, when the adsorbed antibodies are eluted successively with *o*-, *m*-, and *p*-nitrobenzoate, a pattern such as that shown in Fig. 4.8 is obtained. Some antibody combines strongly enough with *o*-nitrobenzoate to be eluted by it. Another antibody increment is eluted by subsequent treatment wtih *m*-nitrobenzoate; a third portion not eluted by the *o*- or *m*-nitrobenzoate treatments is eluted on passage of *p*-nitrobenzoate through the column. Typical results obtained when the orders of elution are changed are shown in Fig. 4.9 (Kitagawa *et al.*, 1965b). Oddly enough, some antibody is eluted by *o*-nitrobenzoate and not by *m*-nitrobenzoate, and some antibody is eluted more effectively

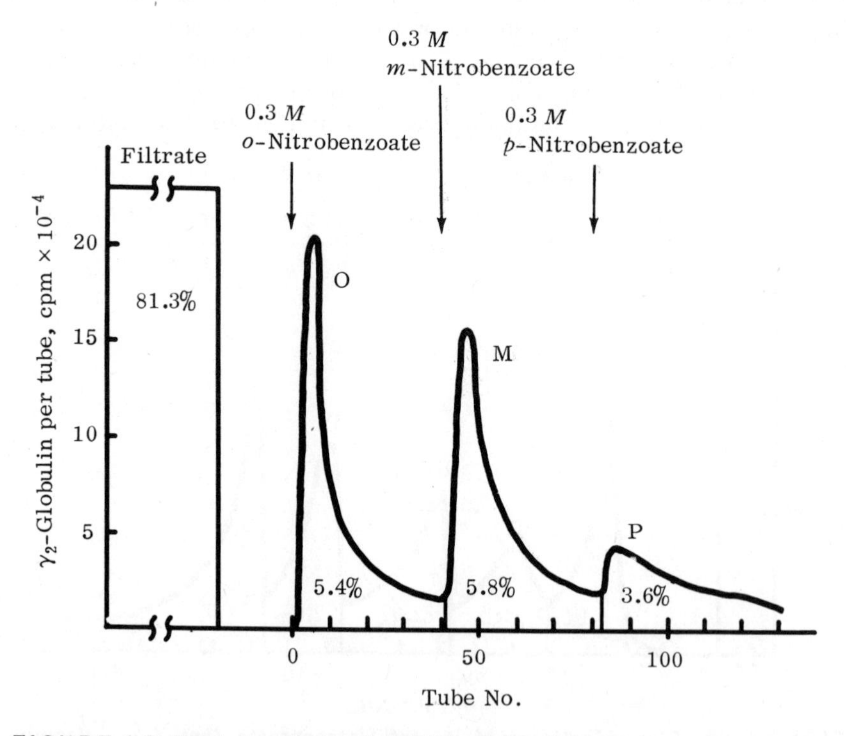

FIGURE 4.8 Elution pattern of anti-X_p γ_2-globulin with *o*-, *m*-, and *p*-nitrobenzoates from the *p*-azobenzoate adsorbent. The recovery with each is expressed as percent of total γ_2-globulin applied. [From Kitagawa *et al.* (1965b).]

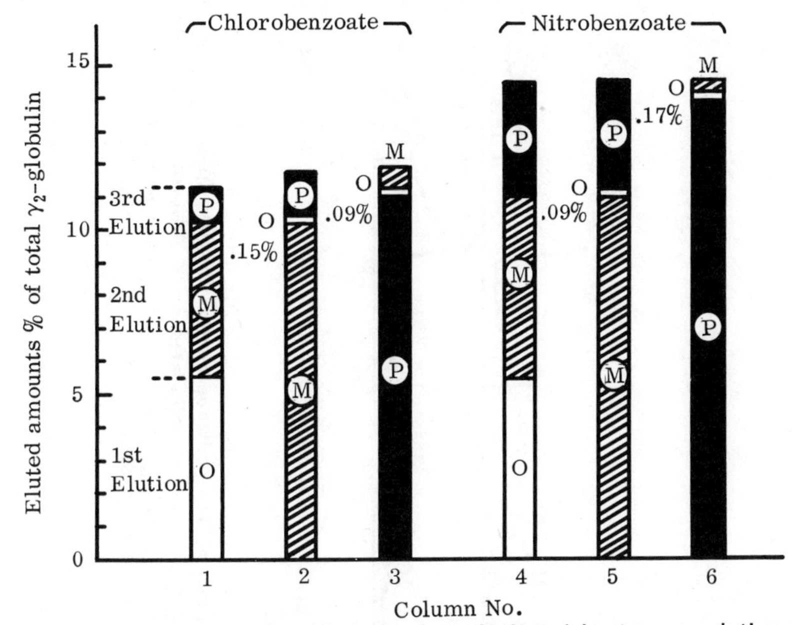

FIGURE 4.9 Effect of order of elution by substituted haptens on elution of antibody. Anti-X_p antibody adsorbed on X_p-RSA-PAS was eluted with *o*-, *m*-, and *p*-chlorobenzoates and nitrobenzoates in the various orders indicated. [From Kitagawa *et al.* (1965b).]

by the *m*-nitrobenzoate than by the *p*-nitrobenzoate (fractions M from columns 3 and 6). This behavior is elicited by chlorobenzoates as well as nitrobenzoates.

The antibody fractions obtained with increasing concentrations of *p*-nitrobenzoate (fractions I, II, III, IV, V), or by successive elution with the *o*-, *m*-, and *p*-nitrobenzoates (fractions O, M, P), show heterogeneity upon refractionation. Fractions of antibody originally eluted at different concentrations of *p*-nitrobenzoate (fractions I, III, and V) have been shown to be heterogeneous with respect to their ability to accommodate ortho, meta, and para substituents by further fractionation using *o*-, *m*-, and *p*-nitrobenzoates successively (see Fig. 4.10). Fractions eluted originally by successive elution with *o*-, *m*-, and *p*-nitrobenzoate each have shown heterogeneity on refractionation with increasing concentrations of the para nitro hapten.

Figure 4.11 shows the van der Waals outline of the *p*-azobenzoate group coupled to the protein of the injected antigen. Antibodies directed against the regions B, D, and F of the surface of the hapten (Fig. 4.11) would accommodate the ortho substituted hapten. However, antibodies such as those encompassing regions C or E in Fig. 4.11, which fit closely

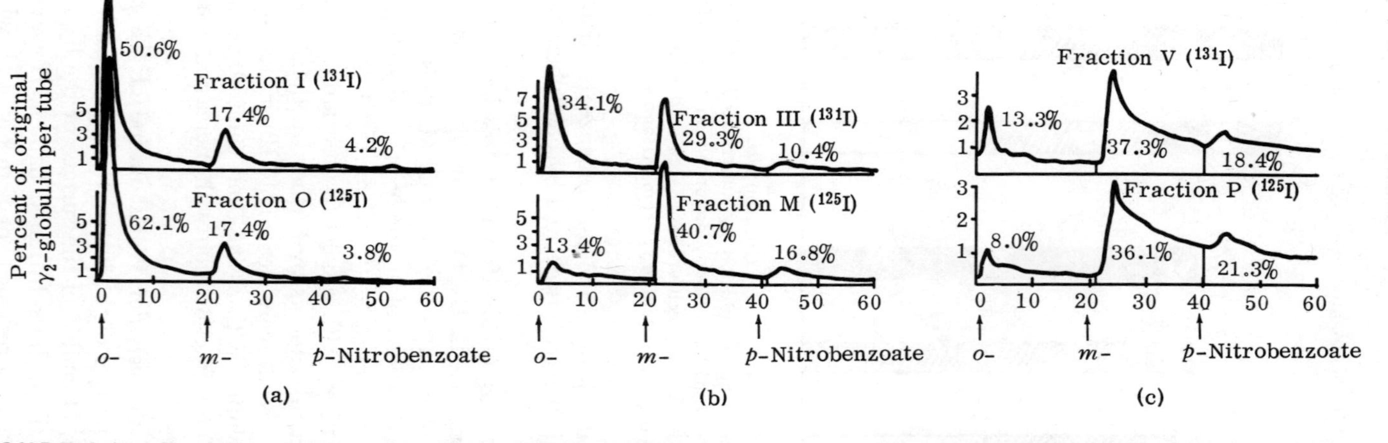

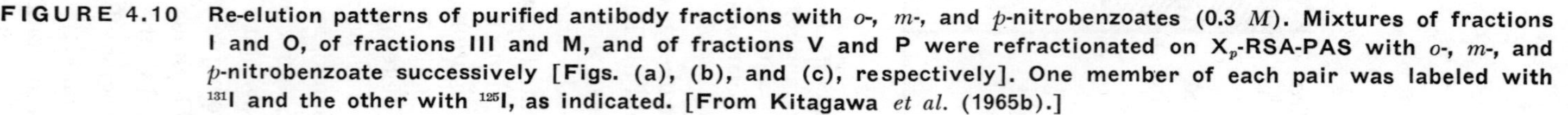

FIGURE 4.10 Re-elution patterns of purified antibody fractions with *o*-, *m*-, and *p*-nitrobenzoates (0.3 *M*). Mixtures of fractions I and O, of fractions III and M, and of fractions V and P were refractionated on X_p-RSA-PAS with *o*-, *m*-, and *p*-nitrobenzoate successively [Figs. (a), (b), and (c), respectively]. One member of each pair was labeled with ^{131}I and the other with ^{125}I, as indicated. [From Kitagawa *et al.* (1965b).]

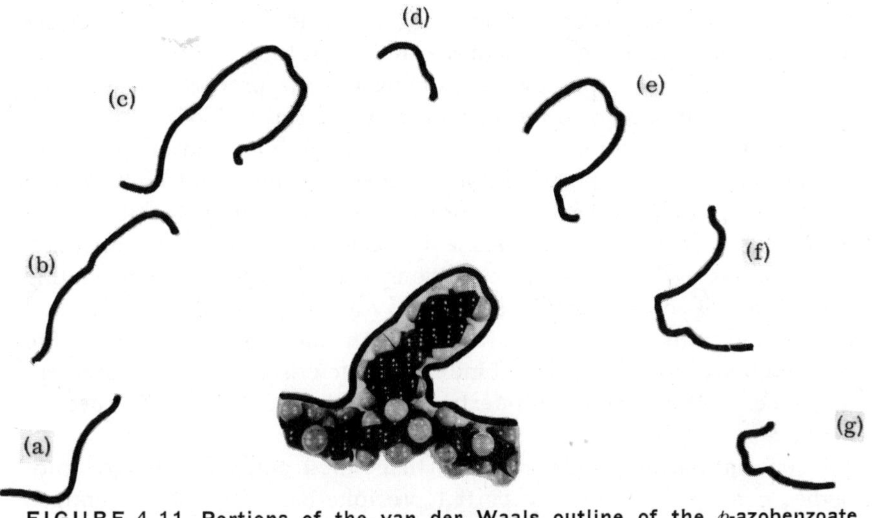

FIGURE 4.11 Portions of the van der Waals outline of the *p*-azobenzoate group coupled to protein which are implicated for various antibodies. [From Kitagawa *et al.* (1965b).]

around the hydrogen in the ortho positions of the hapten, would combine more weakly with the ortho substituted hapten relative to combination with the unsubstituted group on the adsorbent. Fractions M and P apparently contain this kind of antibody.

Some antibodies seem to be directed not only against the haptenic group but also against regions of the protein containing tyrosine, histidine, or lysine residues to which hapten was attached in the immunizing antigens. When the solid adsorbent is made with *p*-(*p*′-azobenzeneazo)-benzoate groups attached to an insolubilized protein, less antibody is adsorbed than when *p*-azobenzoate groups are attached. In the former adsorbent the *p*-azobenzoate group is not attached directly to a protein, but rather is connected through a phenylazo group. This displacement of the benzoate group from the protein surface results in an alteration in the protein contribution to binding. The antibodies which combine poorly with the adsorbent containing the displaced benzoate are probably those for which the protein contribution to binding is more important than it is for antibodies which combine well.

4.5 OTHER EXAMPLES OF HETEROGENEITY

Other examples of heterogeneity with respect to binding site are known. Landsteiner and van der Scheer (1936) found that some of the rabbit antibodies formed against *m*-azobenzenesulfonate cross-react with *o*-aminobenzenesulfonate, *m*-aminobenzoate, and *m*-aminobenzenearsonate. The cross-reacting antibodies could be selectively removed from the antiserum by adsorption with insoluble antigens prepared by coupling the appropriate hapten to red cell stromata. Lerman (1953) was able to show that rabbit anti-*p*-azobenzenearsonate antibody, adsorbed on an immunoadsorbent composed of *p*-azobenzenearsonate coupled chemically to cellulose, could be separated into fractions by gradient elution with increasing concentrations of *p*-arsanilic acid, each of which, upon refractionation under the same conditions, eluted at the original eluting concentrations of *p*-arsanilic acid. Schlossman and Kabat (1962) and Gelzer and Kabat (1964) separated human anti-dextran antibody into two fractions having different binding characteristics by using different oligosaccharides to elute anti-dextran antibody specifically adsorbed on Sephadex.

Eisen and Siskind (1964) reported that rabbit anti-dinitrophenyl antibodies can be separated by partial precipitation with specific antigen into a series of fractions with different binding constants for dinitrophenyl lysine, extending over a range of more than a thousand. Moreover, in connection with investigations of the structure of the protein molecule, Edelman *et al.* (1963) separated guinea pig anti-dinitrophenyl antibodies specifically absorbed on DNP fibrinogen into two fractions, one eluted by dinitrophenol and the other by dinitrophenyl lysine. Different starch gel electrophoretic patterns were found for the two fractions after reduction and alkylation. They speculated that these different electrophoretic patterns were concerned with the binding sites rather than with other differences in the protein.

Although most of the studies on heterogeneity of binding sites have been made with serum pooled from several rabbits, a sufficient number have been performed with serum from individual rabbits to show that heterogeneities exist within such a serum (Nisonoff and Pressman, 1958a; Eisen and Siskind, 1964).

4.6 SIZE OF THE COMBINING SITE OF ANTIBODY MOLECULE

It is difficult to determine precisely the size of the combining site of an antibody molecule because of the heterogeneity of antibody against any particular antigenic site. It would appear that for anti-GIL antibodies the size of the combining site is about that of the GIL group, since it is possible to isolate a fraction containing antibodies which are directed against the total group and require both the G and the L residues for combination. However, antibodies are also made which appear to be directed against just one side of the GIL group. These may well be directed against part of the protein also—though their interaction with the G or with the L haptens indicates that this portion of the antibody combining region alone is of sufficient size to give good combination, although the total combining region of the antibody might be larger.

Some attempts have been made to determine the size of the antibody site by measuring the ability of haptens of increasing size to inhibit precipitation. Thus, Kabat (1960) studied the inhibition of human anti-dextran antibodies with glucose polymers of increasing size. The dextran used as antigen was a 1-6 linked polymer of glucose. Kabat found that glucose polymers of increasing size up to the hexamer gave increased combination with antibody, as indicated by their increasing effectiveness in inhibiting precipitation of the antibody with dextran. He interpreted these findings as indicating that the size of the antibody site is large enough to accommodate a molecule of the length of six glucose units. Actually the size may be much smaller, for the hexamer may exist in a compact configuration not assumed by any of the smaller oligomers. This compact configuration would be the one which exists in the large dextran molecule and the one against which antibody is directed.

5

THE CHEMICAL NATURE OF ANTIBODY COMBINING SITES

As described earlier in this monograph, the specificity of the combining site of the antibody molecule depends on the presence of particular chemical groupings in the site which can interact with complementary groups on the antigen or hapten. The purpose of this chapter is to discuss what is now known about the amino acid residues that make up antibody sites.

Information about the chemical composition of antibody sites has been obtained with four different antibodies—those directed against the *p*-azobenzenearsonate group, the *p*-azobenzoate group, the 3-azopyridine group, and the *p*-azophenyltrimethylammonium group. Information is thus available about antibodies against two negative groups, a neutral group, and a positively charged group. For simplicity, we have adopted abbreviations for these antibodies as follows:

anti-A_p for anti-*p*-azophenyltrimethylammonium ion;
anti-R_p for anti-*p*-azobenzenearsonate ion;
anti-X_p for anti-*p*-azobenzoate ion;
anti-P_3 for anti-3-azopyridine.

According to the discussions in Sections 3.2 and 3.5, the antibody to the positive group (anti-A_p antibody) has a negative charge in the combining site, and the antibody to the negative azobenzoate group (anti-X_p antibody) has a positive charge in the combining site. The results of further studies, to be detailed below, suggest the following additional structural characteristics of the antibody site.

(1) The negative charge in the site of anti-A_p antibodies is due to a carboxylate group.

(2) The positive charges in the combining sites of anti-R_p and anti-X_p antibodies appear to be primarily due to guanidinium groups in these sites. The ammonium group appears to play only a minor role. However, there is evidence that an ammonium group is important in some of the binding sites of anti-azobenzenearsonate antibodies, although not in the sites of the anti-azobenzoate antibodies which have been studied.

(3) All four of the antibodies seem to have a tyrosine in the combining site.

(4) None of them appear to have a disulfide or a histidine in the site.

Most of this information has been obtained from studies of the effect of chemical alteration of antibody on its activity. Such studies are carried out with a reagent which is known to react with a particular chemical group. Loss of activity is taken to indicate an effect in the binding site. However, it must be proven that the loss of activity is not due to chemical alteration of the antibody molecule elsewhere, followed by a change in the conformation of the protein, which in turn disrupts the site. Moreover, although reagents are available which react predominantly with certain groups or amino acid residues, usually at least some reaction takes place with other residues. Therefore it is important to demonstrate just which residue is attacked and to relate the attack of the particular residue to the loss of antibody activity.

For each of these kinds of antibodies, the preparations studied are heterogeneous mixtures of antibody molecules with different combining constants, whose sites must therefore differ. Only the amino acid residues present in an appreciable proportion of sites are recognized when such a mixture of antibody molecules is studied.

5.1 ESTERIFICATION OF ANTIBODIES

It has already been pointed out that the antibodies to the positively charged trimethylphenylammonium group (anti-A_p antibodies) appear to have a negative charge in the combining site. It would seem that this site should contain a carboxylate group to provide the negative charge, and, indeed, the presence of a carboxylate has been shown by chemical means (Grossberg and Pressman, 1960). Anti-*p*-azophenyltrimethylammonium antibodies were treated with the reagent diazoacetamide, which is known to esterify carboxyl groups according to the following reaction:

$$\text{protein—COOH} + N_2CHCONH_2 \rightarrow \text{protein—COOCH}_2CONH_2 + N_2$$

This reaction removes the negative charge on the carboxylate. When this was done the anti-A_p antibody lost its ability to bind specific hapten, as measured by the method of equilibrium dialysis (see Appendix I). The loss of activity parallels the degree of reaction: the greater the number of carboxylate groups esterified, the greater the loss of activity as shown in Fig. 5.1. By the time 25% of the carboxyl groups were esterified, the antibody lost 65% of its binding activity.[1]

However, this result does not necessarily mean that there is a carboxylate group in the active site. That a reaction in the active site is

[1] The term "binding activity" as used throughout this chapter refers to the relative concentration of hapten bound by antibody at a particular free hapten concentration, with the concentration bound by the unaltered antibody at the same free hapten concentration taken as unity. This value is affected both by changes in number of sites and by changes in binding constant.

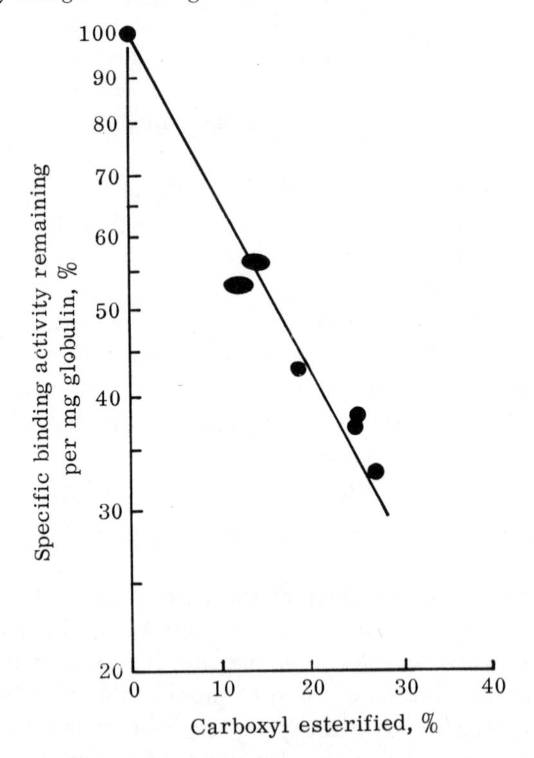

FIGURE 5.1 The effect of esterification of anti-A_p antibody. [From Grossberg and Pressman (1960).]

actually involved in the loss of activity must be proved by a "protection" experiment, in which the antibody is combined with the simple hapten such as the phenyltrimethylammonium ion, and the mixture is esterified with diazoacetamide. In the experiment, esterification is carried out to an extent which is known to destroy antibody activity in the absence of hapten. When the solution is freed of hapten by dialysis it is found that antibody activity is retained; the hapten has blocked the chemical alteration of the site, as illustrated in Fig. 5.2. The reactive group of the antibody site is protected by hapten against esterification; when the

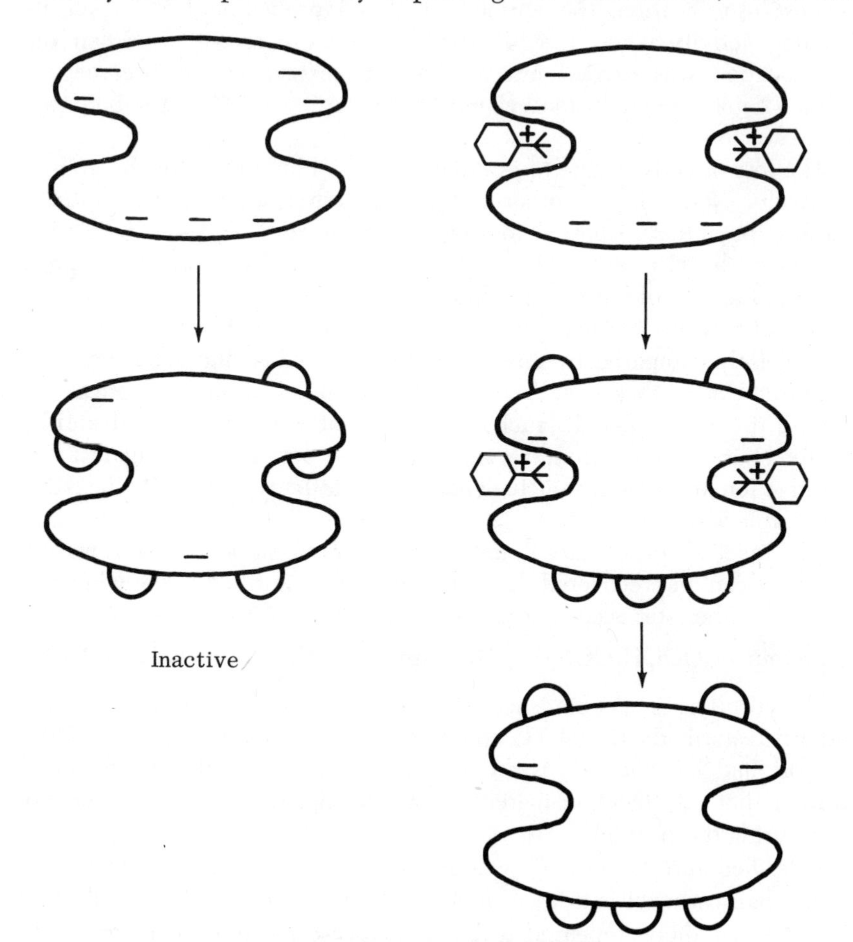

FIGURE 5.2 Protective blocking of antibody sites by hapten during esterification. Evidence that a carboxylate is in the site.

hapten is removed, the antibody site is recovered unaltered, although carboxyl groups in other regions of the antibody molecule have been esterified.

Experiments of this type are useful in proving the presence of a particular group in the antibody site. If treatment with a reagent destroys antibody activity in the absence of hapten but does not do so in the presence of hapten, then the reagent affects a group present in the binding site.

In a typical experiment involving protection of anti-A_p antibody against esterification, the antibody with no protection lost 58% of its binding activity when 18% of its carboxyls were esterified. When the esterification was carried out to the same extent in the presence of 0.005 *M* *p*-iodophenyltrimethylammonium ion, only 19% of antibody activity was lost.

The loss of activity due to esterification was found only for the anti-A_p antibody. None of the other antibodies tested, that is, the anti-R_p, anti-X_p, or anti-P_3, suffered loss of activity on esterification, indicating that no carboxyl group, which is important for combination with hapten, exists in the sites of these antibodies.

The effects of esterification on anti-A_p and on any other antibody can be precisely compared by mixing the two antibodies and esterifying the mixture. Under these conditions both antibodies receive identical exposure to the reagent. In such an experiment with anti-A_p and anti-X_p antibody it is found that the activity is lost for antibody against the positive ion and remains unchanged for the antibody against the negative ion (Table 5.1).

The inactivation of anti-A_p antibody by esterification can be reversed. Activity can be recovered from the esterified antibody following hydrolysis of the ester according to the reaction:

$$\text{protein—COOCH}_2\text{CONH}_2 + \text{OH}^- \rightarrow \text{protein—COO}^- + \text{HOCH}_2\text{CONH}_2$$

This hydrolysis is accomplished, though not completely, by bringing the esterified antibody to pH 11; about 20% of the binding capacity lost by the original esterification is recovered. This recovery of activity shows further that esterification merely blocks the site rather than irreversibly denaturing the antibody.

Esterified anti-A_p antibody was analyzed to determine whether groups other than carboxyl had been modified. At the level of 30% esterification of carboxyls there appeared to be no decrease in amino content of the protein by van Slyke analysis, indicating that less than 3 to 4% of amino groups had reacted. It was estimated that less than 5% of the tyrosine or histidine groups had been alkylated. One or two sulfhydryls were alkylated. From the rate of decrease of binding activity with esterifica-

TABLE 5.1 Effect of Esterification by Diazoacetamide on the Hapten Binding Activities of Mixtures of Anti-A_p and Anti-X_p Antibodies[a]

Sample	Carboxyl esterified (%)	Binding activity[b] of Anti-A_p (% of original)	Binding activity[b] of Anti-X_p (% of original)
Esterified mixture 1	24	36	105
Esterified mixture 2	27	33	106

[a]Data from Grossberg and Pressman (1960).

[b]Binding activity of anti-X_p antibody was determined with ^{131}I-labeled *p*-iodobenzoate. Binding activity of anti-A_p antibody was determined with *p*-(*p*′-hydroxyphenylazo) phenyltrimethylammonium (mixture 1) and with ^{131}I-labeled *p*-iodophenyltrimethylammonium (mixture 2).

tion—70% loss of activity when 30% of the carboxyls are esterified—it appears that a carboxyl in the site is more easily esterified than some of the carboxyls elsewhere on the antibody.

When binding activity is affected by a chemical reaction, such as by esterification in hapten absence, the attack may be directed to an important part of the site as designated by position A in the hypothetical site of Fig. 5.3. Such an attack will drop the binding constant to essentially zero, so that the site becomes undetectable (that is, is "lost"). If esterification is at B or C, on the periphery of the binding site, the constant for the site is decreased, depending on the degree of interference with

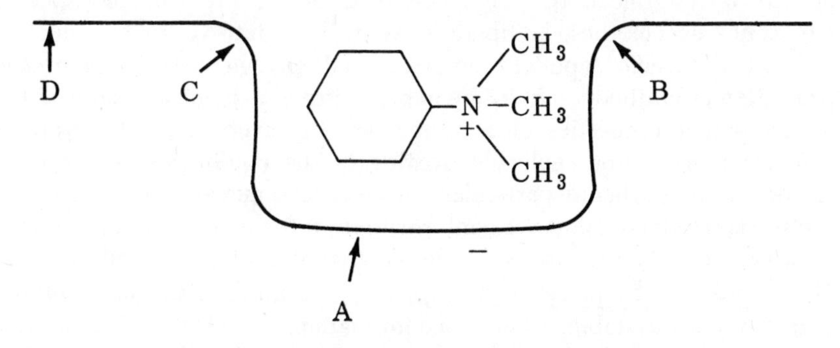

FIGURE 5.3 Effect of chemical alterations on hypothetical combining site of anti-A_p antibody. Alteration at A would have a major effect; at B and C, lesser effect; and at D a minor effect.

binding exerted by the ester group. However, the number of sites present will not be altered because binding still takes place, although a higher concentration of hapten is required to show it. Esterification farther from the site, such as at D, will produce little effect on the binding constant, and of course no effect on the number of sites detectable.

When the chemical alteration is carried out in the presence of hapten, Fig. 5.3 also shows that there would be protection against loss of sites by interference with alteration at point A. Interference by hapten at points B and C results in protection against the decrease in binding constant K_{H} caused by alteration at these points. When the point of alteration is further removed from the site, as in D, the effects of alteration and protection are less.

Chemical alteration, particularly when extensive, changes the shape of a protein molecule, as has been shown by Habeeb *et al.* (1958) for succinylation, which increases the net negative charge on the protein. The repulsion between the negative charges causes expansion of the molecule, as shown by measurements of diffusion and sedimentation constants. Such expansion of an antibody molecule could alter its binding sites. Esterification also changes the net charge on a protein, but by decreasing the number of negative charges. The altered charge interaction probably causes some alteration of the molecule similar to that found when the net negative charge is increased by succinylation, and this might also alter the binding site. However these effects would be expected to be the same for protected or unprotected antibody molecules, since all of the alteration (except for the single group which may be in the site) must take place elsewhere than in the site. Therefore the demonstration of a protection effect gives evidence that the loss of activity is not due to nonspecific general alteration of the antibody molecule. Moreover, the anti-X_p, anti-R_p, and anti-P_3 antibodies showed no loss of activity on esterification, and if distortion of the site were nonspecific we would expect these antibodies, as well as anti-A_p, to be affected.

Another specific type of conformational change could explain the protection of antibody activity by hapten during a chemical modification. The apparent properties of a protein are the average for the various conformations of the molecule existing in the equilibrium mixture. It is possible that when a particular carboxylate somewhere other than in the site is esterified, allosteric conformations of the molecule are stabilized in which the binding site is so altered that it no longer binds hapten. If, in addition, the presence of hapten in the binding site of unaltered antibody causes stabilization of conformations in which the reactivity toward esterification of the particularly important carboxylate mentioned above is decreased, the protection effect would be observed without any reaction in the site. This allosteric effect has been shown to exist for the combination of certain enzymes with substrate, and was suggested to occur for the combination of antibody with hapten as summarized by Koshland (1963).

This mechanism does not seem to apply to esterification which affects only anti-A_p antibodies. If esterification exerted its effect at a distance by the above allosteric mechanism, it is difficult to see why antibodies to other haptens would not be similarly affected. Although it is reasonable that anti-A_p might differ from the other antibodies by having a carboxylate in the site, it is not likely that it should differ from other antibodies by having an important carboxylate elsewhere than in the site.

Figure 5.4 shows the effect of esterification (to the extent of 16% of the carboxyl groups present) on the number of antibody sites and the binding constant of anti-A_p antibody. The binding of ^{131}I-labeled *p*-iodophenyltrimethylammonium ion at several free hapten concentrations was determined with the untreated anti-A_p and with esterified anti-A_p antibody. The binding values are plotted as the reciprocal of the bound hapten concentrations against the reciprocal of the free hapten concentrations. The intercept on the ordinate is the reciprocal of the total concentration of effective antibody sites. The slope of the curve and the intercept give the value of the average combining constant K'_H for the sites (see Appendix I). At this degree of esterification, 42% of the sites were lost and there was a reduction in K'_H value from 8.7×10^5 liter/mole for the unaltered antibody to 5.6×10^5 liter/mole for the esterified anti-

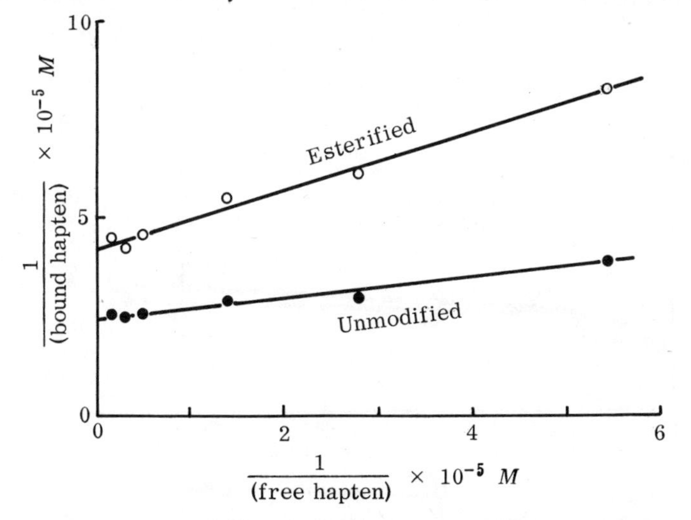

FIGURE 5.4 A comparison of the binding of ^{131}I-labeled *p*-iodophenyltrimethylammonium ion by esterified and by untreated anti-A_p antibody showing loss of effective sites due to esterification by diazoacetamide. [From Grossberg and Pressman (1960).]

body. This reduction in K'_H is probably partially of an electrostatic nature—due to the increased positive charge of the antibody as a whole, which results in a nonspecific decreased attraction (or increased repulsion) for the positive hapten. Steric effects due to esterification of carboxyl group close to but not in the antibody site, or alteration of the molecule as a whole due to increased positive charge, may also contribute to the decrease in binding constant. Another possibility is that the antibody sites having higher binding constants are the ones which are more effectively inactivated. Then the antibody sites remaining after esterification would be those with a lower average K'_H value.

When anti-R_p antibody is esterified to essentially the same extent (20% of the carboxyls esterified) the binding curves are almost superimposable (Fig. 5.5), indicating no loss of sites and minimal difference in binding constant for esterified and unesterified anti-R_p antibody.

5.2 THE EFFECT OF IODINATION ON ANTIBODY ACTIVITY

The four antibodies studied each lose binding activity when iodinated. This loss can be protected against by the presence of the homologous haptens, showing that the loss of activity in each instance is due to chemical reaction of the iodine with a group in the binding site (Grossberg *et al.*, 1962).

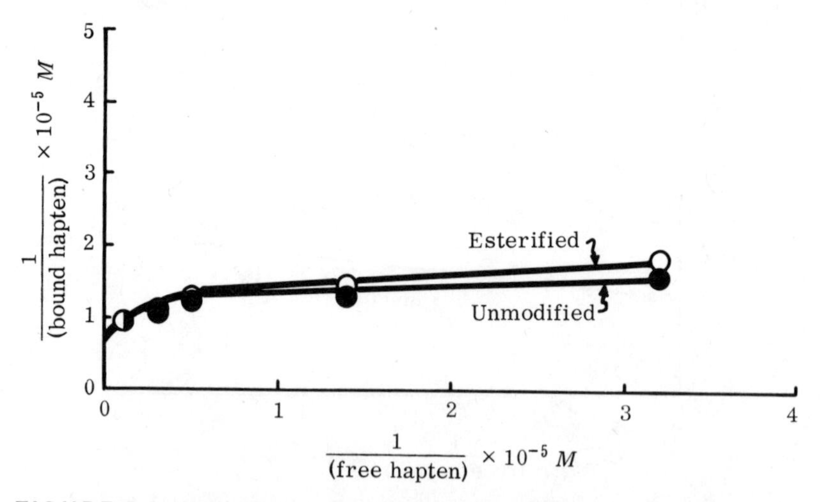

FIGURE 5.5 Similarity of binding of ^{131}I-labeled *p*-iodobenzenearsonate by esterified and by untreated anti-R_p antibody, showing that esterification of this antibody results in no loss of sites. [Data from Grossberg and Pressman (not previously published).]

The reaction of iodine with protein results in the incorporation of iodine as a substituent on tyrosine or to a lesser extent on histidine. The reaction with the tyrosine proceeds in steps as follows:

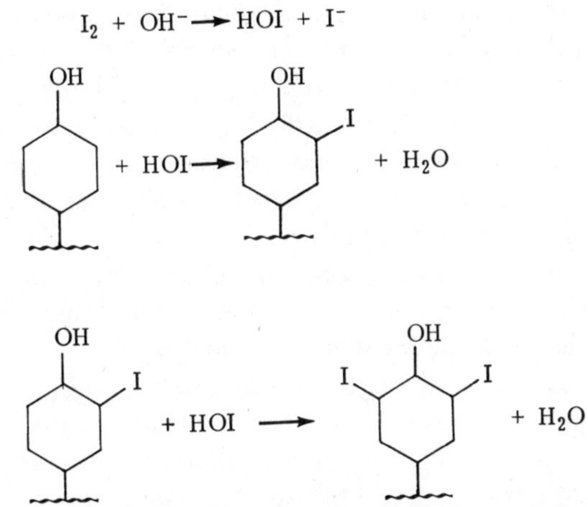

During iodination there may also be some oxidation of tyrosine, histidine, tryptophan, cysteine, cystine and methionine. The degree to which these amino acid residues are affected has been shown by amino acid analyses of the hydrolysates of the iodinated proteins. Table 5.2 shows the loss of amino acid residues by iodine incorporation or by oxidation, as reported by Koshland *et al.* (1963).

When a globulin molecule is altered by chemical reaction such as

TABLE 5.2 Amino Acid Residues in Rabbit γ-Globulin Altered by Iodination[a]

Iodine incorporation (atoms/mole)	Residues lost[b]			
	Tyrosine	Histidine	Methionine	Tryptophan
3.6	2.0		0	
7.6	4.7	0	0	
15.7	7.7	0	0	
22.1	11.3	0.4	0	
30.5	15.0	1.9	0	
55.5	23.9	3.0	0	0
102.1	43.6	8.9	10	6.2

[a]Data from Koshland *et al.* (1963).
[b]Original composition: 57 Tyr; 18 Hist; 13 Meth; 18.6 Tryp.

incorporation of iodine, chemical analysis yields a figure for the average number of atoms incorporated per protein molecule. The number of iodine atoms per single molecule will vary from this figure—some having more, some having less, and some having none, as shown by the hypothetical curve in Fig. 5.6. The shape of the curve for any particular degree of iodination will depend on the relative iodination rates of the various residues. The particular residues iodinated will vary even for molecules which incorporate identical numbers of iodine atoms. Moreover, not even all identical residues, such as the tyrosines (or histidines), iodinate at the same rate.

At very low levels of iodination, where the average number of iodine atoms is much less than one per molecule and most molecules are uniodinated, those molecules which are iodinated have only one iodine atom each. This iodine appears on different residues of the individual molecules depending on their relative iodination rates. The effect of iodination on the binding site of a particular antibody molecule will depend, of course, on which residues are iodinated.

The iodination reaction is further complicated because tyrosine first forms monoiodotyrosine and then diiodotyrosine. Thus at a particular level of iodination—for example at an average of ten atoms per molecule—certain tyrosines of each antibody molecule may be completely con-

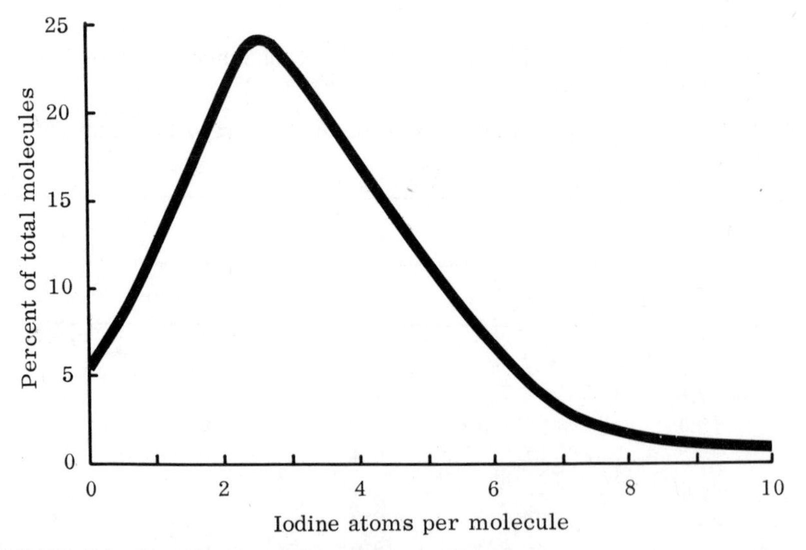

FIGURE 5.6 Distribution of γG-globulin molecules with 0, 1, 2, 3, . . ., iodines per individual molecule in a preparation having an average of 3 iodine atoms per molecule. [See discussion in Pressman and Sternberger (1950).]

verted to diiodotyrosines, other tyrosines may be partially converted to diiodotyrosine so that they are present as a mixture of uniodinated, monoiodinated and diiodinated forms, while still others may be essentially uniodinated or only partially converted to the monoiodotyrosine form.

5.2a Effect of iodination on antibody activity. The effect of iodination on the binding activity of antibody is illustrated by the effect on anti-X_p antibodies. As the degree of iodination is increased the activity decreases. This result is indicated in Fig. 5.7 by a plot of the fraction of the binding activity remaining against the average number of iodine atoms incorporated.

The presence of a simple hapten protects against the loss of activity, which shows that the loss is due to reaction in the anti-X_p site. A comparison of the activity remaining after the iodination of anti-X_p antibody in the presence of 0.25 *M* *p*-nitrobenzoate, with the activity remaining after iodination without protection is given in Fig. 5.7.

There can be some loss of activity by reactions other than iodine incorporation, as is shown by the data in Table 5.3. In this experiment, a decrease in activity of antibody occurred following greater exposure to iodine, although actual iodine incorporation was not increased. The protection effect was apparent only at higher levels of iodination.

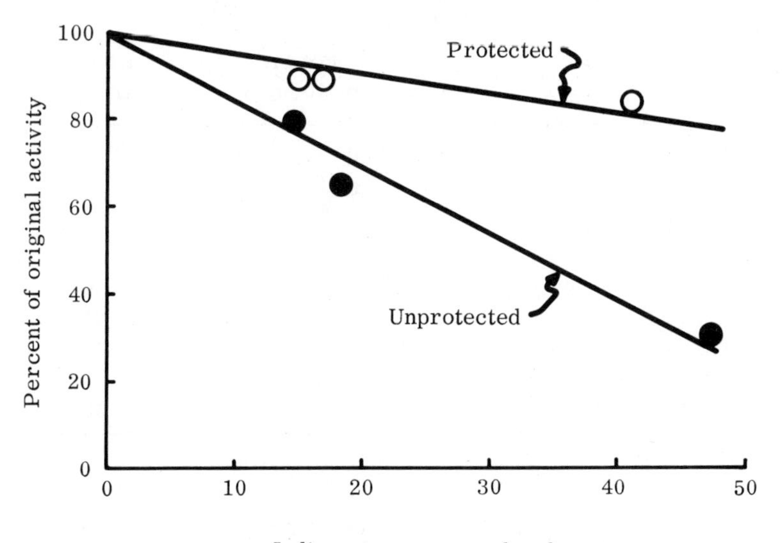

FIGURE 5.7 Effect of iodination in the presence and absence of hapten on the activity of anti-X_p antibody. [Data from Pressman and Radzimski (1960).]

The other antibodies studied, that is, anti-R_p, anti-A_p, and anti-P_3, also show loss of activity upon iodination. A very close comparison of degree of loss of activity of the different antibodies can be obtained by iodinating a mixture of two antibodies in the same solution and determining the effect on the binding for each antibody individually. When the iodination of the two antibodies is done in the same solution they necessarily obtain the same exposure to the reagent. Thus, from Fig. 5.8 it can be seen that anti-R_p activity is more sensitive to loss by iodination than is anti-A_p activity.

Part of the loss in activity for each system has been found to be due to a decrease in binding sites as shown in Fig. 5.9. The loss is partially prevented when hapten is present during iodination. This protection effect shows that each preparation contains antibodies with an iodinatable group in the site itself and that iodination of this group blocks the site.

There is an alternative, more complex, mechanism which can explain protection effects in all studies of chemical alteration of antibody. It

TABLE 5.3 Iodination of Specifically Purified Anti-X_p Antibody in the Presence and Absence of *p*-Nitrobenzoate[a]

HOI used per mole protein (moles)			
With hapten	Without hapten	Iodine incorporated (atoms/molecule)	Binding activity (%)
	0	0	100
10.1		9	91
	10.1	9	90
25.3		19	78
	25.3	20	75
50.5		34	67
	50.5	31	51
101.0		56	50
	101.0	38	30
	0	0	100
94		66	64
	94	65	24
285		71	19
	285	67	6

[a]Data from Grossberg *et al.* (1962b).

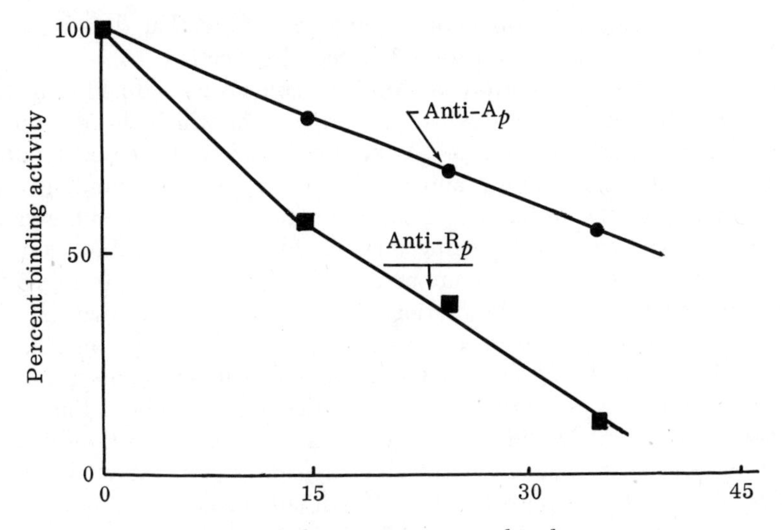

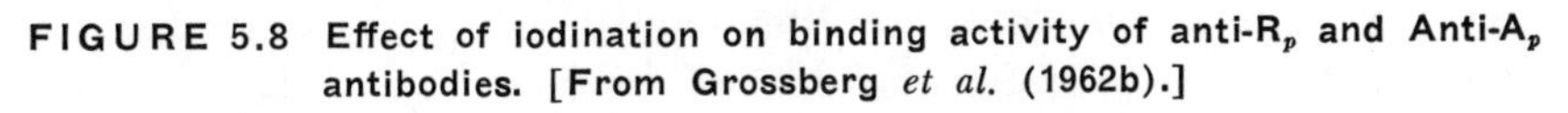
FIGURE 5.8 Effect of iodination on binding activity of anti-R_p and Anti-A_p antibodies. [From Grossberg *et al.* (1962b).]

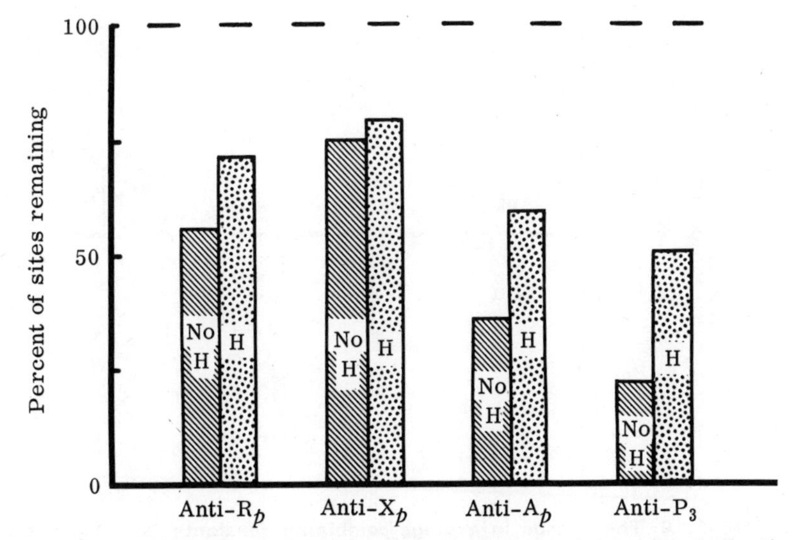

FIGURE 5.9 The percentage of antibody sites remaining after iodination of different antibody preparations in the presence or absence of hapten. [From Grossberg *et al.* (1962b).]

involves a specific conformational change similar to that discussed for the esterification reaction (Section 5.1; see also Section 5.3).

5.2b Effect of iodination on binding constants. Iodination in the absence of hapten has resulted in preparations in which the remaining sites of anti-R_p, anti-X_p, and anti-A_p antibodies show decreased binding constants and the remaining anti-P_3 sites show increased binding constants. The presence of hapten during iodination tends to keep the value of K'_H observed from being reduced in the anti-R_p, anti-X_p, and anti-A_p systems. The observations are summarized by the bar graphs in Fig. 5.10.

In interpreting these observations it should be noted that all the preparations were heterogeneous with respect to binding constants, as revealed by the binding curves. It is probable that for each system the various antibodies comprising such a heterogeneous population have somewhat different binding sites, and these are reflected in the different binding constants. The different sites in each system may also have different susceptibilities to alteration. If iodination results in a preferential loss of binding sites of high K_H value, there results a population with a lower average binding constant after iodination. On the other hand, if iodination causes a preferential loss of binding sites with a low K_H, then K'_H (the average) observed after iodination would be larger.

A hapten protects only those sites which it occupies. The degree of protection depends on the strength of binding and on the importance for binding of the iodinatable group in the site. From these considera-

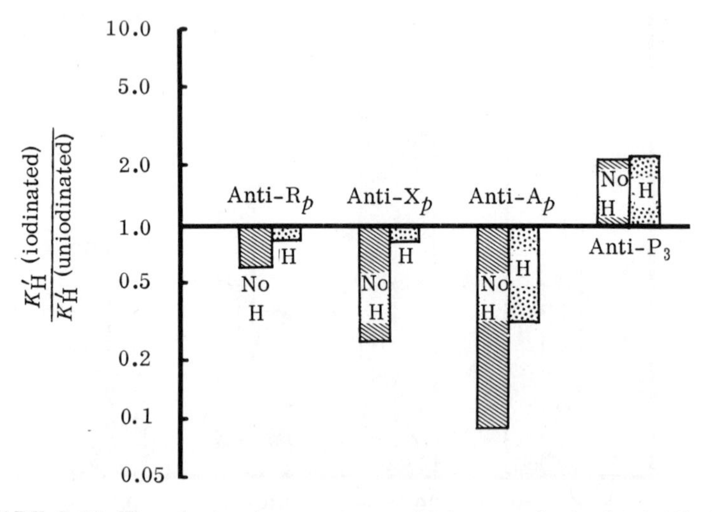

FIGURE 5.10 The change in average combining constants (and ΔF of combination) of antibody sites remaining after iodination of different antibody preparations in the presence or absence of hapten. [From Grossberg *et al.* (1962b).]

tions, it follows that with the preparations of anti-R_p, and anti-X_p, and anti-A_p antibodies studied, iodination in the presence of hapten results in preparations that bind more strongly than do those obtained after iodination in the absence of hapten, because the stronger binding sites, although more sensitive to iodination than the weaker binding sites, are better protected.

With the anti-P_3 preparation the weaker binding sites appear to be more sensitive to iodination. The K'_H for anti-P_3 antibodies has the same high value (compared to the uniodinated preparation) after iodination in the presence or in the absence of hapten. If all sites were equally sensitive to iodination, K'_H would rise somewhat, owing to greater protection of those with high K_H. If the sites with high values of K_H were less sensitive, the rise would be smaller with protection. Since the value of K'_H is about the same regardless of the presence of hapten, it appears that some of the sites with high values of K_H as well as those with low values are affected by iodination.

5.2c Loss of activity by iodination in the presence of hapten. The most plausible explanation for loss of activity in the presence of hapten is that iodination takes place in the combining sites of antibodies that are uncombined with hapten, owing to the equilibrium state. Other possible reasons include iodination of the antibody (or the antibody-hapten complex) so close to the site that the site is blocked, or iodination elsewhere than in the combining site which results in unfolding of the protein in the region composing the site. Such losses of activity would not be protected against by hapten.

These possibilities may explain the results reported by Koshland *et al.* (1965), that iodination of an anti-A_p preparation causes loss of sites which is not prevented by the presence of hapten during iodination. Data which may be considered to demonstrate this type of effect are provided in Table 5.3. The samples of specifically purified anti-X_p which were exposed to 285 moles of HOI per mole of protein incorporated only a few more iodine atoms than did other samples exposed to only 94 moles of HOI, but lost much more activity—a loss which could not be prevented by hapten. It seems a reasonable assumption that the lack of increased incorporation in the more drastically treated samples can be correlated with the occurrence of increased oxidative reactions, which could lead to destruction of the site in the manner suggested. However, it is possible that the loss of activity may be due to increased incorporation of iodine in the combining site, while oxidation effects occurring elsewhere result in a lower total iodine content for the whole molecule.

The possibility also exists that iodination (or oxidation) in other parts of the molecule lowers (or raises) the binding constant of uniodinated sites by electrostatic effect due to change of charge, or by effects such as contraction or expansion of the whole molecule, as described by Habeeb *et al.* (1958). This could be a partial cause of the observed lowering of K'_H in the iodinated anti-R_p, anti-X_p, and anti-A_p preparations or of the increase of K'_H for anti-P_3 (Fig. 5.10). Another possibility is that a tyrosine contributing to a site occupied by hapten may still be iodinated even though blocked on one side by hapten. The resulting increased ionization of the tyrosine hydroxyl, to yield a negative charge in the site, could change the binding energy of hapten-site interaction since such ionization would decrease binding of an anionic hapten. Any reduction of K_H would increase the susceptibility of a site to be iodinated owing to increased dissociation of the hapten.

5.2d Nonspecific effect of iodination of γ-globulin on binding of haptens. There is a charge effect on the nonspecific binding of hapten to normal γ-globulin, as shown by the fact that iodination, which increases negative charge of the protein (by increasing the dissociation constant of the tyrosine hydroxyl), alters the nonspecific binding of hapten. In accord with simple electrostatic theory, nonspecific binding of negatively charged haptens is decreased and nonspecific binding of positively charged haptens is increased somewhat. The opposite effect was observed with esterified globulins in which the negative charge was decreased (Grossberg and Pressman, 1960). The magnitude of this nonspecific charge effect on hapten binding by modified antibody is not clear. However, the differences observed in binding by antibodies iodinated to the same extent in the presence and absence of hapten must be due to differences other than those associated with any such nonspecific charge effect, which must be the same for both preparations.

5.3 THE ISOLATION OF PEPTIDES FROM THE BINDING SITES OF ANTIBODY MOLECULES

The iodination reaction has made it possible to isolate peptides from a digest of iodinated antibody which appear to have come from the combining region of the antibody molecules. These peptides contain iodine-labeled tyrosine, the formation of which is affected by the presence of hapten during the iodination. It has been shown for some antibodies (anti-R_p and anti-X_p) that a tyrosine exists in the combining region which is protected from iodination by the presence of hapten. The technique used is the "Paired Label" iodination technique (Pressman and Roholt, 1961).

One portion of a preparation is iodinated directly with ^{125}I. The other portion is similarly iodinated with ^{131}I but in the presence of hapten. Iodine incorporation is carried out to the same level for each portion. If there is a tyrosine in the site, it is iodinated with ^{125}I in proportion to its reactivity along with other tyrosines on the molecule. However, in the mixture containing the hapten, the rate of iodination by ^{131}I of the tyrosine protected by the hapten is reduced. The two preparations are then mixed and digested with pepsin or another proteolytic enzyme. A portion is placed on a sheet of filter paper and carried through chromatography in one direction followed by high voltage electrophoresis at right angles to the chromatography. This separates the peptides on the sheet. The radioactive peptides are located by making a radioautograph of the paper (Fig. 5.11). The portions of the filter paper corresponding to the location of radioactivity are then cut out and the amounts of ^{125}I and ^{131}I present are determined for each. The amounts of the two isotopes are in the same ratio for most of the spots and for the original digest, but some spots have a high or low ratio of ^{125}I to ^{131}I. These are peptides containing iodinatable residues which are iodinated at different rates in the presence and absence of hapten.

When the peptides containing these aberrant ratios are hydrolyzed to amino acids with pronase and then subjected to high voltage electrophoresis, it is found that the radioactive iodine is present either as mono or diiodotyrosine. It is interesting that the number of binding sites lost for these preparations, as determined from ability to bind hapten, is essentially equivalent to the amount of iodinated tyrosine residues recovered from the "aberrant ratio" peptides. This result indicates that each lost site yields an iodinated tyrosine.

The reason that both high and low ratio peptides are associated with the protected tyrosine (of decreased reactivity) in the site is that some peptides contain diiodotyrosine and others contain monoiodotyrosine. All diiodotyrosine-containing peptides which come from the site will have a high ratio of ^{125}I to ^{131}I, because the protected site is of reduced reactivity. Some of the monoiodotyrosine peptide will have a low ratio because there is more monoiodotyrosine in the peptide from the protected (less reactive) than from the unprotected tyrosine, since not as much of the monoiodotyrosine has been converted to the diiodotyrosine as with the more rapidly iodinating unprotected tyrosine.

The peptides of aberrant ratio are of particular interest because they contain the tyrosine present in the antibody site. By determining the amino acid sequence of such peptides, information can be obtained about the composition of the chain contributing to the binding site.

There remains, however, the possibility that when hapten combines with antibody there is some change in the conformation of the antibody molecule, so that a form is stabilized in which a tyrosine elsewhere than in the combining site is reduced in reactivity (Fig. 5.12). Aberrant ratio peptides could then be due to the conformation change rather than to the protection effect.

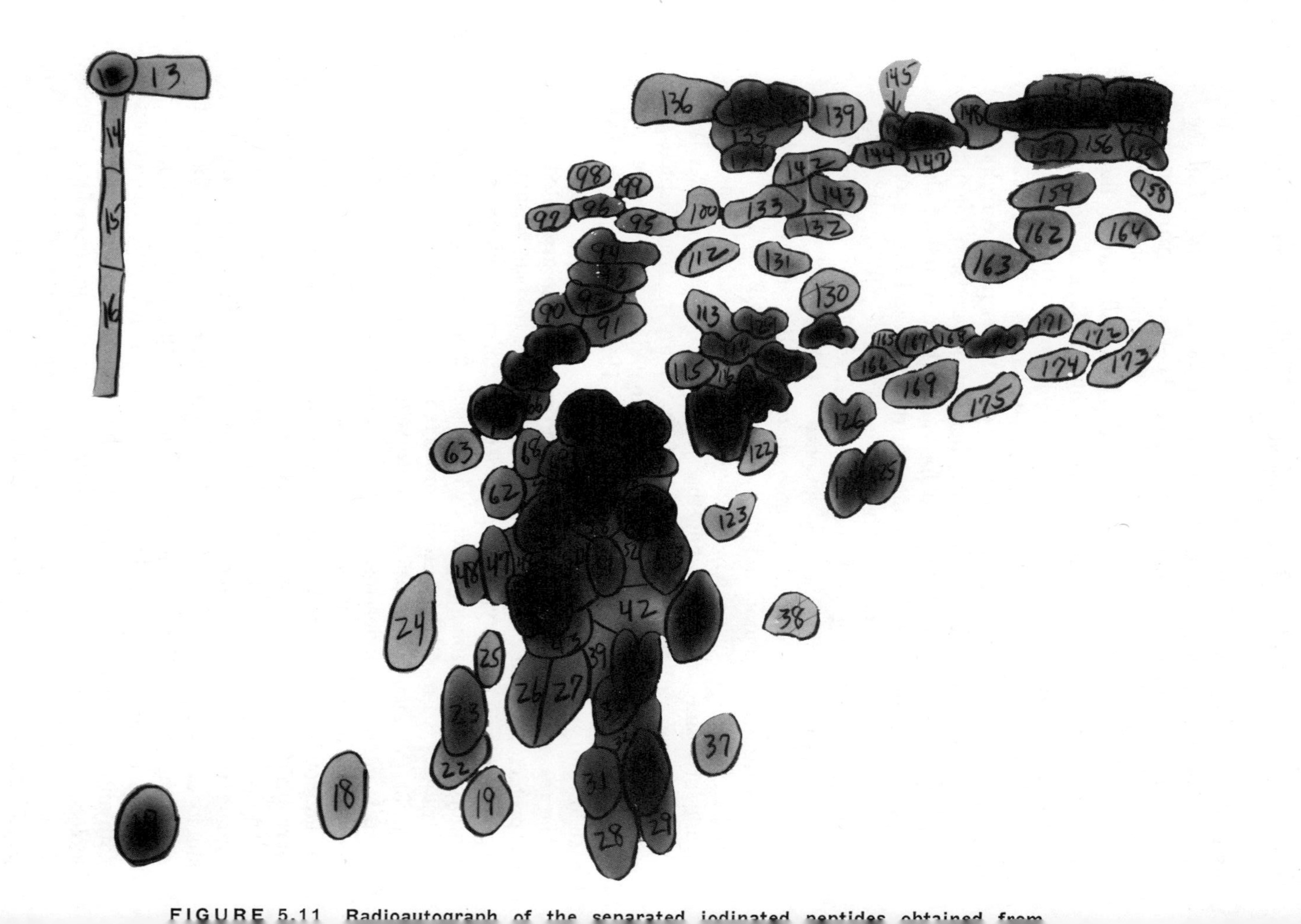

FIGURE 5.11 Radioautograph of the separated iodinated peptides obtained from

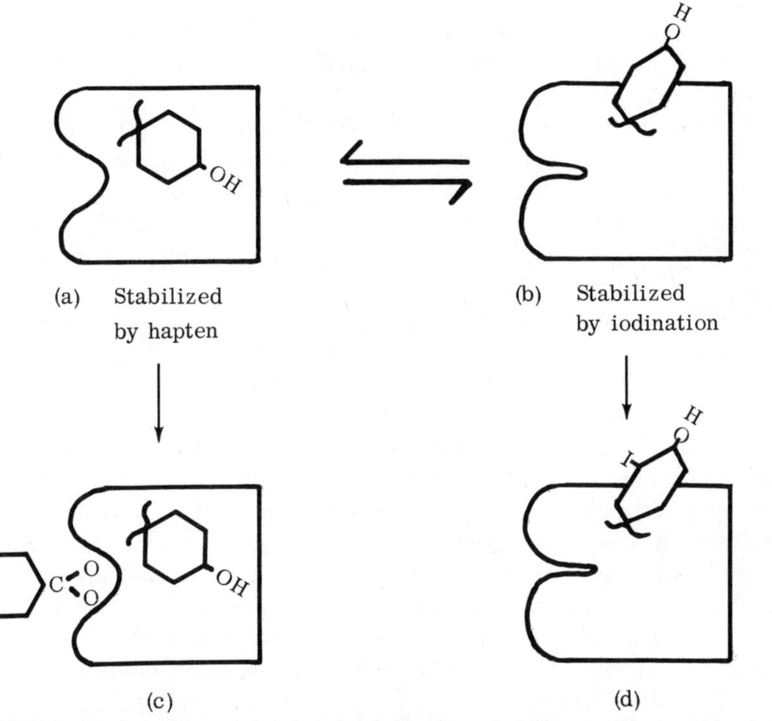

FIGURE 5.12 Possible mechanism for formation of aberrant ratio peptides by iodination of a tyrosine elsewhere than in the antibody site. Equilibrium forms of a portion of an antibody molecule are shown in (a) and (b). Form (a) which has a binding site, has a tyrosine in an unreactive position. Form (b) which has a reactive tyrosine, does not have an effective site. Form (a) is stabilized by hapten so that the equilibrium is shifted in its favor when hapten is present. The tyrosine does not iodinate, that is, the "protection" phenomenon is observed (c). Form (b) is stabilized by iodination and since the equilibrium is then shifted, iodination results in a loss of site (d).

5.4 THE EFFECT OF CYANATE ON ANTIBODY ACTIVITY

Cyanate carbamylates amino groups according to the reaction:

$$\text{protein—NH}_2 + \text{OCN}^- + \text{H}_2\text{O} \rightarrow \text{protein—NH-CO-NH}_2 + \text{OH}^-$$

It converts amino (ammonium) groups to ureido groups which do not carry the positive charge at physiological pH values. A modification reaction of this sort is of particular interest in connection with antibodies such as anti-X_p and anti-R_p, which are directed against negatively charged groups and for which there appears to be a positive charge in the specific binding site. Reaction with cyanate can thus give information about the presence of an amino (ammonium) group in the combining site of such antibodies.

Treatment of anti-R_p antibodies with cyanate until 70 to 80% of the free amino groups were carbamylated was found to result in the loss of 20 to 30% of the antibody sites. That this loss of activity was due to an attack on a group in a site was shown by the fact that the loss could be partially prevented when hapten was present during the carbamylation reaction (Chen *et al.*, 1962).

Anti-azobenzoate antibody loses some activity when reacted with cyanate, but this appears to be due to an attack in the antibody elsewhere than in the specific site, since the loss of activity could not be protected against by the presence of benzoate.

The effects of carbamylation on anti-R_p and anti-X_p antibodies and the abilities of the specific haptens to protect them against loss of activity during carbamylation may be precisely compared by mixing the antibodies and exposing one portion of the mixture to cyanate alone, another portion to cyanate in the presence of a hapten which binds to anti-R_p antibody sites, and still another portion to cyanate in the presence of a hapten which binds to anti-X_p sites. Thus both antibodies are exposed identically to the action of cyanate in each reaction mixture.

The results of such an experiment are shown in Table 5.4. Anti-R_p lost 50% of its activity, while anti-X_p lost only 25% of its activity, when they were carbamylated so that 85% of the amino groups were altered. Only the anti-R_p antibody, however, was protected by its hapten. The *p*-nitrobenzoate did not afford protection of either antibody. This result indicates that the loss in the case of anti-X_p antibody was due to attack elsewhere than in the antibody site.

Anti-A_p antibody sites are not attacked at all by cyanate under the conditions in which anti-R_p sites are attacked, as shown by experiments in which mixtures of anti-A_p and anti-R_p antibodies were carbamylated (Fig. 5.13).

Cyanate is relatively specific in its reaction with amino groups. It does not seem to react with tyrosine residues or guanidinium groups. Although cyanate reacts with SH groups to form a thiourethane, the inactivation of anti-R_p observed is probably not due to such a reaction since the SH group does not appear to be present in this antibody site (see next section).

5.5 THE EFFECT OF IODOACETAMIDE ON ANTIBODY ACTIVITY

The presence of a sulfhydryl group in binding sites was investigated by treating anti-R_p, anti-X_p, and anti-A_p antibodies with iodoacetamide

TABLE 5.4 Carbamylation of a Mixture of Anti-R_p and Anti-X_p Antibodies—Effect of Hapten[a]

Treatment	Free NH_2 (%)	Hapten present during treatment	Hapten binding activity of: Anti-R_p (% of control)	Anti-X_p
Incubated only	100	None	100	100
Incubated with 1 *M* KOCN	15	None	52	78
Incubated with 1 *M* KOCN	15	0.1 *M* $C_6H_5PO_3^{=}$ [b]	69	80
Incubated with 1 *M* KOCN	15	0.1 *M* $O_2NC_6H_4COO^-$	51	78

[a]Data from Chen *et al.* (1962).
[b]Benzenephosphonate binds strongly with anti-R_p (Table 3.19).

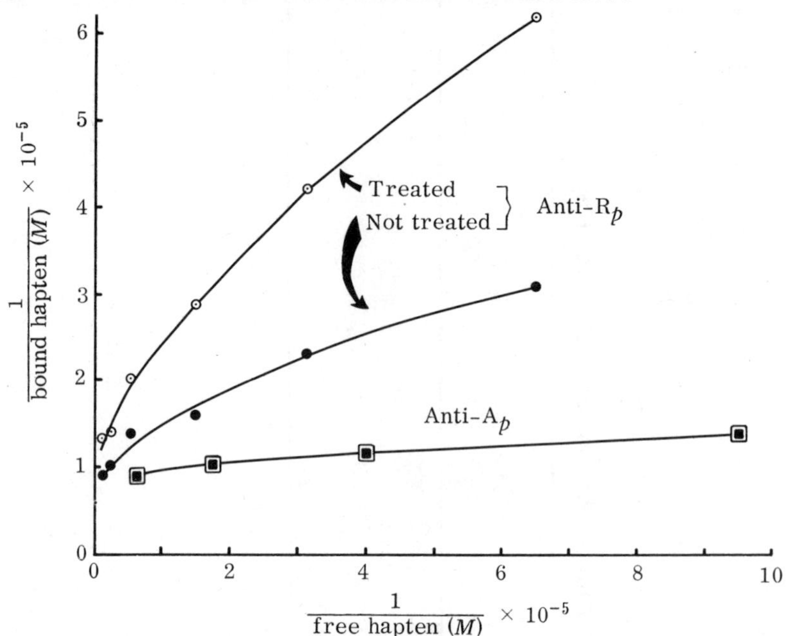

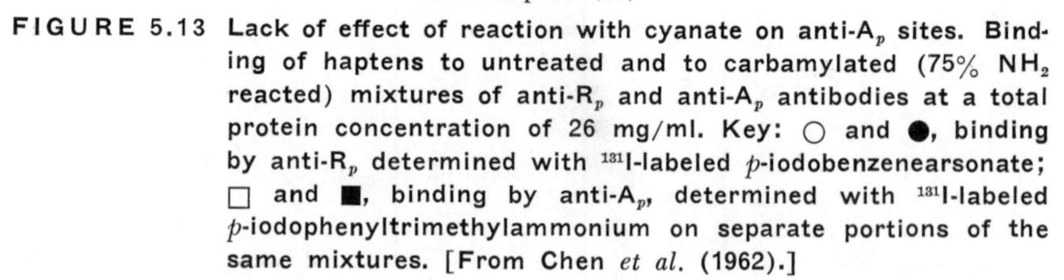

FIGURE 5.13 Lack of effect of reaction with cyanate on anti-A_p sites. Binding of haptens to untreated and to carbamylated (75% NH_2 reacted) mixtures of anti-R_p and anti-A_p antibodies at a total protein concentration of 26 mg/ml. Key: ○ and ●, binding by anti-R_p determined with ^{131}I-labeled *p*-iodobenzenearsonate; □ and ■, binding by anti-A_p, determined with ^{131}I-labeled *p*-iodophenyltrimethylammonium on separate portions of the same mixtures. [From Chen *et al.* (1962).]

under conditions known to alkylate one SH group in γ-globulins. The reaction is

$$\text{protein—SH} + ICH_2CONH_2 + OH^- \rightarrow \text{protein—}SCH_2CONH_2 + I^- + H_2O$$

The alkylation of sulfhydryl groups by this reagent goes much faster than the reaction with amino or hydroxyl groups.

The reaction with these antibodies does not result in appreciable loss of binding activity (Grossberg *et al.*, 1962b) and indicates that no sulfhydryl is involved in the binding sites of any of these antibodies, or is responsible for the inactivation of anti-R_p by cyanate (Section 5.4).

5.6 THE EFFECT OF IODOACETATE ON ANTIBODY ACTIVITY

In view of the possible presence of an amino group in some of the sites of certain antibodies, anti-X_p, anti-R_p, and anti-A_p antibodies have been treated at pH 8 with iodoacetate at concentrations greater than required to react with SH groups. This reaction involves mainly amino groups according to the following equation:

$$\text{protein—NH}_2 + \text{ICH}_2\text{COO}^- + \text{OH}^- \rightarrow \text{protein—NHCH}_2\text{COO}^- + \text{H}_2\text{O} + \text{I}^-$$

Loss of activity of the anti-R_p antibodies, which can be protected against by hapten, has been observed. There is no effect, however, on anti-A_p antibodies which are modified in the same mixture with anti-R_p antibodies (Fig. 5.14). It would appear that an amino group in some of the anti-R_p sites is alkylated. The presence of an amino group in the site of antibenzoate antibodies is uncertain; some loss of activity occurs, but it is not protected against by hapten.

It is interesting to note that the carboxymethylation of amino groups leads to a large increase in net negative charge on the protein molecule. Although, as mentioned above, such increase in net charge as effected by succinylation leads to expansion of γ-globulin molecules (Section 5.1), in the present instance such expansion, if it takes place, does not affect the anti-A_p binding sites. There is an increased nonspecific binding of the positively charged phenyltrimethylammonium hapten to carboxymethylated normal γ-globulin.

5.7 THE EFFECT OF AMIDINATION ON ANTIBODY ACTIVITY

One of the most specific reactions involving modification of amino groups on proteins under relatively mild conditions is that of amidination by ethyl acetimidate. Of the various reactive groups on proteins, only amino groups appear to be modified. The reaction is

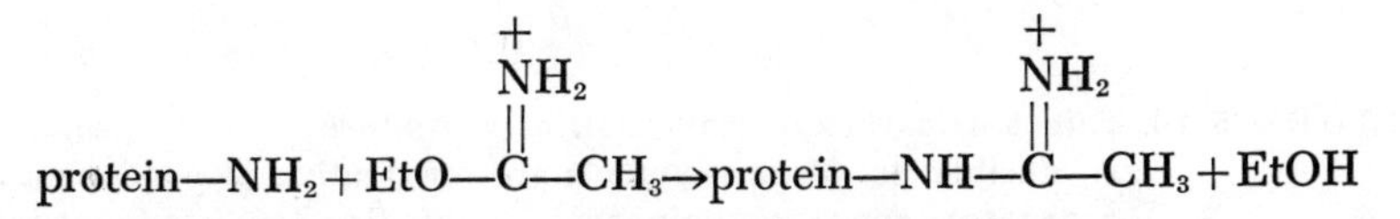

$$\text{protein—NH}_2 + \text{EtO—}\overset{\overset{+}{\text{NH}_2}}{\overset{\|}{\text{C}}}\text{—CH}_3 \rightarrow \text{protein—NH—}\overset{\overset{+}{\text{NH}_2}}{\overset{\|}{\text{C}}}\text{—CH}_3 + \text{EtOH}$$

Wofsy and Singer (1963) extensively amidinated the amino groups in anti-R_p antibody and found a loss of up to 27% in binding activity. This loss might have been due to the amidination of an important amino group in the site of some anti-R_p antibodies, but since protection experiments were not carried out, this point was not clear. However, amidination of other antibodies showed no loss of activity.

The present authors (Table 5.5) have investigated this problem and have confirmed the observation that amidination of specifically purified anti-R_p antibody preparation results in a loss of from 15 to 40% of binding activity in different preparations. The presence of 0.1 *M* phenylarsonate

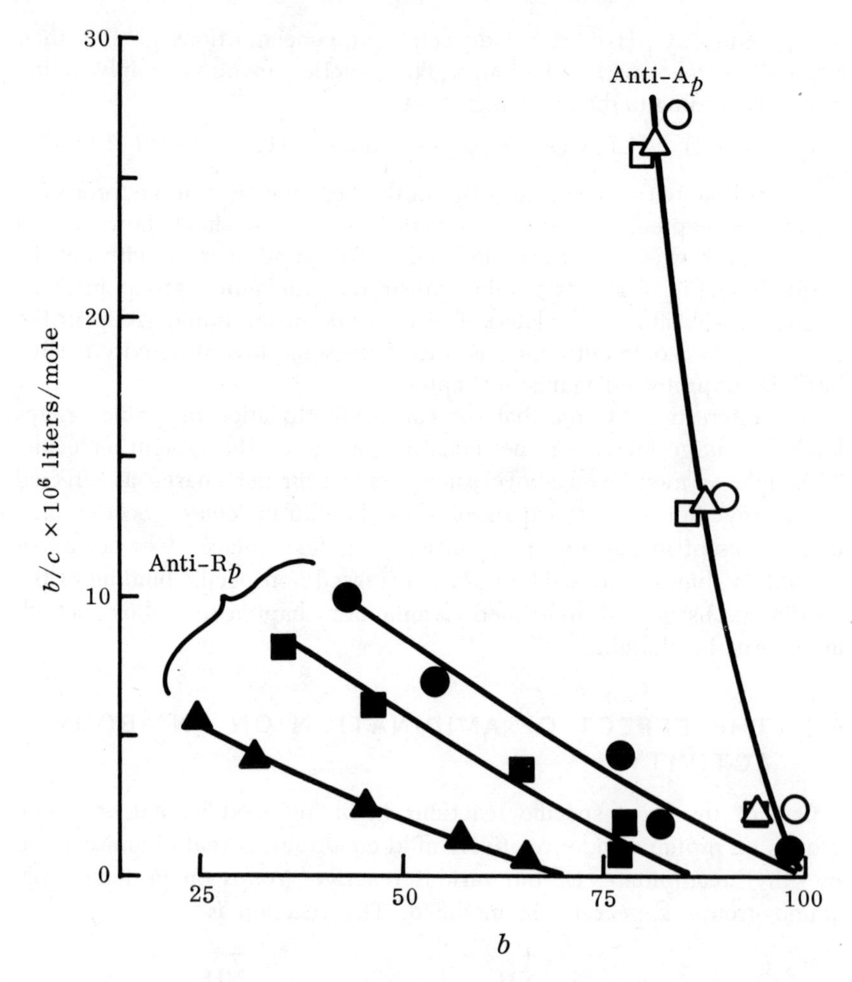

FIGURE 5.14 Effect of carboxymethylation of a mixture of anti-R_p and anti-A_p antibodies. Closed symbols are for binding of *p*-iodobenzene-arsonate; open symbols are for binding of *p*-iodophenyltrimethylammonium. Key: ● and ○, control (untreated) mixture; ▲ and △, mixture carboxymethylated so that 65% of free amino groups were alkylated; ■ and □, mixture carboxymethylated in presence of haptens (0.04 *M* *p*-nitrobenzene-arsonate and 0.08 *M* phenyltrimethylammonium) so that 70% of free amino groups were alkylated. The symbol b is the concentration of hapten bound, expressed as percent of the extrapolated values found for the control mixture; c is the free hapten concentration in the assay by equilibrium dialysis (Data not previously published.)

TABLE 5.5 Effect of Amidination in Presence and Absence of Hapten on Activity of Specifically Purified Anti-R_p Antibodies[a, b]

	Relative binding activity after amidination[c]	
Anti-R_p preparation	With hapten absent	With hapten present
1	0.82	1.00
2	0.77	0.89
3	0.60	0.70
4	0.88	0.88
5	0.96	0.97

[a]Data from Grossberg and Pressman (not previously published).

[b]Antibodies were amidinated by a 2 hour exposure to 1 *M* ethylacetimidate at pH 8.5, without hapten present or with 0.1 *M* phenylarsonate present. In all amidinated preparations more than 70% of amino groups originally present in the protein were modified.

[c]Relative to untreated preparation = 1.00.

during the amidination of these preparations prevented these losses totally or in part, providing evidence that a certain proportion of antibody sites contain an amino group which is important for the combination of hapten with site.

5.8 THE EFFECT OF ACETYLATION ON ANTIBODY ACTIVITY

The effect of reaction with acetic anhydride on anti-hapten antibody activity has been studied with the four antibodies, anti-X_p, anti-R_p, anti-A_p, and anti-P_3. Acetic anhydride reacts with amino and hydroxy groups of proteins to give acetamino groups, protein—$NHCOCH_3$; and acetyl esters, protein—$OCOCH_3$, respectively. The reaction with the amino groups is much more rapid, so that nearly all these groups are acetylated before many hydroxyls react.

5.8a Differences in effect of low and high levels of acetylation of antibodies. Several antibodies can be acetylated so that most amino groups are blocked without much affect on the ability to bind hapten. Thus, when 85% of the amino groups of anti-X_p antibody are acetylated (Nisonoff and Pressman, 1958), only 12% of the binding activity is lost. At this level of acetylation only the amino groups are affected, and as a result it appears that there is no reactive amino group in the anti-X_p site (see Section 5.6). At higher levels of acetylation, however, when hydroxy groups are acetylated, binding activity is lost, and the loss can be prevented by the presence of hapten (Grossberg and Pressman, 1963). Moreover, activity can be recovered by exposure of the acetylated protein to alkali (pH 11) or to hydroxylamine. These treatments do not affect acetylated amines but do split acetylated hydroxyl groups according to the following reactions:

$$\text{protein—OCOCH}_3 + \text{OH}^- \rightarrow \text{protein—OH} + \text{CH}_3\text{—CO—O}^-$$
$$\text{protein—OCOCH}_3 + \text{NH}_2\text{OH} \rightarrow \text{protein—OH} + \text{CH}_3\text{CONHOH}$$

The loss of activity only at high levels of acetylation, its recovery, and the protection effect indicate, therefore, that hydroxy groups are in the anti-X_p sites.

Low levels of acetylation of anti-R_p antibodies have demonstrated some inactivation which appears to be due to acetylation of an amino group in some of the sites. Only some of the anti-R_p antibodies appear to have an amino group in the binding site in accord with the observations on carbamylation (Section 5.4) and amidination (Section 5.7).

Low levels of acetylation have practically no effect on the activity of anti-A_p and anti-P_3 antibodies, but high levels do cause loss of activity, as with anti-X_p and anti-R_p antibodies. In each instance the loss can be partially prevented by protecting the site with hapten during acetylation. Moreover, in each case the effect can be largely reversed by mild hydrolysis.

5.8b Comparison of the sensitivity of anti-R_p, anti-X_p, and anti-A_p antibodies to acetylation. Differences in the effectiveness of acetylation in reducing the binding activity of the various antibodies are shown in Table 5.6. Mixtures of anti-R_p and anti-X_p antibodies, and of anti-R_p and anti-A_p antibodies, were acetylated to several different extents and the hapten binding activities and degrees of amino acetylation measured. The results are plotted in Figs. 5.15 and 5.16. It may be seen that anti-R_p and anti-X_p antibodies (Fig. 5.15) lost activity progressively with increasing exposure to acetic anhydride (as measured to some degree by the loss of free amino groups on the protein); the former antibody seemed somewhat more sensitive. In contrast, anti-A_p was much less sensitive than anti-R_p to acetylation (Fig. 5.16). At a level of amino acetylation at which over 60% of anti-R_p activity was lost, only a few per cent loss of anti-A_p activity was detected. Only at the highest levels of acetylation, at which anti-R_p activity was completely destroyed, were losses of anti-A_p activity apparent.

5.8c Effect of acetylation on combining sites and on hapten binding constants. The fact that protection by hapten against the loss of activity following high level acetylation was observed with anti-X_p,

TABLE 5.6 Acetylation of Anti-hapten Antibodies—Effect of Hapten[a]

Antibody	Amino groups acetylated (%)		Binding activity of antibody after acetylation (% of control)	
	Hapten absent	Hapten present	With hapten absent	With hapten present
Anti-R_p	73	75	23	51
[b] Anti-R_p			1	8
+	92	99		
Anti-A_p			16	43
[b] Anti-A_p			23	52
+	95	91		
Anti-P_3			19	27

[a]Data from Grossberg and Pressman (1963).
[b]Acetylated as a mixture.

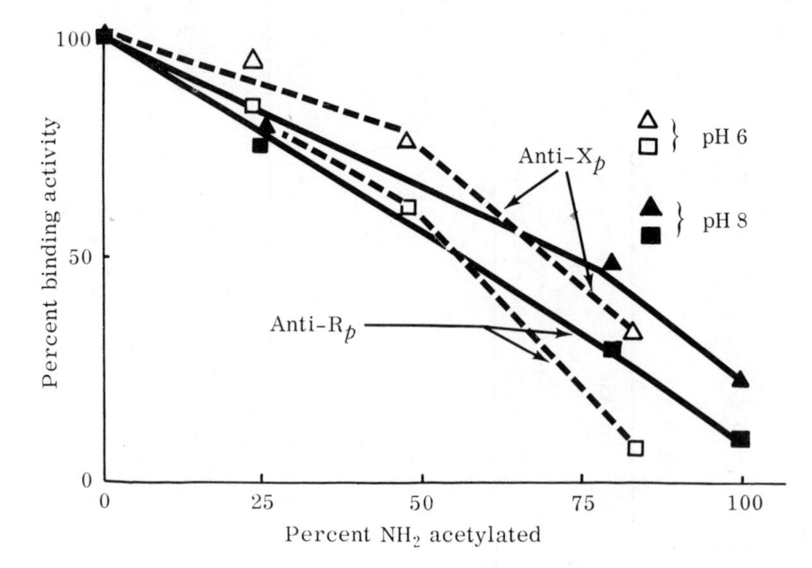

FIGURE 5.15 Effect of acetylation at different levels at pH 6 and at pH 8 on the binding activities of a mixture of anti-R_p and anti-X_p antibodies. Binding of haptens is expressed as percent of the binding by the unacetylated mixture. [From Grossberg and Pressman (1963).]

anti-R_p, anti-A_p, and anti-P_3 antibodies constitutes evidence that in each antibody a group in the combining site was attacked. However, part of the effect of acetylation is due to a decrease in the average binding constant (K'_H) of the sites rather than to a complete block of sites.

Experimental values for the effect of acetylation on the total site concentration (A_o), the average combining constant (K'_H), and heterogeneity index (a) are shown in Table 5.7. The results reveal that acetylation of the more sensitive antibodies, that is, anti-R_p and anti-X_p antibodies, resulted in the loss of binding sites with little or no change in binding constant of the remaining sites. More intensive acetylation of the less sensitive anti-A_p antibodies caused loss of sites, accompanied by a decrease of binding constant to about one-sixth its initial value. Acetylation of anti-A_p antibody in the presence of hapten resulted in essentially complete retention of sites but reduction of their binding constant to about one-fifth the initial value, suggesting that the acetylated group was on the periphery of the site (Fig. 5.4). Acetylation of one anti-P_3 antibody preparation (a comparison with anti-A_p was made by acetylating a mixture of the two) resulted in no loss of binding sites, but in a decrease of K'_H to one-third its initial value. The presence of hapten during acetylation of this anti-P_3 antibody afforded no protection against altera-

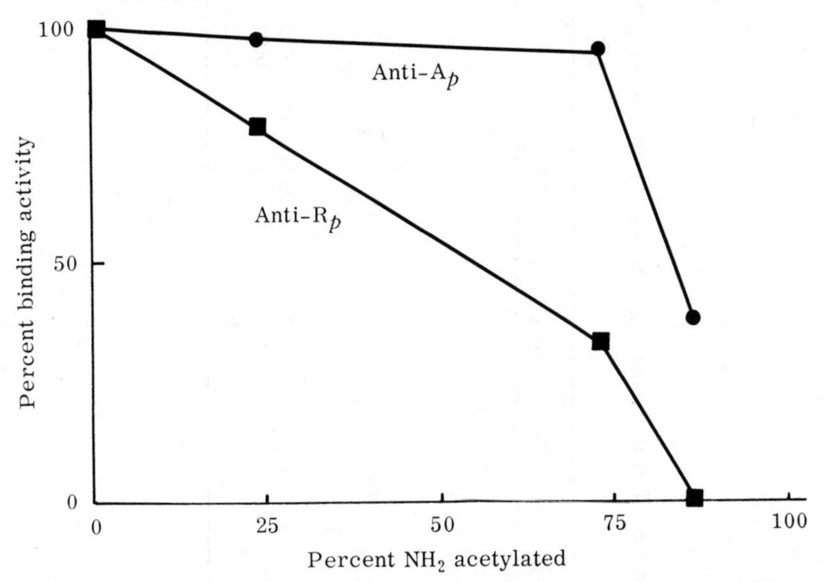

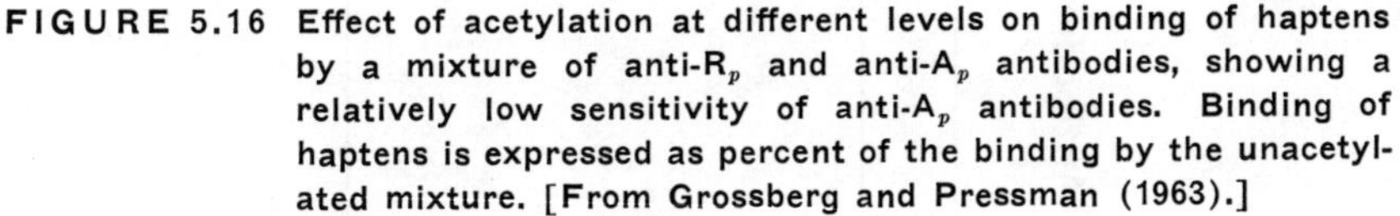
FIGURE 5.16 Effect of acetylation at different levels on binding of haptens by a mixture of anti-R_p and anti-A_p antibodies, showing a relatively low sensitivity of anti-A_p antibodies. Binding of haptens is expressed as percent of the binding by the unacetylated mixture. [From Grossberg and Pressman (1963).]

tion of the binding constant (K'_H was the same as it was when the antibody was acetylated with hapten present).

Another anti-P_3 preparation, when acetylated at a still higher level of exposure in the absence of hapten, lost about 30% of its active sites. This loss was completely prevented by the presence of hapten. Acetylation of this preparation also resulted in a large decrease in the average binding constant of the remaining sites (to about one-sixtieth of the original value). Hapten prevented some of this decrease.

5.8d Reversal of acetylation effects by hydroxylamine. Various antibody preparations which lost activity following acetylation have been hydrolyzed by treatment with hydroxylamine. Their binding activity after removal of hydroxylamine was compared to that of the corresponding unhydrolyzed acetylated materials, and also to that of unmodified antibodies. The results (Table 5.8) indicate that binding activity lost upon acetylation can be recovered following hydrolysis.

5.8e Interpretation of effects of high levels of acetylation. There is considerable evidence for the participation of a hydroxyamino acid in the site of each of the four antibodies studied. The fact that the four can be protected by their specific haptens from loss of activity or sites due to extensive acetylation indicates that a residue in each antibody

TABLE 5.7 Effect of Acetylation of Anti-hapten Antibodies on Total Binding Sites and Average Combining Constants[a]

	Anti-R_p	Anti-X_p	Anti-A_p[b]	Anti-P_3[b]	Anti-P_3
Amino groups acetylated (% of original)					
In absence of hapten	75	80	95	95	97
In presence of hapten	—	—	91	91	95
Binding sites remaining after acetylation (% of original)					
In absence of hapten	44	66	61	100	71
In presence of hapten	—	—	100	100	100
Average binding constants (liters/mole $\times 10^{-5}$)					
Before treatment	1.6	0.21	4.0	0.40	0.91
After acetylation in absence of hapten	1.1	0.21	0.65	0.13	0.014
After acetylation in presence of hapten	—	—	0.87	0.15	0.029

[a] Data from Grossberg and Pressman (1963).
[b] These two preparations were treated in a mixture.

TABLE 5.8 Reversal of Acetylation by Hydroxylamine for Anti-hapten Antibodies[a]

Antibody	Binding activity (%) of acetylated samples[b]	
	Prior to hydrolysis with hydroxylamine	After hydrolysis with hydroxylamine
Anti-R_p	31	60
	10	57
	8	42
	1	35
Anti-X_p	60	83
	35	67
	25	56
Anti-A_p	27	73
Anti-P_3	71	82
	20	50

[a]Data from Grossberg and Pressman (1963).
[b]Calculated as

$$\frac{\text{Hapten bound by acetylated sample}}{\text{Hapten bound by unacetylated sample}} \times 100$$

site is attacked by acetic anhydride. In addition, the reversal by hydroxylamine of the loss of activity caused by acetylation indicates that a hydroxyl group in the sites is being attacked. In view of the evidence from iodination studies that tyrosines are present in these sites, it would appear that the hydroxyl groups involved in acetylation are from these tyrosines.

Analysis of the effects of acetylation in terms of proportion of sites lost and effect on binding constants (Table 5.6) indicates that the acetylatable group in the site is involved to a variable degree in the specific interaction of site with hapten. With some antibodies, that is, anti-R_p and anti-X_p, acetylation of the group in the site appears to destroy binding activity effectively, whereas acetylation elsewhere on the molecule does not affect the activity of the site (that is, sites on such antibodies have the same binding constant as those on unmodified antibody). These sites must also be unaffected by any distortion due to the radical change in charge distribution (the protein as a whole suffered a net increase in negative charge of 40 to 50 units), or due to the steric effects of introduction of acetyl groups.

The anti-A_p site is less readily affected by acetic anhydride. The group in this site which can be acetylated appears to be important for specific interaction, although less reactive with the reagent than the group acetylated in anti-R_p and anti-X_p sites, since anti-A_p sites are lost when sufficient acetylation of the molecule has occurred. This extent of modification also decreases the binding constant of remaining sites appreciably. It is probable that alterations in other parts of the molecule produced by the more intensive exposure to acetic anhydride affect the anti-A_p site. Such alterations do not appear to include anything brought on by increased net negative charge in view of the lack of effect of carboxymethylation (Section 5.6).

The anti-P_3 site is relatively resistant to alteration by acetylation, even more so than the anti-A_p site (Table 5.6, columns 3 and 4). A hydroxyamino acid is involved in the site in some manner, as evidenced by hydroxylamine reversal of acetylation effects (Table 5.7). The greater resistance may be due either to the fact that its acetylatable group is less reactive or that it has less importance for binding. More intensive exposure of the anti-P_3 molecule to acetic anhydride (Table 5.6, column 5) leads to detectable loss of sites. At the same time there is an even greater effect on K'_H (compare columns 4 and 5, Table 5.6), which indicates that the anti-P_3 site is sensitive to an alteration which seems to have little to do with over-all charge effects (since amino acetylation was essentially complete in both instances). In all probability, hydroxyl acetylation accounts for the effect.

5.9 THE EFFECT OF DIAZONIUM COUPLING ON ANTIBODY ACTIVITY

In view of the apparent presence of tyrosine in their sites, two of the antibodies, anti-X_p and anti-R_p, were coupled with *p*-sulfobenzenediazonium chloride. This compound couples with proteins on the tyrosine, histidine, and lysine groups according to the following reactions:

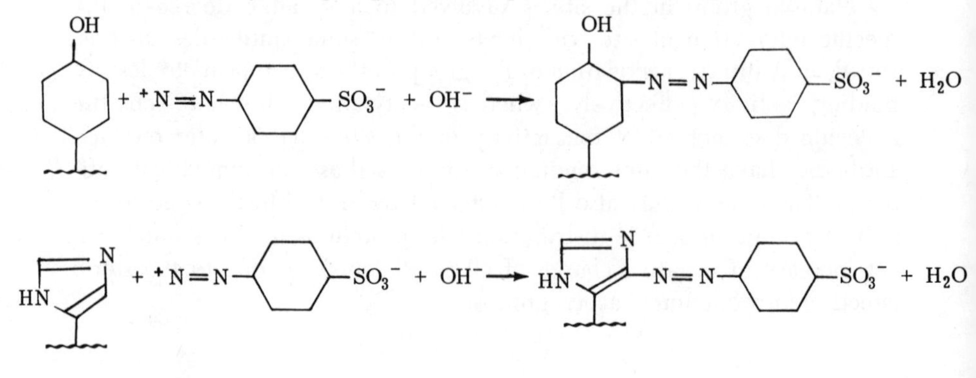

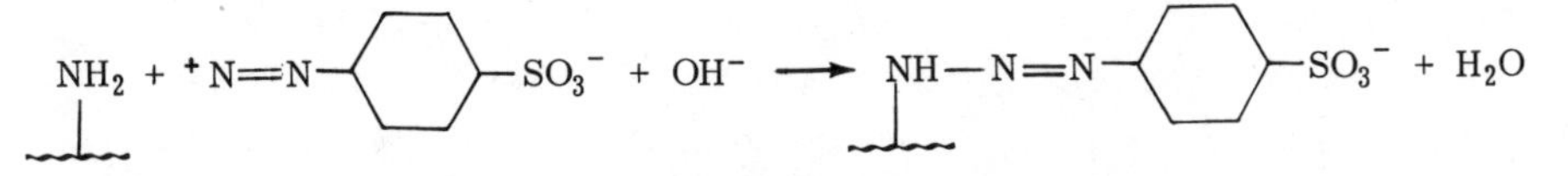

With anti-R_p antibody it was found that antibody activity was lost with coupling, but the effect could be prevented by the presence of hapten. This indicates that a residue is present in the binding site which reacts with diazonium ion. With anti-X_p there was loss of activity which was not prevented by the presence of hapten (Grossberg and Pressman, unpublished). Thus the effect on anti-X_p of diazonium coupling is more complicated than simple coupling with the tyrosine known to be present in its site.

5.10 EFFECT OF pH ON BINDING

The binding of haptens to anti-X_p, anti-R_p, anti-A_p, and anti-P_3 antibodies becomes weaker as the pH of the equilibrated mixtures goes from 8 to 9 to 10. The number of sites and their average K'_H value has been determined at different pH values for the binding of *p*-iodobenzoate to anti-*p*-azobenzoate antibody (Table 5.9). No appreciable difference is observed in the total concentration of combining sites associated with changes in pH. The decrease in the binding constant with increasing pH is in accord with the presence in the active site of an essential group which can lose a proton at higher pH values. A decreased binding due to such a loss of a proton would lead to a straight line relationship in a plot of the reciprocal of the concentration of hapten bound and the reciprocal of the hydrogen ion concentration at a particular value of the concentration of the free hapten (Fig. 5.17) (Pressman *et al.*, 1961b). From these curves the value for the dissociation constant, K_a for an acidic groups in the site is calculated to be 1.4×10^{-10} and is consistent with the presence in the active site of an ionizable group with a pK value

TABLE 5.9 Effect of Variation in pH on A_t, the Total Number of Combining Sites, and on K'_H Values, of Specifically Purified Anti-*p*-azobenzoate Antibody[a]

pH	A_t ($M \times 10^5$)	K'_H (liter/mole $\times 10^{-4}$)
8	2.4	8.2
9	2.3	7.1
10	2.2	3.9

[a]Data from Pressman *et al.* (1961).

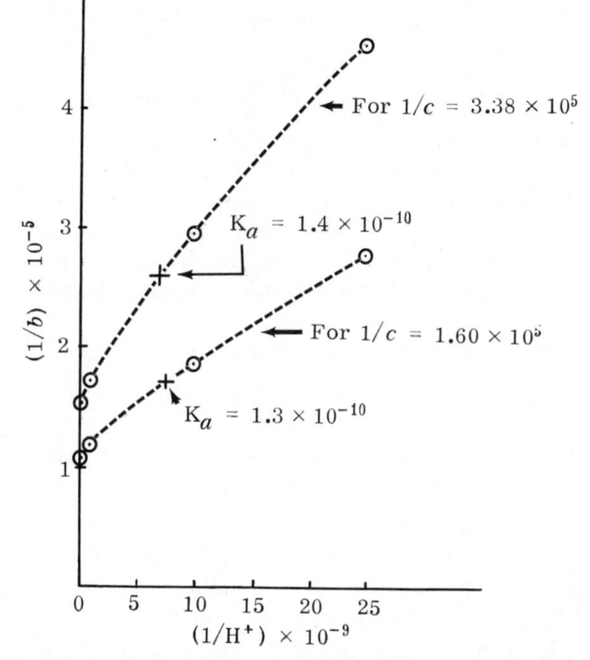

FIGURE 5.17 Effect of hydrogen ion concentration on binding of *p*-iodobenzoate by anti-X_p antibody (*b* is concentration of hapten bound at free hapten concentration, *c*, and hydrogen ion concentrations indicated). [From Pressman *et al.* (1961).]

of about 9.8. The phenolic hydroxyl of tyrosine, an α-ammonium, the ε-ammonium of lysine, and the sulfhydryl of cysteine all have p*K* values in this range. The effect observed, however, is probably due to the ionization of the phenolic hydroxyl of tyrosine, because it is the only group which appears to be in the site of all four antibodies.

The K'_H for anti-X_p antibody does not change appreciably between pH 8 and pH 6 (Pressman *et al.*, 1961b). This indicates that histidine is probably not involved in the anti-X_p binding site.

When the pH is dropped below 5 there is decreased combination with specific hapten in the anti-A_p system (Grossberg and Pressman, unpublished). This is probably because the essential carboxylate group present in the site is protonated, decreasing the number of effective sites.

5.11 REDUCTION OF EXPOSED DISULFIDE BONDS

Mild reduction of several disulfide bonds and subsequent alkylation does not affect the activity of anti-X_p, anti-R_p, and anti-A_p antibodies, indicating that an easily reduced disulfide bond is not important for maintaining the configuration of their sites. Since the alkylation of the cysteine residues thus liberated does not affect antibody activity, it is also apparent that the cystine residues concerned cannot be present in the antibody sites (Grossberg *et al.*, 1962c).

5.12 EFFECT OF PHOTOOXIDATION

In the oxidation of protein by use of ultraviolet light and an activating dye, the most easily oxidized group appears to be histidine, although tryptophan, methionine, and tyrosine are somewhat affected too. Photooxidation of anti-R_p antibody was reported by Koshland *et al.* (1963) to destroy some antibody activity. The loss of activity was probably due to oxidation somewhere other than in the site, since protection by hapten was not observed.

5.13 AFFINITY LABELING

A novel method for modification of residues of antibody molecules is that of affinity labeling, introduced by Wofsy *et al.* (1962). The designed objective of this method is to carry out a reaction specifically in the combining site by taking advantage of the binding properties of antihapten antibodies. A similar approach has been applied to the modification of enzyme molecules by Schoellman and Shaw (1962). A reagent is employed which specifically binds to the active site and which contains a chemically reactive group. First the chemically reactive hapten binds to the antibody site, and then the reactive group forms a covalent bond with a particular residue of the protein. The residue must be of the kind and so situated that it can react with the hapten fixed in the antibody site. This approach is illustrated in Fig. 5.18 for the reaction of the diazonium salt of benzenearsonate by this mechanism.

Such studies have employed reagents with a diazonium group on

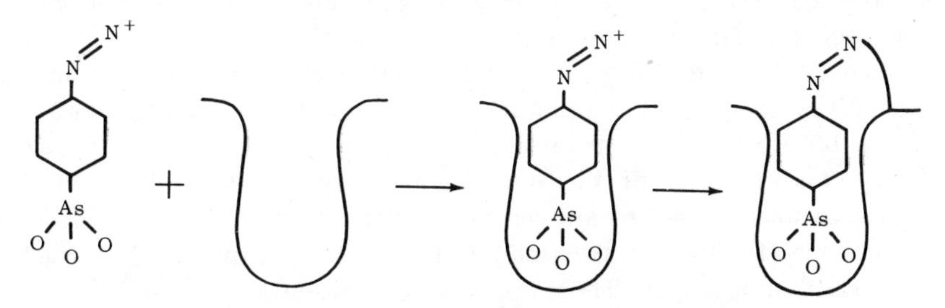

FIGURE 5.18 Mechanism involved in affinity labeling, that is, coupling in the vicinity of the antibody site.

benzenearsonate, nitrobenzene, or phenyltrimethylammonium. These substances are reacted with the specific antibodies anti-R_p, anti-dinitrophenyl, or anti-A_p, respectively. The reaction is very rapid compared to the action of the diazonium compounds with normal γ-globulin or with the antibody molecule whose binding sites are reversibly blocked by hapten. Although the rapid reaction appears to take place with tyrosine, there is a question as to whether the tyrosine being attacked is part of the site. The diazonium group on the hapten may well react with any tyrosine close to the site and in the proper orientation to react while the hapten is combined with antibody as shown in Fig. 5.17. Indeed a tyrosine in the site could be blocked from reacting by the inert part of the hapten. Thus the tyrosine found in the site by iodination studies may well be a different one from that affected by the affinity label.

It has been difficult to establish that antibody sites are irreversibly blocked by the affinity-labeling reaction. Although reduction of binding activity of anti-dinitrophenyl antibodies by this reaction has been demonstrated, it cannot be said that this effect is necessarily due to the modification of a group in the antibody site, since a dinitrophenyl group on one antibody molecule could reversibly bind with the antibody sites of a second molecule to give the observed loss of binding activity. Nonetheless, inasmuch as this method of labeling an antibody molecule apparently can give relatively restricted reaction with certain residues of the molecule, it should prove of use in mapping antibody structure.

5.14 OTHER EVIDENCE FOR THE PRESENCE OF A CHARGED GROUP IN SOME ANTIBODY SITES

In Chapter 3 the presence in the anti-A_p antibody of a negatively charged group in the combining site was suggested by the difference in binding energies of a hapten containing a charged trimethylammonium group and a hapten containing the isosteric but uncharged tertiary butyl benzene group. Similar evidence has been obtained for the presence of a positive charge in the sites of anti-X_p antibody and other antibodies against carboxyl group haptens.

Other evidence that the combining region of anti-A_p antibody contains a negative charge has been obtained from the effect of simple inorganic salts at high concentrations on the binding of haptens (Grossberg *et al.*, 1962a). The binding of the homologous hapten is decreased by inorganic cations but not by anions. This appears to be due to the competition between the inorganic cation and the hapten for the negative charge in the combining region. There appears to be essentially no binding at the antibody site by the various anions tested, Cl^-, Br^-, I^-, NO_3^- and ClO_4^-, because for any single cation there is no variation in the effect of these anions on the binding. The magnitude of the effects for cations is in the order $Cs^+ > Rb^+ > NH_4^+ > K^+ > Na^+ > Li^+$. This is essentially the reverse order of the radii of the hydrated ions. Thus the cations whose centers of charge can approach most closely to the combining region of the antibody seem to have the greatest effect.

In an analogous manner, with anti-X_p antibody, the binding of homologous hapten is decreased by univalent inorganic anions but not by cations (Pressman *et al.*, 1961). The magnitude of the decrease of specific binding caused by these anions is in the order $CNS^- > NO_3^- > I^- > Br^- > Cl^-$, which is the order of decreasing size. (Fluoride gives a slight increase.) Anions, except for fluoride, are not very hydrated. Their effects are probably due to a charge interaction with a positive group in the antibody site. The size of the anion apparently affects its degree of binding and thus the degrees of competition with the homologous hapten are different. When the anion is phenolate it shows still higher binding, since it is closer in structure to the benzoate, having a benzene ring as well as a negatively charged group. The phenolate is small enough to fit in the region of the antibody directed against carboxylate.

5.15 OTHER EFFECTS OF CHEMICAL ALTERATION ON ANTIBODY ACTIVITY; EFFECT ON THE PRECIPITATION REACTION

To determine the effect of a chemical alteration on the binding site of the antibody molecule, it is necessary to use a method which measures binding directly; for example, the equilibrium dialysis method. It is inadvisable to use the precipitation reaction because chemical alteration affects the precipitability of the antibody.

It has been found (Nisonoff and Pressman, 1958) that when anti-X_p antibody is acetylated the precipitating activity is lost much more rapidly than are binding sites. Precipitating activity was reduced 60% and binding activity only 5% upon acetylation of 20% of the amino groups. Precipitating activity was completely lost while binding activity was reduced only 12% on acetylation of 85% of the amino groups. Thus, a very low degree of acetylation destroys the ability of the antibody to precipitate although the binding activity is not affected.

Marrack and Orlans (1954) first pointed out that acetylation of an anti-protein antibody reduced its ability to precipitate but that the antibody so acetylated could be precipitated when mixed with intact antibody. What apparently happens is that the increased negative charge of the antibody, due to acetylation, prevents precipitation. Normally the antigen and antibody are both negatively charged and there is just enough energy of interaction to hold these large charged particles together. However, a single antigen molecule has to hold several antibodies around it. Acetylation of antibody increases its net negative charge so that the energy of interaction is no longer large enough to hold the antigen and the mutually repelling antibodies together. Although complexes of antigen and acetylated antibody form, they are not large enough to precipitate. Increasing the net negative charge on an antibody decreases the binding of a simple negative hapten to an extent proportional to this net negative charge, whereas antibody-antibody repulsion in antigen-antibody complexes is proportional to the square (or more) of the net charge.

Iodination of antibody produces an effect opposite to that of acetylation, in that iodinated antibody is more precipitable. Ordinarily, anti-X_p antibody does not completely precipitate with antigen; some molecules form soluble complexes and precipitate only with difficulty. When this antibody is iodinated it becomes more precipitable, presumably owing to the increased hydrophobic attraction induced by the additional iodine atoms (Pressman and Radzimski, 1962). This means that when iodination of antibody decreases the amount of specific precipitate formed, the effect cannot be used to determine the number of antibody sites affected, since some antibody molecules which would not have precipitated in any event are now brought down.

5.16 SUMMARY

In determining whether a chemical reaction has affected the binding site of antibody and whether certain amino acid residues are present in the site, use is made of the following criteria. (1) There is a loss of binding activity such as measured by equilibrium dialysis. A loss of precipitating activity is not conclusive because the chemical reagent could affect precipitation of antibody without affecting the site. (2) The presence of hapten during the chemical reaction protects the site against inactivation. (3) The amino acid residue affected is isolated and identified as coming from the site by, for example, the paired label technique.

Although loss of activity on chemical alteration and protection by the presence of hapten against such loss strongly implicates a reaction in the site, the possibility remains that the effective reaction takes place elsewhere on the molecule and stabilizes a conformation of the molecule in which the binding site is altered. However it would then be necessary for the presence of hapten in the site to stabilize a conformation in which the reactivity of this key residue is reduced (Fig. 5.12). This indirect mechanism is unlikely on the basis of present evidence, at least for the effects of esterification.

A summary of the chemical modifications so far carried out on the four model anti-hapten antibodies is given in Table 5.10. A summary of the groups thought to be in each antibody site, along with corroborating evidence, is given in Table 5.11.

Charge: Inorganic ion effects on specific binding and a comparison of the binding of charged haptens with that of the isosteric uncharged hapten indicate that there is definitely a charged group in the sites of anti-X_p and anti-A_p antibodies.

A *carboxylate* group is present only in sites of anti-A_p antibodies; it is absent in the sites of antibodies to the other groups. This has been shown by esterification, reversal of the esterification, and the effect on the hapten-antibody combination of reducing the pH.

A *hydroxyl* group is present in the sites of all four antibodies, as shown by acetylation and reversal of the acetylation reaction. This hydroxyl group appears to be that of a *tyrosine,* as shown by the effect of the iodination reaction for all four antibodies, the effect of diazonium coupling for those tested, and the isolation of a tyrosine from the sites of anti-R_p and anti-X_p antibodies by the paired label technique. The presence of tyrosine in sites is also implied by the decrease in binding at high pH values for the four antibodies.

The presence of an *amino* group is implicated in some anti-R_p antibody sites by carbamylation, carboxymethylation, amidination, and a low level of acetylation. The anti-X_p antibody shows loss of binding activity by acetylation and carboxymethylation. However, it is not certain that an amino group is present in the anti-X_p site because protection could not be achieved. The particular reactions used to alter amino groups have no effect on anti-P_3 or anti-A_p antibodies.

There does not seem to be a *disulfide* in the sites of the four antibodies; neither does there appear to be a *histidine,* as indicated by the absence of pH effects on the binding in the pH region of histidine protonation.

Guanidinium contributes the positive charge present in the sites of most anti-R_p and anti-X_p antibodies (Grossberg and Pressman, 1967).

TABLE 5.10 Effect of Chemical Modification on Binding Activity of Antibodies[a]

Modification	Antibody			
	Anti-R_p ($AsO_3^{=}$)	Anti-X_p (COO^-)	Anti-P_3 (Pyridine)	Anti-A_p ($N(CH_3)_3^+$)
Esterification	–	–	–	+
Iodination	+	+	+	+
Acetylation of OH	+	+	+	+
Carbamylation	+	–		–
Carboxymethylation	+	?		–
Acetylation of NH_2	+	?		–
Amidination	+			
Alkylation of SH	–	–		–
Diazonium coupling with $NN\langle\text{ring}\rangle SO_3^-$	+	?		?
Diazonium coupling by specific, that is, "affinity" labeling	+			+
Photoxidation	?			

[a]Key: + = loss of activity which can be protected against by the presence of hapten
– = No loss of activity
? = Loss of activity not affected by the presence of hapten

TABLE 5.11 Groups Implicated as Being in the Antibody Site (Rabbit Antibody)

	Anti-R_p ($AsO_3^=$)	Anti-X_p (COO^-)	Anti-P_3 (Pyridine)	Anti-A_p ($N(CH_3)_3^+$)
CHARGE		**+**		**+**
Ion effects		+		+
Hapten		+		+
CARBOXYLATE	**−**	**−**	**−**	**+**
Esterification	−	−	−	+
Reversal				+
pH4				+
HYDROXYL	**+**	**+**	**+**	**+**
Acetylation	+	+	+	+
Reversal	+	+	+	+

TABLE 5.11 *(continued)*

	Anti-R_p ($AsO_3^=$)	Anti-X_p (COO^-)	Anti-P_3 (Pyridine)	Anti-A_p ($N(CH_3)_3^+$)
TYROSINE	**+**	**+**	**+**	**+**
Iodination	+	+	+	+
Diazonium coupling	+	+		+
pH	+	+	+	+
Paired label	+	+		
AMINO	**+**	**(?)**	**−**	**−**
Acetylation (low level)	+	(?)	−	−
Carbamylation	+	−		−
Carboxymethylation	+	(?)		−
Amidination	+			
DISULFIDE	**−**	**−**		**−**
Reduction	−	−		−
HISTIDINE		**−**		**−**
pH		−		−
GUANIDINIUM	**+**	**+**	**−**	**−**
By chemical modification	+	+	−	−

6

ACTIVE SITES OF ANTIBODIES IN RELATION TO γG-GLOBULIN STRUCTURE

This chapter is concerned with the structure of the γG-globulin antibody molecule, and particularly with the regions which make up the two active sites. The basis for the view presently held of the polypeptide chain structure of γG-globulins will be outlined, followed by a more detailed discussion of the way in which this structure is thought to relate to the active sites of antibodies.

6.1 BIVALENCE OF ANTIBODY

Although antibodies were considered to be multivalent because of their participation in the precipitation reaction, the first definitive evidence of bivalence was obtained by Pappenheimer *et al.* (1940). They found that the sedimentation properties of anti-diphtheria toxin when combined with excess diphtheria toxin indicated a complex of two toxin molecules with one antibody molecule.

The bivalence of anti-hapten antibody was demonstrated by Eisen and Karush (1949), using equilibrium dialysis measurements on anti-benzenearsonate antibody.

Since antibodies are bivalent, it appeared plausible at first that some antibody molecules might have one site directed against one antigenic group, whereas the other site might well be directed against another antigenic group. Many experiments were carried out in attempts to demonstrate such heteroligating antibody molecules, that is, those with the combining sites directed against different antigenic groupings. The most definitive of these experiments were carried out by Eisen *et al.* (1954) and Nisonoff *et al.* (1959b), who showed that both sites of an antibody molecule are at least directed against the same hapten or antigenic group. In the latter work antisera were used which had been obtained by injecting X_p-γ-globulin. These contained large amounts of both anti-γ-globulin antibody and antibody capable of binding *p*-iodobenzoate groups. Anti-γ-globulin antibodies were removed by adsorption on a specific solid absorbent. No binding activity for the *p*-iodobenzoate was removed. These experiments led to the conclusion that none of the anti-γ-globulin antibody molecules contained an anti-benzoate site.

6.2 THE POLYPEPTIDE CHAINS OF RABBIT γG-GLOBULIN

The 6S rabbit γG-globulin molecule consists of four polypeptide chains—two light and two heavy chains. The molecule is composed of two halves which appear to be identical. Each half consists of one heavy chain of ~55,000 molecular weight and one light chain of ~20,000 molecular weight. In most molecules, the chains seem to be joined by only three disulfide bonds in the manner indicated in Fig. 6.1 (Porter, 1962; Cohen and Porter, 1964). The single disulfide bond joining the two heavy chains appears to be the most labile since it is usually reduced first when the molecule is exposed to reducing reagents such as β-mercaptoethanol or sulfite. After such reduction, the two halves are no longer covalently linked, but are still held together by noncovalent bonds.

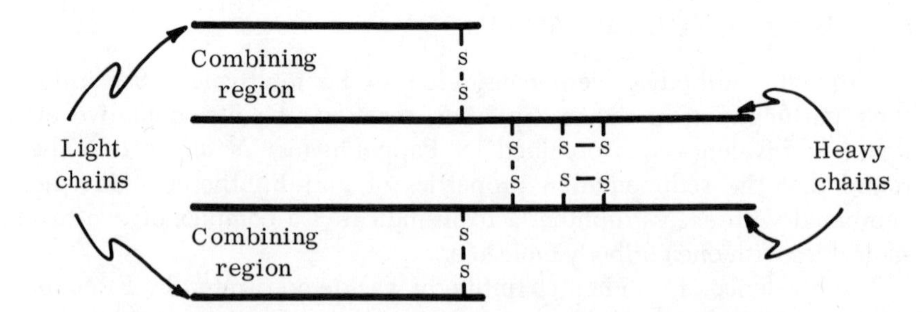

FIGURE 6.1 Schematic structure of the γG-globulin molecule. The exact number of disulfide bonds between the heavy chains is uncertain due to the possibility of disulfide interchange; see discussion in Cohen and Porter (1964).

These bonds can be weakened by placing the molecule in dilute HCl solution so that the two half molecules separate, but the halves go back together again at neutral pH (Palmer *et al.*, 1963). Further treatment of the molecule with a reducing agent results in the splitting of the disulfide bonds linking the light and heavy chains. Even after this reduced molecule is alkylated (for example with iodoacetamide), the four chains remain together by virtue of the noncovalent bonding so that the molecule continues to behave as a hydrodynamic unit of about 150,000 molecular weight. In addition, the noncovalent bonds maintain the chains in the orientation required for antibody activity.

The light and heavy chains can be physically separated if the reduced and alkylated molecules are placed in a solvent such as 1 *M* propionic acid, concentrated urea or guanidine, or a solution of a detergent such as decylsulfate. Under these conditions the noncovalent bonds are sufficiently weakened so that the heavy chains may be separated from the light chains by a molecular sieving process, such as passage through a column of Sephadex (Fleischman *et al.*, 1962). The separated light chains, when returned to neutral salt solution, then exhibit the hydrodynamic properties of a 20,000 molecular weight molecule. The separated heavy chains of rabbit γG-globulin tend to aggregate and are rather insoluble in neutral salt solution. However, if an amount of light chain equivalent to that originally associated with the heavy chains is added to the separated heavy chains, reassociation takes place to produce the 150,000 molecular weight molecule. Moreover, such reassociation of chains from antibody molecules yields reconstituted antibody sites, as will be discussed in Section 6.5.

6.3 FRAGMENTS OF γG-GLOBULIN PRODUCED BY PROTEOLYSIS AND DISULFIDE BOND REDUCTION

When the γG-globulin antibody molecule is subjected to limited proteolysis by pepsin at pH 6 a smaller molecule (M.W. ~105,000) is produced, which differs from the original in that the carboxyl-terminal portions of the heavy chains are digested away, as illustrated in Fig. 6.2. As indicated, the remaining portions of the heavy chains are still joined by a single disulfide bond (Nisonoff *et al.*, 1961). In addition, the 105,000 molecular weight protein fragment so produced still contains both of the antibody sites, making it bivalent and hence precipitable by antigen. Reduction of the disulfide bond joining the two heavy chain remnants produces two 50,000 molecular weight fragments, each containing a single antibody site. There is no loss of antibody sites by this procedure, therefore, but the fragments are no longer precipitable by antigen, since

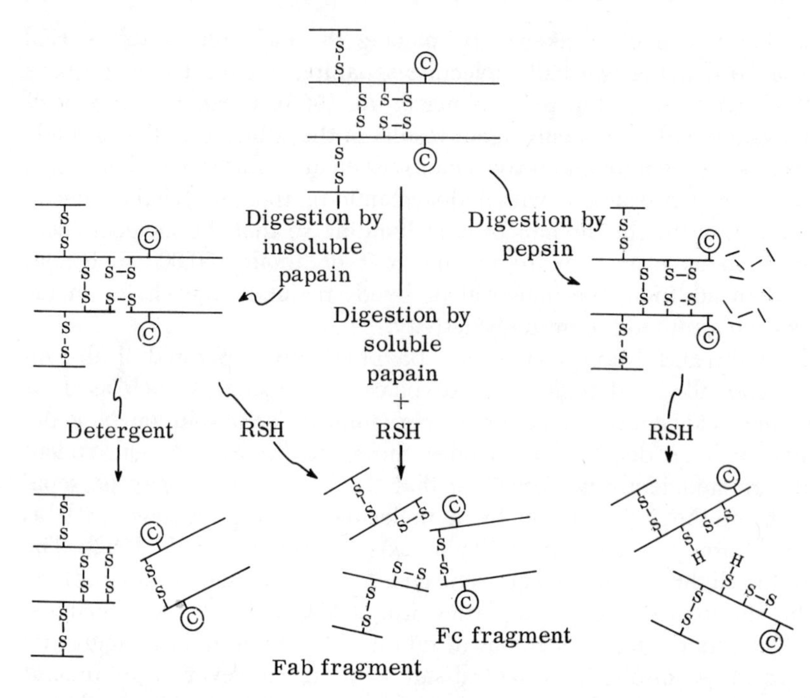

FIGURE 6.2 Fragmentation of the γG-globulin molecule mediated by pepsin and papain. The presence of carbohydrate is indicated by encircled C. The disulfide bond involvement between heavy chain components is uncertain as noted in Fig. 6.1.

they are univalent. They can still bind hapten as well as does the bivalent 105,000 molecular weight piece from which they were derived.

When γG-globulin antibody is subjected to limited digestion by insoluble papain in the absence of reducing agent, only three to five peptide bonds in the heavy chains are broken and the molecule remains unchanged in molecular weight (Cebra *et al.*, 1961). However, subsequent treatment with reducing agent causes it to fall apart into two fragments (Fab fragments) each containing an antibody site, and a third fragment (the Fc fragment) which is not active as antibody. This mixture of antibody fragments still exhibits fully active binding properties due to the antibody sites of the Fab fragments, but it does not exhibit antigen precipitating activities since the Fab fragments are univalent. Furthermore, if the molecule is treated with a detergent instead of a reducing agent, it separates into an Fc fragment and an 85,000 molecular weight bivalent piece very similar in its properties to the bivalent molecule produced by pepsin action (Cebra, 1964). The disulfide bonds appear to be rearranged by disulfide interchange mediated by the presence of a trace of sulfhydryl groups.

The fact that the molecule falls into smaller pieces on reduction indicates that the insoluble papain breaks peptide bonds, and that the resulting peptides are held together by disulfide links as shown in Fig. 6.2. Each disulfide may be an intrachain disulfide between two cysteines on a heavy chain as shown, or it may be an interchain one between the two heavy chains as suggested by Utsumi and Karush (1965).

The exact relationship between the heavy chain positions which are attacked by insoluble papain and by pepsin has not been established. The lower molecular weight of the material produced by insoluble papain suggests that it digests the heavy chains farther away from their carboxyl terminus than does pepsin. Moreover, the bivalent molecule produced by pepsin action still retains some of the carbohydrate associated with the original γG-globulin molecule, whereas the Fab fragments produced by the action of insoluble papain plus reducing agent do not contain any carbohydrate.

When the γG-globulin antibody molecule is digested by soluble papain at pH 6.5 to 8.5 in the presence of reducing agent, peptide bonds and disulfide bonds are both cleaved; the molecule separates into the two Fab fragments and the Fc fragment, as diagrammed in Fig. 6.2 (Porter, 1959). These fragments can be physically separated. If the mixture is dialyzed against distilled water or low ionic strength (0.01 *M*) acetate buffer (pH 5.4), the Fc fragment crystallizes, and the Fab fragments remain in solution. Separation can also be achieved by gradient elution from carboxymethylcellulose. The Fab fragments are eluted first, usually in two major heterogeneous fractions in varying proportions. The Fc fragment is eluted last as a relatively homogeneous fraction.

Not all γG-globulin molecules yield the same Fab fragments, although an individual molecule apparently yields two identical ones. Usually the Fab fragments which are produced from a heterogeneous mixture of γG-globulin molecules are separable into two major fractions, each of which is relatively less heterogeneous than the mixture. Some specifically purified antibody preparations yield Fab fragments which chromatograph on carboxymethylcellulose largely in one of these fractions. The γG-globulin molecules themselves can be fractionated similarly by chromatography on carboxymethylcellulose. The Fab fragments derived from each of these fractions show differences in chromatographic properties similar to the differences observed with the parent molecules. Thus the Fab fragments from the intact globulin eluted at low ionic strength are themselves eluted from carboxymethylcellulose by low ionic strength buffer, whereas the Fab fragments derived from the globulin eluted at high ionic strength are themselves eluted from carboxymethylcellulose at higher ionic strength (Palmer *et al.*, 1962). However, in no case as yet has a separated Fab fragment fraction, even when apparently homogeneous, been induced to crystallize.

These observations indicate that γG-globulin preparations are heterogeneous with respect to the Fab fragments obtained from them, but relatively homogeneous with respect to the Fc fragments produced. This appears to be the case for the whole γG-globulin fraction from serum, as well as for specifically purified antibody preparations, whether derived from a single animal or many animals. In addition, the marked homogeneity of the Fc fragments of rabbit γG-globulin, indicated by their crystallization, may not extend to the γG-globulins of other species.

The Fab fragments have been shown to be each composed of the entire light chain of the intact antibody and a portion of the heavy chain (the Fd piece) (Porter, 1962). The chains are joined by a single disulfide bond.

When the two chains of a Fab fragment are reduced and alkylated they are still held together by noncovalent bonds, as in the intact molecule. These chains, when in 1 *M* propionic acid, can be separated by elution from Sephadex under conditions similar to those which separate the light chain from the intact heavy chain. Under such conditions the Fd pieces apparently tend to associate (as do the heavy chains). Separated light chains from Fab fragments have an amino acid composition identical to that of light chains derived from the intact parent molecule, showing that the light chains are not affected by the proteolysis (Fleischman *et al.*, 1963).

6.4 PARTICIPATION OF THE PEPTIDE CHAINS OF γG-GLOBULIN ANTIBODY TO FORM THE ANTIBODY SITE

The combining site of the antibody has thus been shown to lie in the Fab fragment, which includes both a light and part of a heavy chain. Current evidence suggests that the antibody site in γG-globulin is formed from portions of both chains. It is likely, however, that the relative contributions of the two chains vary, depending on the particular antigenic determinant involved, the kinds of γG-globulin protein which make up the heterogeneous antibody preparations studied, and the animal species whose γG-globulin is considered. There is evidence that isolated heavy chain, separated from light chain, retains antibody site activity (Cohen and Porter, 1964).

It is quite possible that the antibody site is composed of two partial sites, one on the light chain and one on the heavy chain, each of which contribute arithmetically to the binding energy of the intact site. In order for a partial site on an individual chain to be measurable by the equilibrium dialysis methods usually employed, it must have a free energy of binding of at least 4.5 kcal. If partial sites on the heavy and light chains contributed equally to the free energy of binding of an antibody site with a K_H value as high as 10^6 ($\Delta F = -7.7$ kcal) neither chain alone with its intact partial site would show measurable binding, for a chain could contribute 4 kcal and still appear to contain no site.

Another possibility is that one chain (or both) carries the residues composing the site, but the configuration of the site can only be assumed when both chains are present (Edelman *et al.*, 1964). That is, only when interaction between the chains occurs is the tertiary structure of the site assumed. No direct evidence on this point is available.

The information available at present concerns chiefly anti-hapten antibodies produced in the rabbit or guinea pig, together with limited information on anti-protein antibodies in the rabbit, guinea pig, or horse. Some representative studies will now be discussed to indicate the kinds of evidence that have been brought to bear on the question. No attempt has been made to be all inclusive in dealing with published reports.

6.5 EVIDENCE FOR THE CONTRIBUTION OF LIGHT AND HEAVY CHAINS TO THE ANTIBODY SITE

Extensive evidence has been obtained by Roholt *et al.* (1964 and 1965b) that when rabbit antibodies specific for the *p*-azobenzoate group or the *p*-azobenzenearsonate group are reduced, alkylated, and separated into their component light and heavy chains, the light chain portions show little or no ability to bind hapten. Representative data demonstrating this point for anti-*p*-azobenzoate antibody are presented in Table 6.1: the antibody light chains bound little more hapten than did normal γ-globulin light chains. These light chain preparations were completely soluble, as mentioned above, and could be shown subsequently to recombine with heavy chain to give 6S γG-globulin molecules. Thus, their lack of activity cannot be explained by any irreversible denaturation or other nonspecific inactivation of the chain. The heavy chain portions of these preparations, as noted, were only partially soluble in neutral salt solution, so that tests for their antibody activity were accomplished by complexing them with light chains from normal γ-globulin. Such complexes of antibody heavy chains with non-antibody light chains showed some ability to bind hapten. However, when the antibody heavy chains were recombined with the antibody light chains, full activity—up to 80% of the original antibody activity present—was restored. This result represents an elevenfold increase in binding activity over that found for the complex of antibody heavy chain with normal light chain.

Confirmation of these results was obtained in other experiments (Roholt

TABLE 6.1 Binding of Hapten by Light and Heavy Chains from Anti-X_p Antibody and Normal γ-Globulin, and by Mixtures of Such Chains[a]

Equivalents of each chain			*p*-Iodobenzoate bound[b]	Relative activity[c]
$H(X_p)$	$L(X_p)$	L(N)		
	1		0.39	0.04
		3	0.26	0.01
	5		1.25	0.03
		9	0.50	—
1		9	1.12	0.07[d]
1	1		7.27	0.79
1	5		7.17	0.78

[a]Data from Roholt *et al.* (1965b).
[b]Moles per liter × 10^6 at a free hapten concentration = 18×10^{-6} *M*.
[c]Activity relative to that of original anti-X_p preparation.
[d]Corrected for binding by the L(N) chains.

et al., 1965b) with the same or similar preparations in which antibody activity was measured by the method of radioimmunoelectrophoresis (Yagi *et al.*, 1962). The antibody preparation was subjected to electrophoresis in agar on a slide and the separated proteins were precipitated with goat antibody to rabbit globulin according to the general procedure for immunoelectrophoresis (Grabar and Williams, 1953; Grabar, 1958). The arcs were then stained with ^{131}I-labeled *p*-azobenzoate or *p*-azobenzenearsonate protein antigen. Antibody activity of a protein was detected by the presence of radioactivity in its arc of precipitation as shown by radioautography. It was found that, whereas the intact antibody and the reconstituted antibody showed strong binding of antigen, both the light chain and the heavy chain preparations showed only slight binding. These results extend and fully confirm the results of measurements of hapten binding activity by equilibrium dialysis (Table 6.1).

Similar evidence had been obtained by Edelman *et al.* (1963). These workers, using guinea pig antibodies against f1 and f2 phages and against the dinitrophenyl hapten group (DNP), demonstrated that much more activity was obtained when isolated heavy and light chain preparations of these antibodies were recombined with their original partners, than was obtained when they remained isolated. In the experiments with antiphage antibody preparations (containing normal globulin) some activity by heavy chain preparations alone was observed, amounting to 0.5 to 1% of the activity shown by the original preparations of intact antibody. However, a three- to five-fold enhancement of heavy chain activity was observed when corresponding light and heavy chains were combined. The activity for the recombined chains was essentially that of a preparation in which the chains were dissociated and allowed to recombine without prior isolation, where only 5% or less of the original antibody activity was present after the antibodies were reduced, alkylated, and treated with propionic acid. In the experiments with guinea pig anti-DNP antibody some binding activity for dinitrophenol, as measured by equilibrium dialysis, was found with both light and heavy chain preparations separately, but marked enhancement, amounting to 17-fold, was observed for the recombined chains. The anti-DNP antibody preparations (which apparently were only 25% pure) showed better resistance to this treatment than did anti-phage antibody: about 58% of their activity remained. This recovery is comparable to activity retained by specifically purified anti-X_p and anti-R_p antibodies following a similar treatment (Roholt *et al.*, 1965b).

Similar results were obtained by Franek and Nezlin (1963) in studies of equine antibodies against diphtheria and tetanus toxins. In these experiments disulfide bonds joining light and heavy chains were split by sodium sulfide in the presence of copper ions, and the chains dissociated in 6 *M* urea and 0.05 *M* formic acid. Direct reassociation following this treatment resulted in recovery of only 3% of the original activity. The chains when separated showed essentially no activity but when recombined showed the above 3% activity. Some indication was also obtained that mixtures of heavy chains of diphtheria antitoxin with light chains of tetanus antitoxin (and the reverse mixture as well) showed partial fixation of toxin specific for the heavy chain, but not of that specific for the light chain.

Evidence has been obtained that preparations of heavy chains from horse IgA anti-protein antibodies (Fleischman *et al.*, 1963; Porter and Weir, 1966) and from a rabbit IgG anti-hapten antibody (Utsumi and Karush, 1964) contained a significant portion of the activity originally present in the intact antibody preparations.

With the horse antibodies—anti-rabbit γ-globulin and anti-diphtheria toxin—the heavy chains from the former could specifically coprecipitate with intact antibody and antigen, while the heavy chains from the latter could specifically inhibit the precipitation of intact antibody and antigen. In the anti-rabbit γ-globulin system, the heavy chains were about 70% as effective as an equivalent amount of intact antibody, while in the anti-toxin system an amount of heavy chain equivalent to the intact antibody present completely inhibited precipitation of toxin. In both instances the light chains completely lacked effect. In additional studies (Weir and Porter, 1966) in which binding of ^{125}I-labeled toxin to anti-toxin chains was measured following electrophoresis of mixtures on cellulose acetate, it was found that the horse IgA antibody heavy chains bound toxin 20% as effectively as an equivalent amount of intact antibody. Recombination of heavy chains with specific light chains restored activity to 60% of the original, whereas recombination with nonspecific light chains restored 40% of original activity. It was suggested that these results favor the heavy chain as the major site of specific binding activity. However, the data may also be interpreted as indicating that the heavy chains make the major contribution in 40% of the molecules and the light chains make the major contribution in 20%.

It should be noted that horse IgA antibody heavy chains are soluble in neutral salt solution and thus could be tested in the above manner—in contrast to most preparations of rabbit IgG antibody heavy chains, which are only slightly soluble under these conditions. Thus the structures of heavy chains of the two different classes (from the two different species) appear to differ somewhat, and this may be important with respect to which polypeptide chains contribute to the antibody sites.

The rabbit anti-hapten antibody studied by Utsumi and Karush was the anti-*p*-azophenyllactoside antibody mentioned previously (Section 3.22). The methods which they employed to separate the heavy and light chains differed from that of Fleischman, Pain, and Porter (1962), which was used in the other investigations mentioned in this chapter. Thus, the chains were dissociated in a detergent, 0.05 *M* sodium decylsulfate, in pH 8 Tris-HCl buffer rather than in 1 *M* propionic acid. The separated heavy chains thus obtained remained largely soluble (from 50 to 80%) in neutral salt solution but required the presence of about 10^{-5} *M* detergent, and were still highly aggregated. Measurement by equilibrium dialysis of the binding sites present in this heavy chain preparation, which had no more than 5% contamination by light chain, indicated that at least 70% of the binding sites present in the reduced and alkylated antibody could be accounted for. The K'_H value for binding by this preparation was about one-tenth that exhibited by intact antibody, indicating that the light chains contribute to the binding energy as discussed in Section 6.4.

6.6 PREFERENTIAL RECOMBINATION OF CHAINS TO FORM ANTIBODY MOLECULES

Heavy (H) and light (L) chains combine to give globulin molecules. Even association of chains from diverse species occurs (Fougereau *et al.*,

1964). However, heavy chains of antibody show a preference for recombining with their corresponding light antibody chains to give active antibody sites, rather than with light chains of normal globulin or light chains of other antibody to give nonantibody globulin (Roholt *et al.*, 1966b). Thus when anti-X_p antibody is separated into H_X and L_X chains and anti-R_p antibody is separated into H_R and L_R chains, the chains can be individually combined to give the essentially inactive hybrids, H_XL_R and H_RL_X. When these hybrids are mixed, exposed to propionic acid to dissociate the hybrids, and then brought back to neutrality, there is complete reshuffling of the hybrids to give H_XL_X and H_RL_R, as indicated by the recovery of binding activity. The recovery is greater than that expected on the basis of random recombination. Moreover, when heavy chains from antibody are combined with a mixture containing an equivalent amount of light chains from antibody and a large amount of light chains from normal globulin, the binding activity recovered is much greater than would be expected on the basis of random recombination. This also demonstrates preferential association of the chains which give effective antibody.

The combination of H and L chains to form a binding site approximating the original one seems to require either a correct alignment of the two chains (cooperative site formation), or the modulation of one chain by the other to form a site. It is not necessary that the two chains which combine to yield a site come from the same molecule, since in recombination experiments it is found that effective sites are formed when H chain and L chain preparations made from different portions of the same pool of serum are mixed. In this case the H and L chains could not have come from the same molecule.

It seems possible that two chains from very closely related antibody molecules might cross-combine to form a site closely related to the original, either by cooperative site formation or by modulation. However, antibodies formed by a single rabbit, even against a single hapten, are known to be heterogeneous in specificity (Chapter 4) and it is not readily apparent how the chains from any two such different molecules could recombine in an exchange to form an active site. For example, if, as shown schematically in Fig. 6.3, the L chain of one anti-X_p antibody site were directed against the azo group, and the L chain from another anti-X_p antibody site were directed against the carboxylate group, cross combination between the H chain of one and the L chain of the other would not yield an effective site.

Separated chains from antibody against the same hapten but from different rabbits do not always give effective binding sites upon recombination, although association of the chains does occur. There is a specificity of combination such that only chains from antibodies

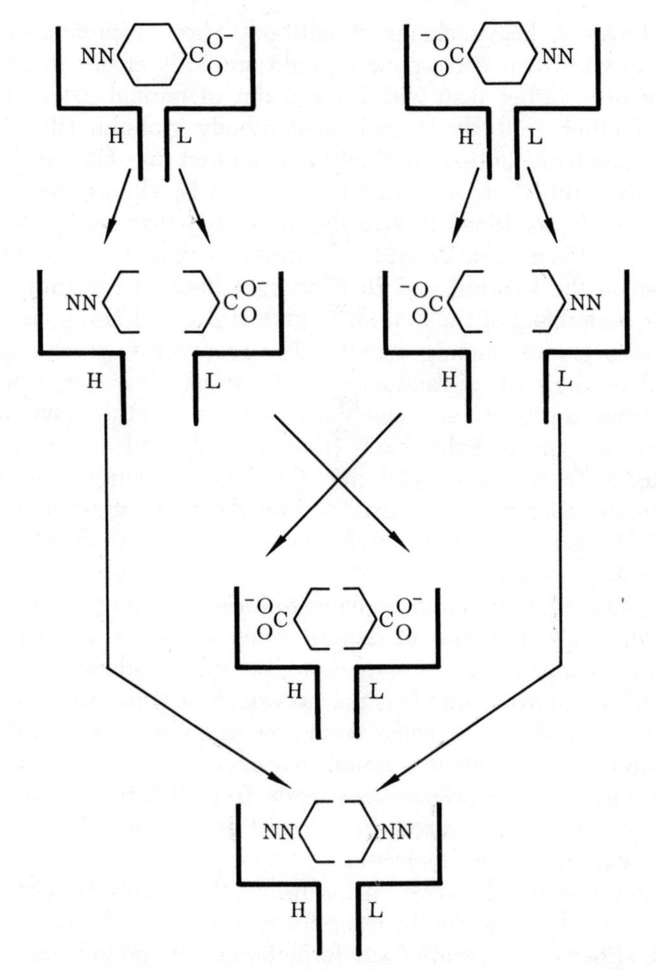

FIGURE 6.3 **Hypothetical cross combination of H and L chains from two different anti-*p*-azobenzoate antibodies to yield antibodies of hybrid specificity not effective in binding *p*-azobenzoate. [From Roholt *et al.* (1965b).]**

of the same (or perhaps a genetically related) rabbit form effective binding sites (Roholt *et al.*, 1965a).

Metzger and Mannik (1964) have observed in the case of anti-DNP antibody an increased yield of antibody-active recombination of H and L chains when hapten is present, suggesting that hapten may have aided in the re-association process by orienting the chains in the most favorable manner or by bringing the correct ones together. This effect was observed in two kinds of situations—the competition between nonantibody L chains and antibody L chains for combination with antibody H chains, and the formation of partially active recombinants composed of antibody H chains and normal L chains. In both kinds of mixtures the presence of hapten aided in the formation of active sites.

6.7 EXPERIMENTS ON DISSOCIATION AND RECOMBINATION OF CHAINS OF RABBIT ANTIBODY FRAGMENTS (Fab FRAGMENTS)

If the picture given for the structure of an antibody molecule is correct, it follows that separation of the Fab fragment into two chains, the light chain and the Fd fragment, should give a qualitatively similar effect, with regard to the antibody site, to that obtained upon separation of heavy and light chains. This has been proven to be the case. As previously noted, in the case of Fab fragments from anti-R_p and anti-X_p antibodies, reduction and alkylation of exposed disulfide bonds results in little loss of antibody sites. When separated, however, light chains and Fd fragments, both of which are soluble in neutral salt solution, show essentially no specific binding activity. When equivalent amounts of the separated light chains and Fd fragments are again mixed, Fab molecules are reconstituted along with their specific binding activities (Table 6.2). In this case, also, selective association of L chains and Fd fragments to give effective antibody sites occurs (Roholt *et al.*, 1966).

TABLE 6.2 Effect of Light Chains on the Binding of Hapten by Anti-X_p Fd Fragments[a]

Equivalents of			
Fd(X_p)	L(X_p)	L(N)	Relative activity[b]
1	1	0	0.71
1	0	1	0.04
1	0	0	0.07

[a]Data from Roholt *et al.* (1966).
[b]Activity relative to that of the original anti-X_p preparation.

6.8 RECOVERY OF ANTIBODY ACTIVITY FROM UNFOLDED CHAINS OF Fab FRAGMENTS

When the disulfide bonds of a Fab fragment are completely reduced, the chains can be unfolded by exposure to 6 *M* guanidinium chloride. Haber (1964) and Whitney and Tanford (1965) have shown that when the unfolded product is dialyzed against neutral buffer, so that the guanidinium concentration is slowly reduced, and slow oxidation of sulfhydryls takes place, antibody activity is recovered. This experiment indicates that the configuration of the Fab fragment, including the active site, is determined by the primary sequence of the amino acid residues constituting the chains.

6.9 LABELING EXPERIMENTS TO DETERMINE THE CHAIN SOURCE OF RESIDUES IN ANTIBODY SITES

Paired label iodination (Section 5.3) has been utilized by Roholt *et al.*, (1963) to determine whether the tyrosine residue in anti-R_p antibody, whose iodination is inhibited by the presence of hapten, is on a light or a heavy chain. The result indicates clearly that the light chain contains such a tyrosine. There is also some contribution of a tyrosine to the site by the heavy chain, since deviant ratio peptides were obtained from both chains. This finding provides strong support for the idea that both chains are involved in the antibody site.

The affinity-labeling technique (Section 5.13) also provides evidence that both chains contribute to the site, or at least are closely situated to it (Metzger *et al.*, 1964; Doolittle and Singer, 1965; Singer and Doolittle, 1966). Tyrosine residues in both light and heavy chains of anti-R_p, anti-A_p, and anti-DNP antibodies were labeled by the affinity-labeling technique but to different extents for different antibody preparations (Table 6.3). This means that tyrosines on both chains are within coupling distance of the reactive diazonium group of the affinity labeling reagent. It does not necessarily mean that the reactive tyrosine is in the active site.

The variation would appear to be due to differences between the distributions or reactivities of tyrosines for the two chains in different antibody molecules. Singer and Doolittle (1966), however, neglect the variation and claim that the relative distributions are a constant value, 2:1. On this basis they interpret their results with the three antibodies to mean that part of the site involves a conservative region.

TABLE 6.3 Extent of Labeling of Chains by Affinity Labeling Reaction[a]

Type of antibody	Labeling reagent	Mole ratio of label, heavy chain/light chain
Anti-R_p	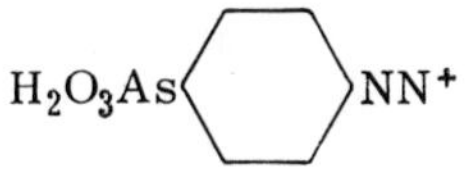 H_2O_3As–C_6H_4–NN^+	2.1
Anti-DNP	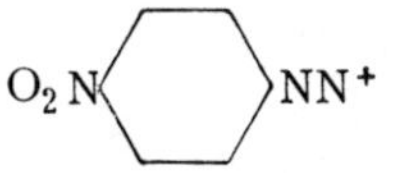 O_2N–C_6H_4–NN^+	1.3
	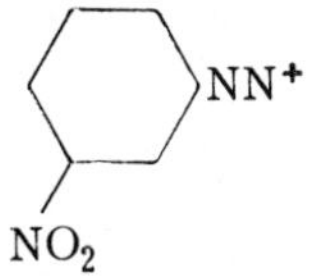 $C_6H_4(NO_2)$–NN^+ (meta-NO_2)	1.8
Anti-A_p	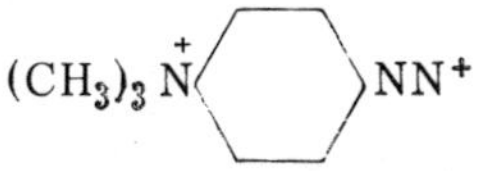 $(CH_3)_3\overset{+}{N}$–C_6H_4–NN^+	1.5

[a]Data from Singer and Doolittle (1966).

6.10 EVIDENCE FOR CONFORMATIONAL CHANGE OF ANTIBODY ON COMBINATION WITH HAPTEN OR ANTIGEN

There is evidence that the presence of hapten in an antibody site affects the conformation of the polypeptide chains of the molecule. Thus Grossberg *et al.* (1965) have found that when the sites of antibody molecules or Fab fragments are occupied by hapten, the molecules are attacked by chymotrypsin at a slower rate than are the molecules or fragments free of hapten. This difference in the rate of proteolysis points to a difference in availability of bonds susceptible to the enzyme action, presumably due to a change in conformation of the molecule.

Electron micrograph studies of the complexes of anti-ferritin antibodies with ferritin (Feinstein and Rowe, 1965) have shown a different kind of change in the conformation of the antibody molecule when it is combined with equivalent amounts of a multivalent, macromolecular antigen. The antibody alone is in a compact form with both binding sites apparently on the same side, but when combined with equivalent amounts of such an antigen, the molecule is open as shown in Fig. 1.1.

In the extended form it appears that regions of the molecule are exposed, while they are inaccessible in the compact form. It would appear that the exposed part corresponds to the Fc fragment which is concerned with various activities such as complement fixation and tissue sensitization.

7

USE OF ANTIBODIES TO DELINEATE MOLECULAR STRUCTURE AND CONFIGURATION

One of the most promising applications of antibodies is in describing the structure and configuration of molecules in aqueous medium—that is, in defining the preferred orientations of simple molecules which can exist in several possible forms in aqueous solution, and in defining the states of hydration of these molecules. Antibodies are also useful in describing the surface structure of macromolecules, either soluble or insoluble. These characteristics are fundamental for the binding of physiologically and pharmacologically active substances by receptor sites. In the design of drugs and chemotherapeutic compounds it is necessary to realize that the structure of interest is the structure in aqueous medium, and it is this structure which becomes accessible to study by the use of antibodies.

The antibody that reacts with a hapten acts essentially as a mold outlining the hapten. By determining the ability of substances of known configuration to react with the antibody, it is possible to map the outline defined by the antibody site. This information, in turn, aids in determining the outline of a related substance which combines with the site but which can exist in several configurations. In addition, information on the hapten configuration which stimulates antibody formation can be obtained by determining which related substances of known configuration fit the site.

It was by such argument that the coiled configurations for the succinanilate group and the β-benzoylpropionate groups were suggested as described in Sections 3.16 and 3.19.

The use of antibody as a template gives evidence concerning another configurational aspect of molecular structure—the tilt of the carboxylate ion out of the plane of the benzene ring brought about by the presence of an ortho substituent, as described in Section 3.2.

Still another important aspect of structure of molecules in aqueous solution is indicated by the interactions of certain ortho substituted benzoates with anti-*p*-azobenzoate antibody. Although most substituent groups in the ortho position of benzoate result in a K_{rel} value of considerably less than 0.1, owing to steric hindrance or tilt effects, exceptional behavior is shown by the amino group and other proton donor groups in the ortho position, as mentioned in Section 3.21. How these groups cause the increased value of K_{rel} still remains to be determined.

7.1 THE HYDRATION OF MOLECULES IN AQUEOUS SOLUTION

The water of hydration attached to proton acceptors and proton donors is a structural feature of major importance in connection with the combination between molecules in aqueous solution, including the binding of a molecule to a biological receptor site. The state of hydration must be a contributing feature in the combination. When the water is attached strongly it behaves sterically as a substituent on the molecule. Many of the groups present in biologically reactive compounds and receptors contain groups which would be expected to be hydrated in water: for example, OH, NH_2, NH, CO, COO^-, azo groups, and ring nitrogen. In all of these the water of hydration probably remains an integral part of the molecule during its biologically significant interactions.

The problem of hydration has been difficult to study by physical chemical techniques. Use of antibodies to hydrated structures allows the problem to be attacked.

For example, in connection with the anti-3-azopyridine system it has been shown in Section 3.6 that the antibodies appear to be directed against a hydrated structure that includes water attached to the nitrogen of the pyridine ring. That pyridine is hydrated in aqueous solution is apparent from the fact that it is miscible with water, whereas benzene is only slightly soluble. Moreover, the heat of hydration of pyridine has been found to be 12 kcal/mole (Briegleb, 1949). This water of hydration is a large structural feature in the reaction of pyridine compounds with antibody (Fig. 7.1). Thus antibodies against the *o*-, *m*-, and *p*-azobenzoate ions (anti-X_o, -X_m, and -X_p) and the *p*(*p*-azophenylazobenzoate) ion (anti-X'_p) react with the pyridine carboxylate ions (*o, m,* and *p,* that is, picolinate, nicotinate, and isonicotinate) as though there were a large substituent on the ring in the position occupied by the nitrogen atom (Pressman and Siegel, 1957).

The values for K_{rel} are shown in Fig. 7.1, in which the van der Waals outline of the hydrated form of the pyridine carboxylate ion is superimposed on the outline of the hapten against which the antibody is directed; the number under each figure is K_{rel}. Isonicotinate acts like a

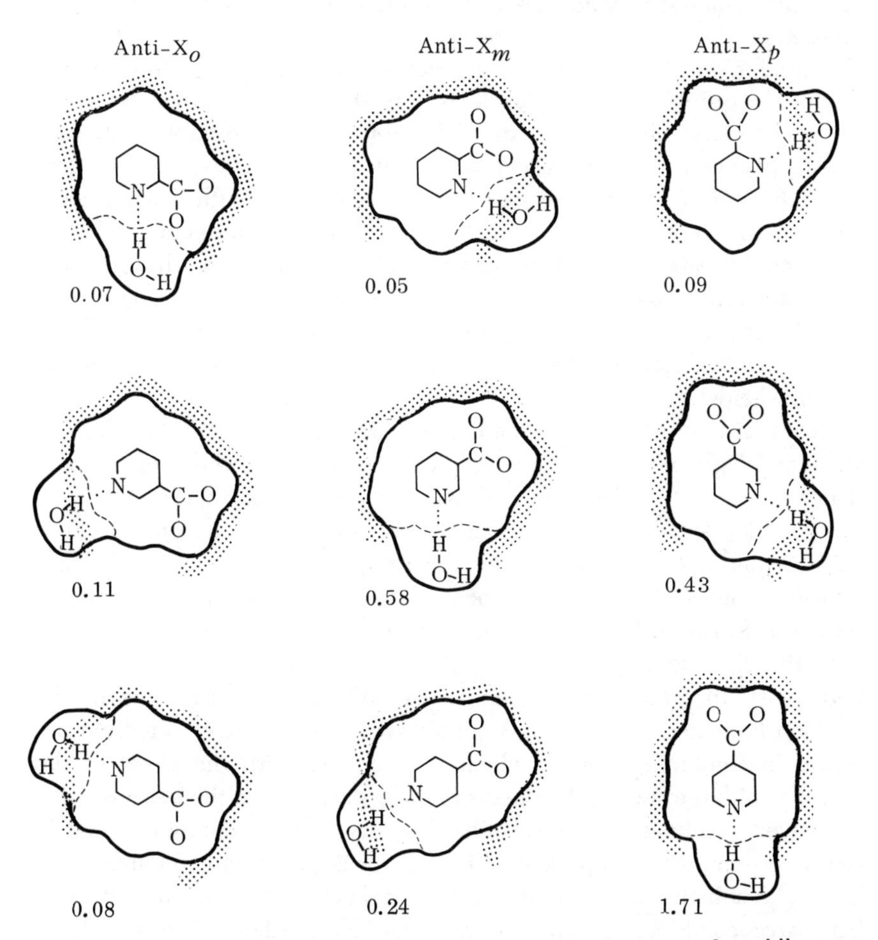

FIGURE 7.1 Van der Waals outline of the hydrated form of pyridine carboxylate ion superimposed upon the outline of the immunogenic hapten. The number under each figure is the relative combining constant K_{rel}. [From Pressman and Siegel (1957).]

benzene with a large substituent in the para position, and is the one which combines best with anti-X_p antibody. Nicotinate, with the nitrogen in the meta position, combines best of the three ions with anti-X_m antibody. However, the K_{rel} for its combination with the anti-X_m antibody is less than 1, that is, 0.58, whereas K_{rel} for benzoates with various substituents in the meta position is greater than 1 with this antibody. A probable reason for the low value for the nicotinate ion is that the water of hydration constitutes too large a substituent to fit in the region of the antibody that fits the hydrated azo group of the immunogen. Finally, with anti-X_o the combination of all three ions is poor. The effect of a large amount of water next to the carboxylate is not understood at present.

A similar set of observations has been made concerning the combination of the quinoline carboxylate ions with these three antibodies, which shows the effect of replacing an α-CH group of α- or β-naphthoate ions with a nitrogen atom (Pressman and Siegel, 1957). Thus the quinoline 2-, 3-, 6-, and 7-carboxylate ions may be compared with β-naphthoate ion, and the quinoline 4-, 5-, and 8-carboxylates may be compared with the α-naphthoate ion. α-Naphthoate itself acts as a 2,3-disubstituted benzoate, and β-naphthoate acts as a 3,4-disubstituted benzoate. The quinolines act as though a large substituent (water) were also present at the position occupied by the nitrogen, as has been described for the pyridine acids.

As an aid in discussing combination of antibody with hapten, the van der Waals outlines of the α-naphthoate structure, the β-naphthoate structure, and the quinoline carboxylates are shown superimposed on the van der Waals outline of the *p*-, *m*-, and *o*-azobenzoates in Figs. 7.2, 7.3, and 7.4. The number on the upper left corner of each figure indicates the position of the carboxylate group relative to the nitrogen. Values of K_{rel} are listed under each figure.

In the X_p system (Fig. 7.2) K_{rel} for the combination of anti-X_p antibody with the β-naphthoate ion is 3.1. When the nitrogen is in the position indicated for the 2 or 3 quinolinate, there is a six- to tenfold decrease in combining power, which is in accord with the effect of the presence of large steric substituents in these positions on the benzene ring. Moreover, picolinate is known to have a very low combining constant in the X_p system, which is paralleled by K_{rel} for 2-quinolinate. 3-Quinolinate is a 3,4,5-substituted benzoate, and it is known that 3,5-disubstituted benzoates combine very poorly with anti-X_p antibody (Section 3.2b).

Nitrogen in the 6 or 7 quinolinate does not hinder combination but actually increases combining power slightly, which is to be expected, especially with 6-quinolinate in view of the ability of anti-X_p antibody to

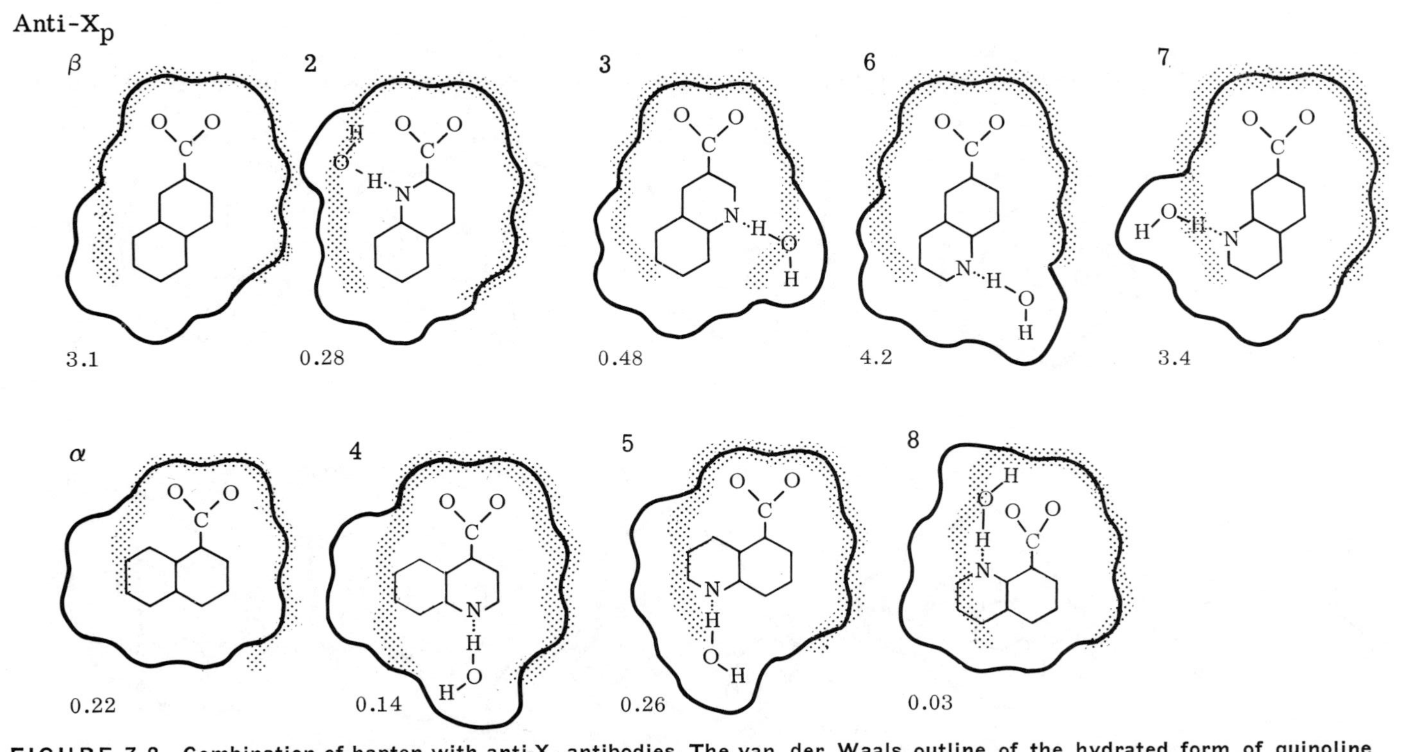

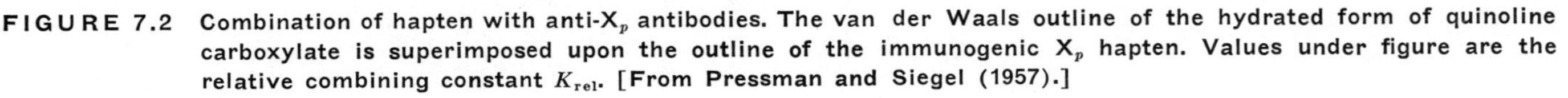

FIGURE 7.2 Combination of hapten with anti-X_p antibodies. The van der Waals outline of the hydrated form of quinoline carboxylate is superimposed upon the outline of the immunogenic X_p hapten. Values under figure are the relative combining constant K_{rel}. [From Pressman and Siegel (1957).]

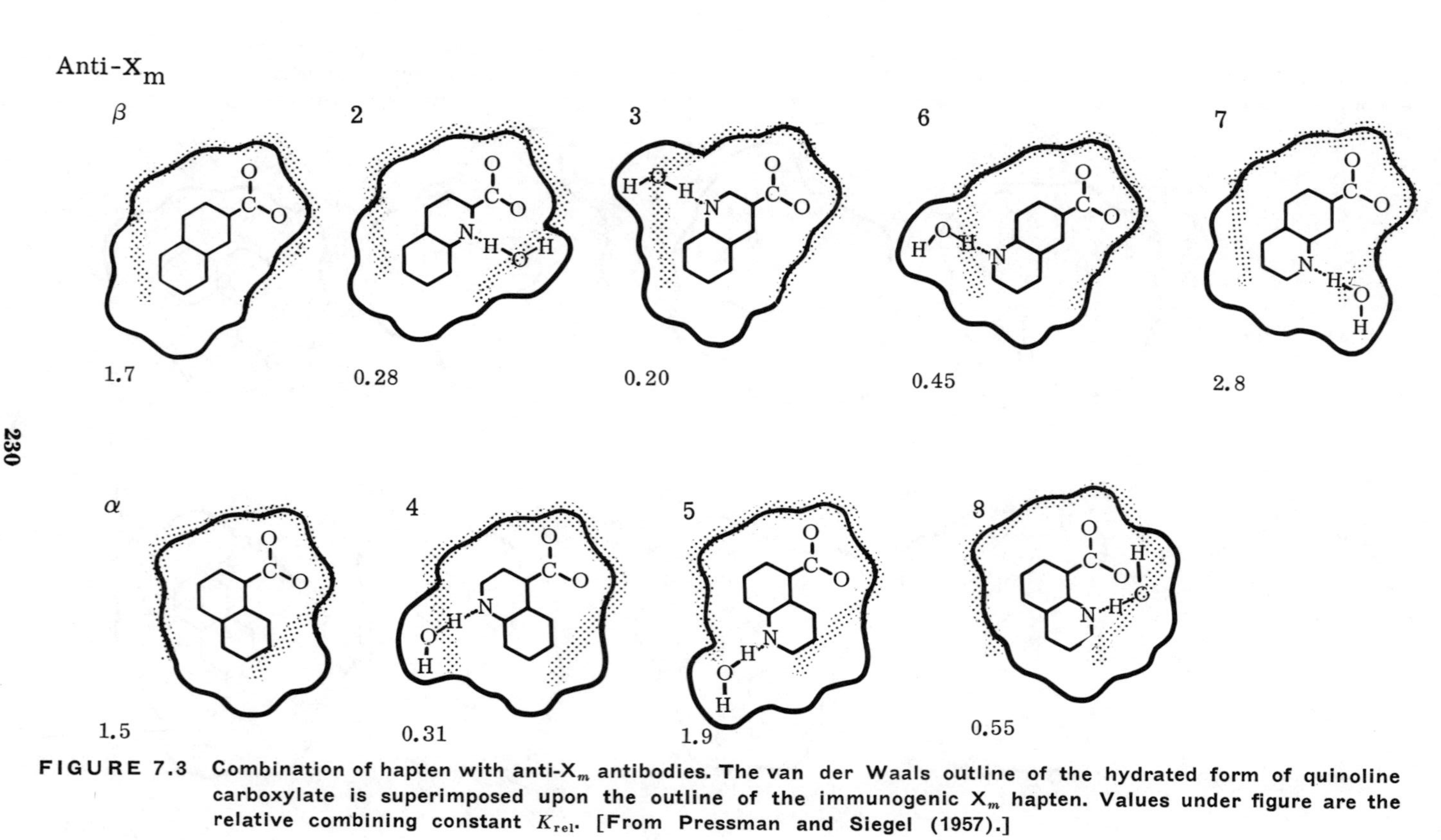

FIGURE 7.3 Combination of hapten with anti-X_m antibodies. The van der Waals outline of the hydrated form of quinoline carboxylate is superimposed upon the outline of the immunogenic X_m hapten. Values under figure are the relative combining constant K_{rel}. [From Pressman and Siegel (1957).]

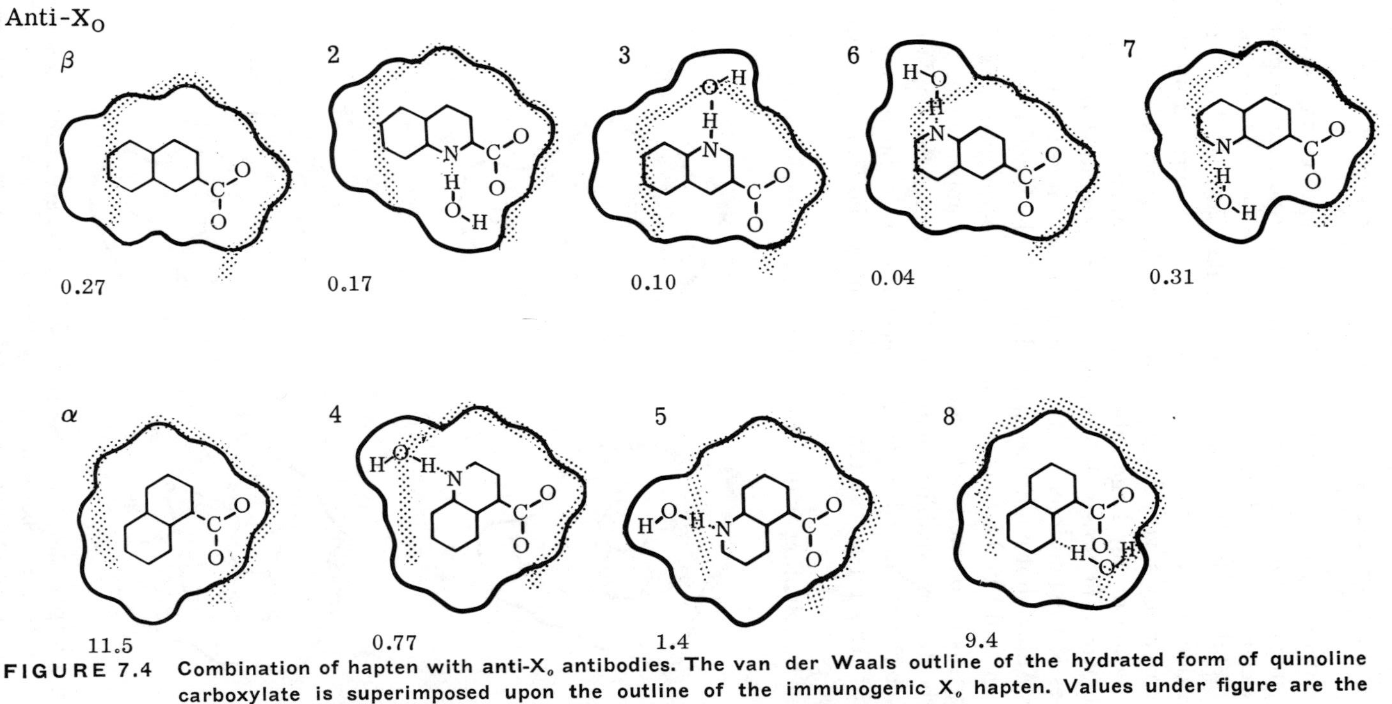

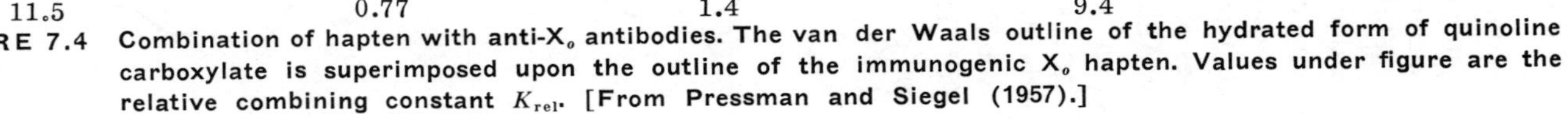

FIGURE 7.4 Combination of hapten with anti-X_o antibodies. The van der Waals outline of the hydrated form of quinoline carboxylate is superimposed upon the outline of the immunogenic X_o hapten. Values under figure are the relative combining constant K_{rel}. [From Pressman and Siegel (1957).]

accommodate large substituents in the para position and even some (iodine and bromine) in the meta position corresponding to position 7.

The second group of haptens consists of those related to α-naphthoate ion. α-Naphthoate itself has a K_{rel} value of 0.22, attributable to the size and position of the second ring. Insertion of the nitrogen atom in the 8-position causes a very large decrease in K_{rel}, as would be expected from insertion of any large substituent in a position around which the antibody would fit closely. Insertion of the nitrogen in the 4 position also decreases K_{rel}, while insertion into the 5 position increases the constant slightly. Although it might be expected that the hydrated nitrogen in the 4 position could be best accommodated, the experiment shows that the 5-nitrogen is accommodated most easily. It thus appears that when the α-naphthoate ion combines with the X_p antibody, the naphthoate is tilted somewhat in order for the second ring to be accommodated (Fig. 7.5). This tilt and resultant rotation place the 5-nitrogen in a less hindered position.

In the combination with anti-X_m antibodies β-naphthoate has a K_{rel}

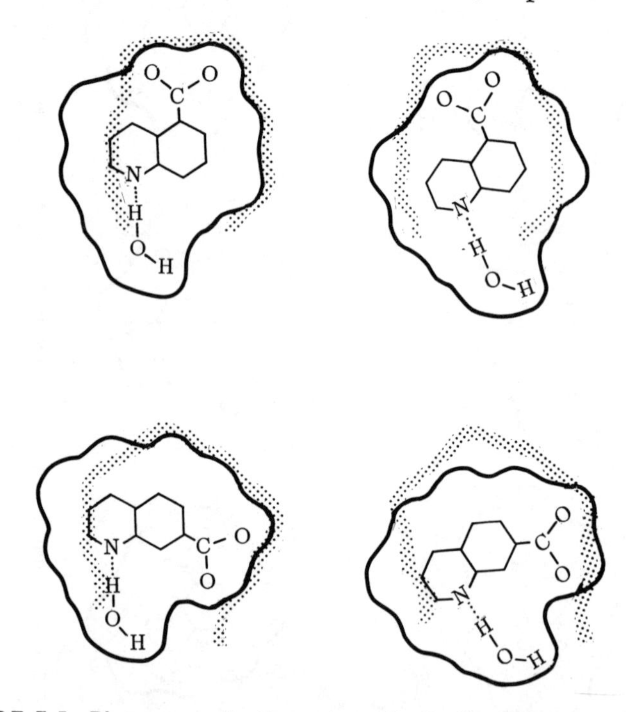

FIGURE 7.5 Diagrams indicating schematically the better accommodation of the 5-carboxyquinoline by the anti-X_p antibody and the 7-carboxyquinoline by the anti-X_o antibody when the haptens are tilted. [From Pressman and Siegel (1957).]

value of 1.7, replacement of the —CH— in the 8 position by hydrated nitrogen increases the constant to 2.8. From Fig. 7.3 it can be seen that a large substituent in this position can be accommodated. The increase is probably due to increased van der Waals interaction of the water with the antibody. Placement of the nitrogen in the other positions causes a decrease in combining constant, as would be expected on the basis of the results obtained with the chlorosubstituted benzoates (Section 3.2). Again, with the α-naphthoate analogs it can be seen that a large substituent can be accommodated in position 5 most readily, the 5-carboxylate having the highest constant in this group of quinoline carboxylates. The presence of a large substituent in the 4 or 8 positions causes decreased combination, as would be expected on the basis of close fit in these positions and the assumption of hydration.

In the combination with anti-X_o antibodies (Fig. 7.4) the β-naphthoate structure itself is not well accommodated, and the K_{rel} value is 0.27. Replacement of the —CH— by the hydrated nitrogen atom in the 2, 3, or 6 quinolinates lowers the combining constant by a factor of 1.5 or more. The low value of the quinoline-2-carboxylate is in line with the anomalously low constant of the related picolinate ion (Fig. 7.1).

Presence of the nitrogen in the 7 quinolinate gives a $K_{rel}=0.31$, an increase somewhat over that of the parent β-naphthoate. This effect is to be expected for a large substituent in this case, since the β-naphthoate is probably already tilted somewhat in order to be accommodated by the anti-X_o site. This tilt would bring a large substituent into a region where it could be accommodated by the anti-X_p antibody, and the increased van der Waals attraction for the hydrated nitrogen could come into play.

In the combination of the α-naphthoate group of haptens with anti-X_o antibody, α-naphthoate itself shows a high constant of 11.5 (Fig. 7.4). The nitrogen in the 8 quinolinate is easily accommodated, $K_{rel}=9.4$, and as is seen from the drawing, a large substituent in this position could be accommodated. However, the drawing indicates that hydrated nitrogen atoms in the 4 and 5 position would not be accommodated easily, and that is actually what has been observed. The existence of a hydrated ring nitrogen is also inferred from the reaction of picoline dicarboxylate and pyrazine dicarboxylate with antibodies to the 4-azophthalate ion (Section 3.12). The replacement of the ortho CH of phthalate ion by a single nitrogen lowers the combining constant by a factor of 3, and the replacement of the second ortho CH by a ring nitrogen results in another lowering by a factor of 3, apparently due to the hydration of the molecules.

7.2 THE STRUCTURE OF MACROMOLECULES

When a macromolecule such as a polysaccharide or a protein is antigenic, the antibody fits essentially as a mold against various surface "patches" of the macromolecule. By determining the ability of smaller substances of known configuration to react with this antibody, information is obtained about the structure of the surface of the original macromolecule. For example, structures of the blood group substances, the pneumococcus polysaccharides, and the dextrans have been elucidated (after the structural details have been determined by chemical reactions), by determining the extent to which antibody to the polysaccharide will react with known chemical derivatives. Kabat (1962) has shown that various dextrans are made up of glucose units with different glucoside linkages. Some dextrans have the glucose units in 1-2 linkages, others in 1-3 and 1-4 linkages, and still others, in 1-6 linkages. Subsequently, he showed that antibodies against various dextrans reacted specifically with small oligosaccharides containing the particular group of which the dextran was composed. Similar methods have been used to define the more complex antigens from bacterial cell walls; for examples see the reviews by Luderitz *et al.* (1966) and Robbins and Uchida (1962).

With DNA, Levine (1962) has isolated oligonucleotides which comprise part of the antigenic structure of the parent molecule. For example, oligonucleotides containing a glucosylated hydroxymethylcytidylic acid residue were the only ones of those isolated from DNA of T-4 bacteriophage which reacted with antibody against the parent DNA. The antigenic determinant thus appeared to comprise in part such a residue and to be larger than a mononucleotide. Polypeptides isolated from hydrolysates of silk inhibited the reaction between silk fibroin and its antibodies. Cebra (1961) has studied these compounds further and has found that the most effective inhibiting peptide has the following composition and partial sequence:

$$\text{Gly-(Gly}_3\text{,Ala}_3\text{)Tyr}$$

This peptide must represent an antigenetically active patch on the surface of the silk fibroin molecule.

Benjamini *et al.* (1964) and Anderer and Schlumberger (1966) have isolated peptides from the tobacco mosaic virus surface patch which constitutes an important antigenic site of the virus. The antibody against the tobacco mosaic virus is inhibited by these peptides in its reaction with the virus. Brown (1962) has been able to define partially the antigenic regions of ribonuclease by isolating peptides from ribonuclease which inhibit its reaction with antibody. LaPresle and Webb (1965) have isolated antigenetically important portions of the serum albumin molecule.

Crumpton and Wilkinson (1965) have been able to separate from digests of the myoglobin molecule several different peptides which combine effectively with antibody directed against the intact myoglobin and inhibit the homologous precipitation. The peptides are structurally unrelated to each other. Each of these effective peptides combines with only some of the antibody produced; presumably each reacts only with the antibody directed against the part of the myoglobin from which the particular peptide was derived. Since the structure of myoglobin, including the folding of the polypeptide chain, is known (Kendrew *et al.*, 1961), the position occupied by each peptide in the surface of the myoglobin molecule is determined. Thus it is possible to map the particular antigenic regions on the surface of the molecule. This result is shown in Fig. 7.6, where the known structure of the myoglobin molecule is shown and the known antigenic patches are indicated.

The effective peptides must exist in aqueous solution in a configuration close enough to their configuration in the intact myoglobin to permit their combination with antibody. Thus those active peptides that are derived from the portions of the myoglobin where the polypeptide chain exists in a coiled configuration must themselves exist in the same coiled configuration to react with the antibodies.

Myoglobin does not contain repeating units, and thus a mixture of antibodies against more than one antigenic region is required in order to give a specific precipitate. If antibodies were formed only against a single antigenic site no precipitate would form, since the required formation of large complexes would not take place. To give precipitation, antibodies directed against at least two sites on the antigen molecule are required.

This requirement is clearly shown in anti-hapten systems with simple substances containing one *p*-azobenzoate group and one *p*-azobenzenearsonate per molecule. These simple substances give no precipitate with anti-benzoate or with anti-benzenearsonate antibodies alone, but they do give a precipitate with a mixture of the two antibodies (Pauling *et al.*, 1944).

Some proteins which can be separated into subunits have been analyzed to determine whether the isolated subunits contain antigenic determinants in common with the parent molecule. In immunoglobulin G both the heavy and the light chains contain antigenic regions which are also present in the original molecule (Cohen and Porter, 1964); and in insulin, Yagi *et al.* (1965) have similarly found that the B chain carries antigenic components in common with the intact insulin. In addition, an antigenic site on certain human immunoglobulin G molecules has been described (Polmar and Steinberg, 1964) which depends on an association of the light and heavy chains, since it is present on the intact molecule, is not

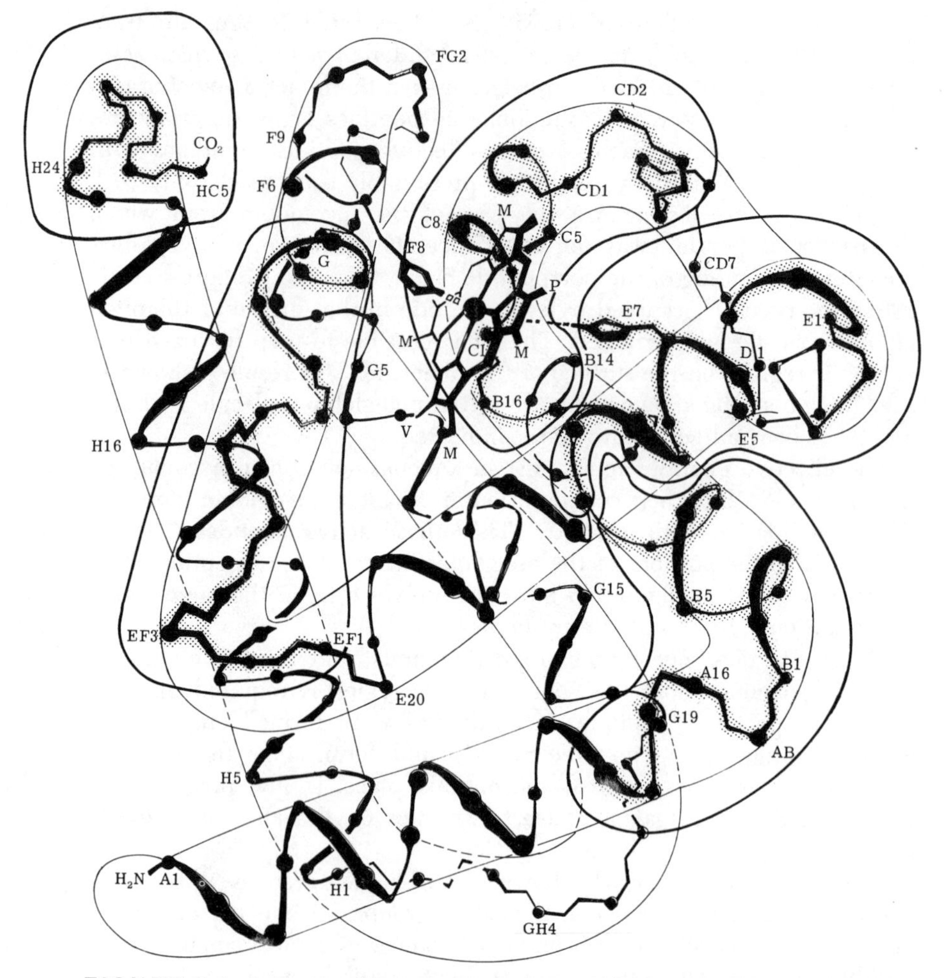

FIGURE 7.6 **Active peptides from whole myoglobin. Peptides enclosed by heavy lines are those which when isolated have been found to combine with part of the antibody formed against intact myoglobin (according to Crumpton and Wilkinson, 1965).**

present on either of the separated chains, but reappears when the separated chains recombine. Similarly, intact insulin contains an antigenic determinant which cannot be detected in either of the insulin polypeptide chains (Yagi *et al.*, 1965).

By the use of synthetic polypeptides Sela and Arnon (1960), Sela *et al.* (1962), Fuchs and Sela (1963), Gill and Doty (1960, 1961, 1963), and Maurer *et al.* (1959, 1964) have made major contributions to the problem of what constitutes immunogenicity—a subject which falls outside the scope of this monograph.

The nature of the specificity of the antibodies formed against some of these polymers has been elucidated by inhibition with small compounds of known composition. Although some of the synthetic polypeptides may obviously be simpler than proteins, there are major problems in connection with their complexities of configuration. The work in this field has been reviewed by Maurer (1964) and by Sela (1966).

In a reciprocal structural relationship, antibodies which have been prepared against simple substances are reacted with more complex macromolecules, permitting the identification of portions of these larger substances. For example, antibodies made against glucuronic acids react with complex plant gums and bacterial polysaccharides (Goebel, 1938) which contain the same grouping against which the antibody was directed. Graf, Yariv, and Rapport (1965) found that antibodies against lactose react with many structures in tissues which contain the lactose grouping. Similarly, antibody can be formed against the simple purines and pyrimidines as haptens and will then react with the more complex nucleotides as has been shown by Butler *et al.* (1962), Tanenbaum and Beiser (1963), and Sela *et al.* (1964).

Appendix I

DETERMINATION OF ANTIBODY SITE CONCENTRATION, AVERAGE BINDING CONSTANT, AND HETEROGENEITY INDEX BY THE METHOD OF EQUILIBRIUM DIALYSIS

In Section 2.2, it was pointed out that because of the heterogeneity of antibody preparations with respect to the species of binding sites present, calculations of an average binding constant for the sites must assume that the distribution of binding constants follows a particular function. A convenient function for this purpose is provided by the equation for binding proposed by Sips (1948), as applied by Nisonoff and Pressman (1958a). The Sips equation corresponds to a distribution of combining energies for the sites which closely resembles a Gauss error function, but has an advantage over other such distributions proposed (Pauling *et al.*, 1944; Karush, 1956) since it can be integrated analytically rather than approximated by curve fitting.

The mass action expression for the combination of hapten with a homogeneous population of sites, that is, with a single combining constant (Eq. 2.1) may be put in the form

$$b = K_H\, c(A_0 - b) \qquad \text{or} \qquad \frac{1}{b} = \frac{1}{A_0 K_H}\left(\frac{1}{c}\right) + \frac{1}{A_0} \tag{I-1}$$

where A_0=total concentration of antibody sites, b=concentration of hapten bound to antibody site, and c=concentration of unbound (free) hapten.

The corresponding Sips equation for binding by a heterogeneous group of sites is

$$\frac{1}{b}=\frac{1}{A_0}\left(\frac{1}{K'_{H}c}\right)^a+\frac{1}{A_0} \quad (0<a<1) \tag{I-2}$$

The additional symbol, a, is the heterogeneity index, and K'_H is the average combining constant corresponding to the apex of the distribution curve. For a homogeneous group of sites $a=1$. Then Eq. I-2 reduces to Eq. I-1 and $K'_H=K_H$. Decreasing values of a correspond to increasing degrees of heterogeneity of combining constants, as illustrated in Table I-1.

Equation I-1 predicts that when $1/b$ is plotted against $1/c$ a straight line will be obtained. However, such a plot for binding by a heterogeneous antibody preparation exhibits downward curvature (Fig. I-1a). By choosing the proper value of a, and plotting $1/b$ against $(1/c)^a$, a straight line is obtained (Fig. I-1b) as predicted by Eq. I-2. In the case of either a curved or straight line plot the intercept of such a plot on the $1/b$ axis, that is, at infinite free hapten concentration $1/c=0$, gives the value of $1/A_0$, the inverse concentration of total antibody sites.

When A_0 has been determined, K'_H and a are most accurately obtained by making use of the logarithmic expression of Eq. I-2, that is,

$$\log\left(\frac{A_0}{b}-1\right)=a\log\left(\frac{1}{K'_H}\right)+a\log\left(\frac{1}{c}\right) \tag{I-3}$$

Thus a logarithmic plot of $[(A_0/b)-1]$ vs. $(1/c)$ gives a straight line whose slope is a. The intersection of this line with the value $[(A_0/b)-1]=1$ (that is, when half the sites are occupied by hapten) corresponds to the point at which the expression $\log K'_H=\log(1/c)$ is satisfied, so that the value of $1/c$ at this point gives the value of K'_H.

TABLE I-1 Distribution of Combining Constants Corresponding to Several Values of the Heterogeneity Index a

a (Sips equation)	Range containing 75% of sites
0.5	0.025 to 40 K'_H
0.7	0.16 to 6 K'_H
0.8	0.27 to 3.7 K'_H

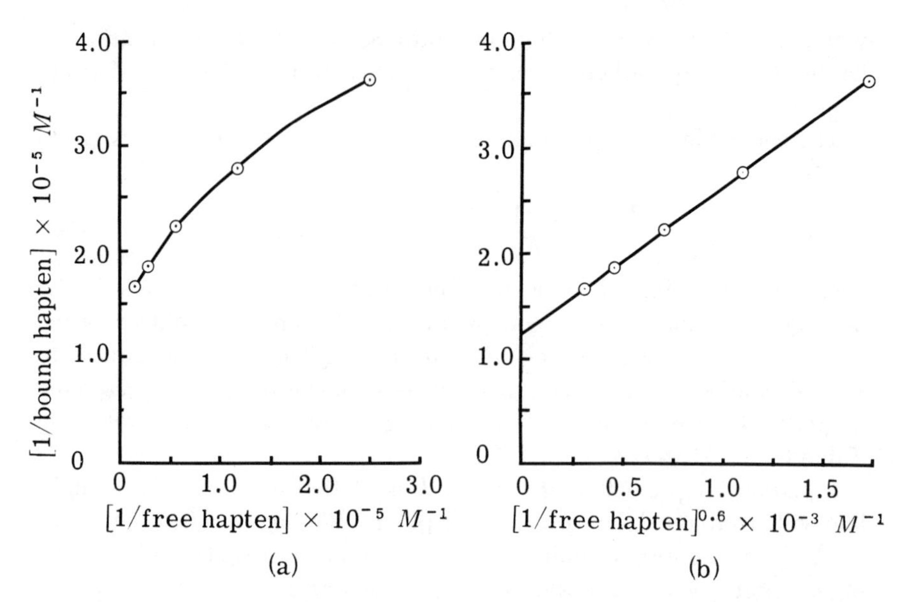

FIGURE I-1 (a) Binding curve for antibody-hapten interaction, plotted according to Eq. I-1. (b) Same data as in (a), plotted according to Eq. I-2, with $a = 0.6$. [Data from Grossberg *et al.* (1962b).]

An additional useful form of plotting is that in which Eqs. I-1 or I-2 are recast in the form

$$\frac{b}{c} = K_{\mathrm{H}}A_0 - K_{\mathrm{H}}b \tag{I-4}$$

or

$$\left(\frac{b}{c}\right)^a = K'^{a}_{\mathrm{H}}A_0 - K'^{a}_{\mathrm{H}}b \tag{I-4a}$$

For Eqs. I-4 or I-4a a plot of b/c or $(b/c)^a$ against b gives a value of $A_0 = b$ when the curve (or straight line) is extrapolated to the abscissa. As with the other forms of plotting the data, when $b = A_0/2$, K_H or $K'_{\mathrm{H}} = 1/c$.

From the above it is apparent that A_0, K'_{H}, and a cannot be determined independently. If the highest degree of accuracy is desired the method of choice for a γ-globulin preparation containing an unknown amount of antibody would seem to be to determine the value of a which gives the best straight line fit of the data plotted according to Eq. I-2, utilizing values of a from 0.45 to 1.00, in steps of 0.05. The sum of the squares of the deviations from a straight line are calculated for each plot and the value of a giving the minimum deviation is chosen. A_0 and K'_{H} are then calculated.

An alternative method is to obtain a rough estimate of A_0 by plotting the data according to Eq. I-1 or I-4, and then to utilize values of A_0 around this value until the best straight line fit of the data according to Eq. I-3 is obtained.

If the binding of a specifically purified antibody preparation is being determined, use of Eq. I-3, with A_0 chosen to be twice the molar concentration of antibody, gives reasonably accurate determinations of K'_H and a.

Examples of the treatment of equilibrium dialysis data are given by Nisonoff and Pressman (1958a) and by Eisen (1964a). These references also describe in detail the experimental procedures used to obtain data. In the procedure adopted by Nisonoff and Pressman, hapten concentration is determined both inside and outside the dialysis bag at equilibrium. In the alternative procedure described by Eisen, the total volume of the system is accurately fixed, free hapten concentration outside the bag is determined at equilibrium, and bound hapten inside the bag is calculated from the total amount of hapten known to be in the system, together with a correction for the amount of hapten nonspecifically adsorbed to surfaces, as determined in a separate experiment. The former procedure is especially convenient when comparison of the binding by more than one antibody preparation is to be made, since bags containing them can all be dialyzed against a common outside solution.

Appendix II

ANTIBODY-HAPTEN COMBINATION DETERMINED BY INHIBITION OF PRECIPITATION

This procedure for describing the relative combining constant K_{rel} ($K'_{\text{H}}/K'_{\text{ref hapten}}$) of a hapten with antibody takes into account heterogeneity of antibody sites, and it assumes that the combining constant can be described by the distribution of constants around a mean value K'_{H}, according to a probability distribution function which is an error function in the effective free energy of combination of hapten and antibody (Pauling *et al.*, 1944). The distribution of the molecules of antibody with different values of combining constant K_{H} relative to the average value K'_{H}, for different degrees of heterogeneity (σ), is shown in Fig. II-1.

Curves showing the theoretical dependence of the amount of precipitate obtained on the concentration of hapten added, for different combining constants (but for the same degree of heterogeneity), are given in Fig. II-2. These are quite similar in shape to those obtained experimentally. The corresponding curves plotted logarithmically are shown in Fig. II-3. It can be seen that all the curves now have the identical shape. The effect of changing K'_{H} is merely to shift the curves along the abscissa (log hapten axis).

Similar curves for different degrees of heterogeneity (heterogeneity constant σ) but for a single average combining constant are given in Fig. II-4. The same curves plotted logarithmically with respect to hapten

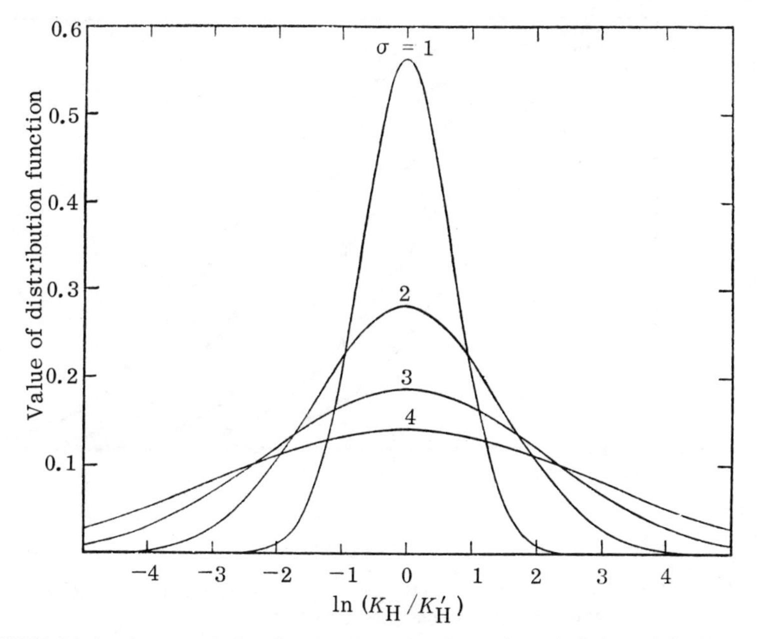

FIGURE II-1 Assumed distribution function for values 1, 2, 3, and 4 of heterogeneity index σ, plotted against ln K_H/K'_H. [From Pauling *et al.* (1944).]

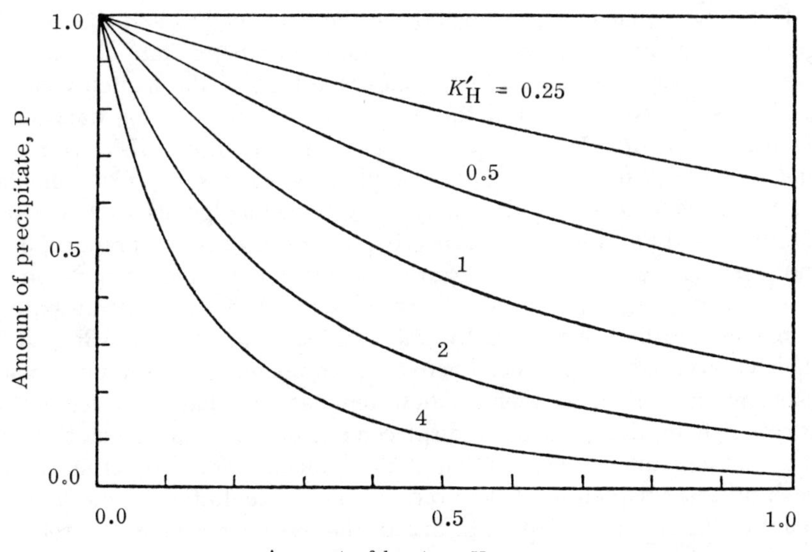

FIGURE II-2 Family of curves with $\sigma = 1.5$ and $K'_H = 0.25$, 0.5, 1.2, and 4, showing dependence of amount of precipitate on K'_H for fixed σ. [From Pauling *et al.* (1944).]

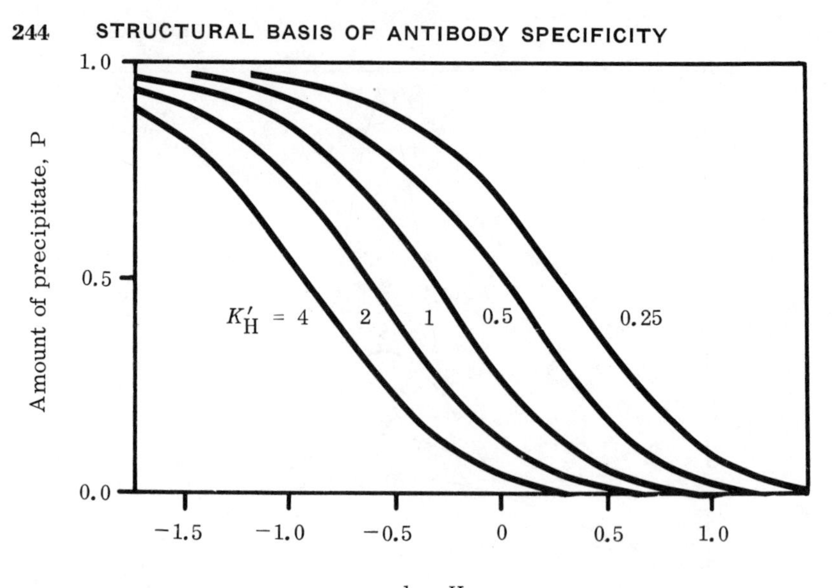

FIGURE II-3 Same family of curves as in Fig. II-2, but plotted logarithmically. [From Pressman (1964).]

concentration are given in Fig. II-5. The curves in Fig. II-5 are very useful for comparing the combination of different haptens with antibody.

In the experimental determination of the value of K_{rel} and the heterogeneity constant σ, the fraction of the amount of precipitate obtained in the absence of hapten is plotted against the $\log_{10}$ of the hapten concentration as abscissa on centimeter cross section paper (0.2 log units/cm). Transparent templates, corresponding to the curves in Fig. II-5, are made and a curve is drawn using the template which fits the experimental data. To evaluate K_{rel} and σ, only 2 experimental points each for the hapten tested and for the reference hapten are needed. In practice, 3 or more points are usually taken. Experimental points have been found to follow the theoretical curves very closely. The set of transparent templates can be constructed by tracing each of the curves in Fig. II-5, which is accurately reproduced here on a centimeter scale. A fiducial point as shown is marked on each of these templates so that displacement of curves can be determined by displacement of the fiducial point. Then the relative hapten concentration at the fiducial point is determined for each different hapten used. The ratio of the concentration at the fiducial point of the reference hapten to that of the test hapten gives the relative combining constant for the hapten. A value of heterogeneity is obtained at the same time for each hapten. An example of this calculation is given in Fig. II-6, which shows three experimental points each for two haptens, one of which is the reference hapten. The template curve with $\sigma = 3$ fits

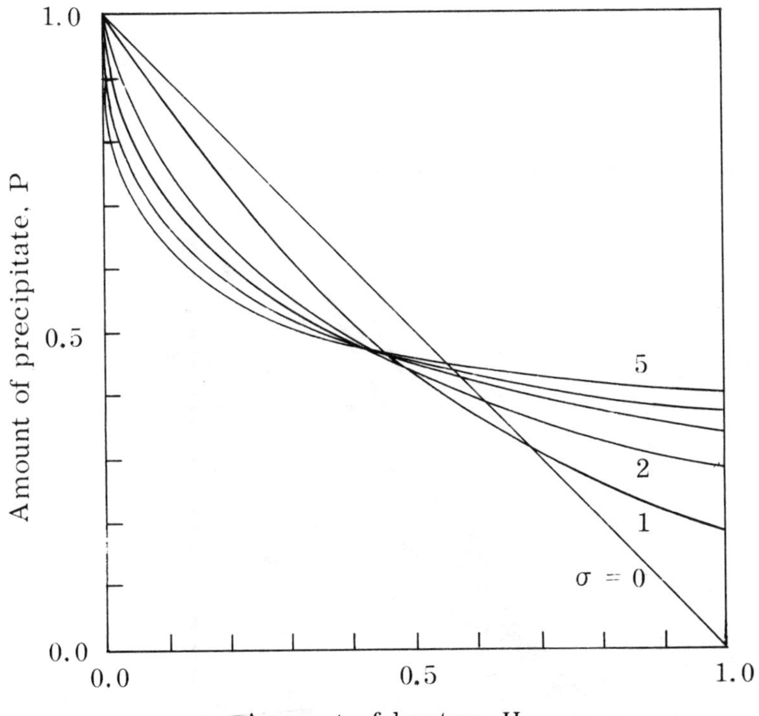

FIGURE II-4 Theoretical curves showing dependence of amount of precipitate, P, on amount of hapten, H_{total} for $\sigma = 0$, 1, 2, 3, 4, and 5 and $K'_H = 1$. [From Pauling *et al.* (1944).]

the points for the experimental hapten, while curves for $\sigma=2$ and $\sigma=4$ do not. The fiducial point falls at concentration 0.00105 *M*. The curve with $\sigma=2$ fits the reference hapten. The fiducial concentration here is 0.00178 *M*. Therefore the value of K_{rel} for the test hapten is 0.00178/0.00105 = 1.69.

In practice, the globulin fraction of the antiserum, or the specifically purified antibody, is used in order to avoid the presence of serum albumin which might compete for the hapten (Pressman and Siegel, 1953). The binding of hapten by albumin is important only in certain systems where the hapten is bound strongly to the albumin, and it is important only for the haptens which are very strongly bound to antibody, since they are effective at low concentrations where binding to albumin may change the concentration appreciably. The antibody solution is brought to a concentration such that 1 ml will yield 100 μg or more of precipitate at optimal antigen concentration. The globulin is made up in an appropriate buffer (usually borate buffer, pH 8), and is mixed with an equal volume

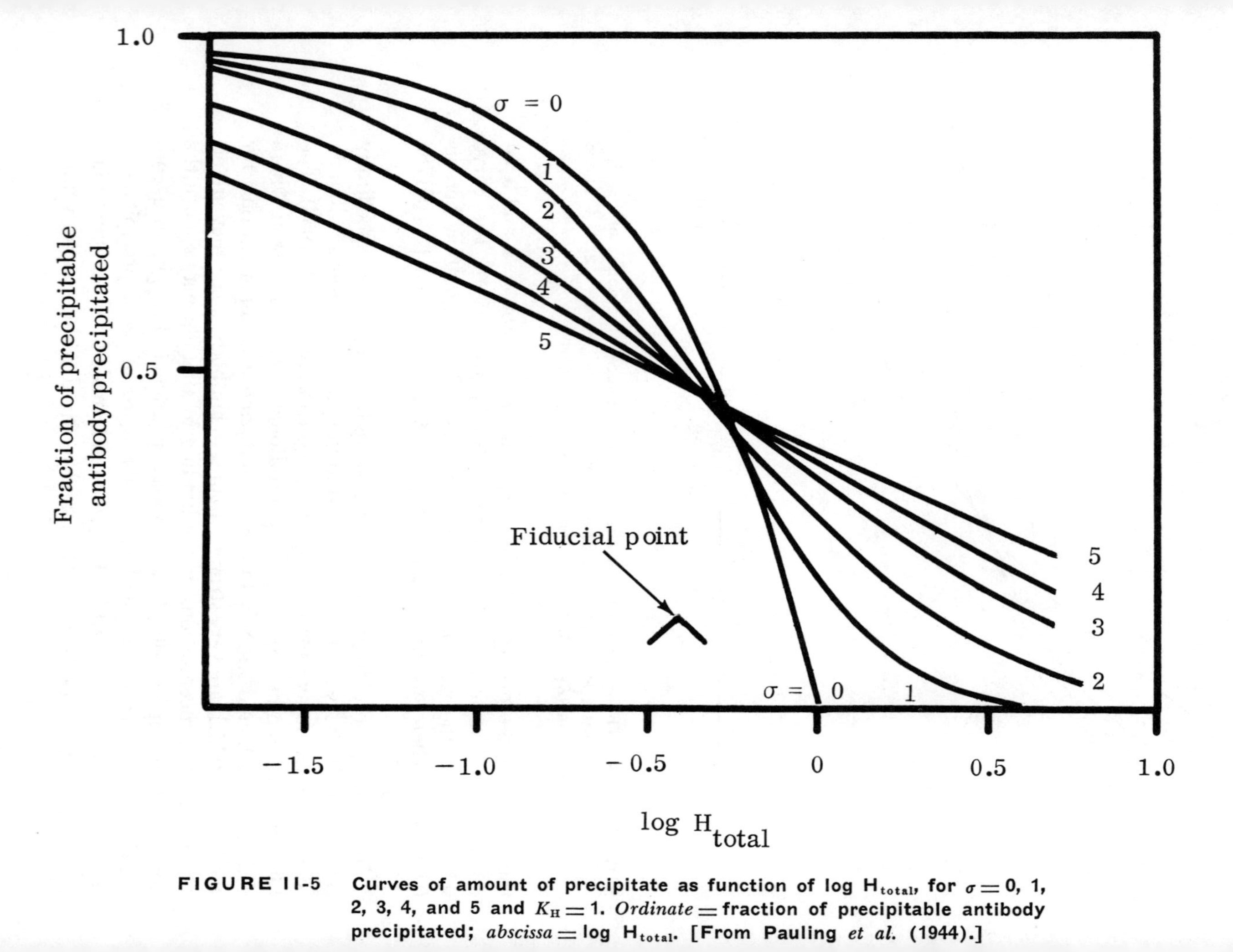

FIGURE II-5 Curves of amount of precipitate as function of log H_{total}, for $\sigma = 0$, 1, 2, 3, 4, and 5 and $K_H = 1$. *Ordinate* = fraction of precipitable antibody precipitated; *abscissa* = log H_{total}. [From Pauling *et al.* (1944).]

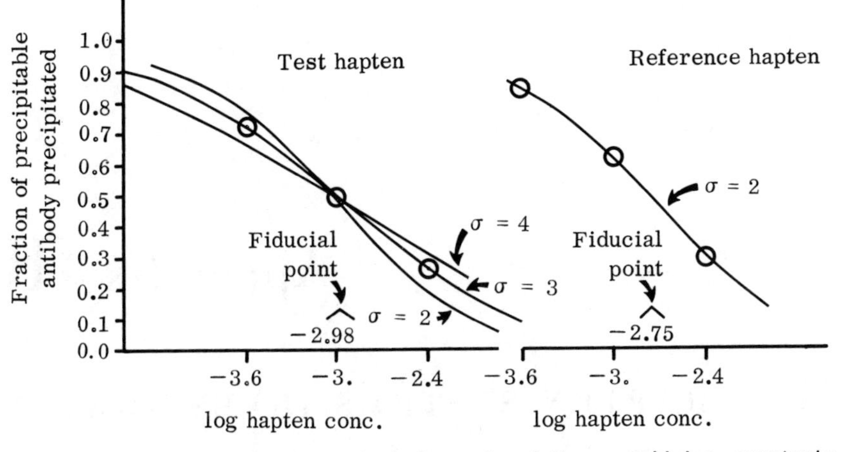

FIGURE II-6 Example for calculation of relative combining constants. [From Pressman (1964).]

of hapten solution (also in buffer) and the optimal amount of antigen. The tubes are usually set up in triplicate, and 4-fold concentration changes are used for the hapten. A preliminary experiment is set up with single tubes, using 10-fold variations in hapten concentration (usually 0.1, 0.01, and 0.001 *M*, respectively), to determine the amount of hapten which decreases the amount of precipitate by 50%. This hapten concentration is then used, as well as one 4-fold greater and one 4-fold less. The mixtures of antigen, antibody, and hapten are mixed and kept at 37°C for one hour and then allowed to stand at 5°C for 2–5 days. Quite suitable data are obtained with even briefer incubations. The precipitates are centrifuged and washed three times with 10 ml saline, and the amount of precipitate is determined by absorption spectrum, by Folin reagent, or by any other quantitative method for the determination of protein.

Appendix III

HAPTEN SYSTEMS INVESTIGATED

Group	Mode of attachment to protein	Reference
	CARBOXYLATE ION DERIVATIVES	
Carboxymethyl	direct	Pillemer *et al.* (1939)
α-Carboxyethyl	direct	Pillemer *et al.* (1939)
α-Carboxy-*n*-propyl	direct	Pillemer *et al.* (1939)
α-Carboxyisobutyl	direct	Pillemer *et al.* (1939)
Phenylacetate	*p*-azo	Landsteiner and van der Scheer (1934a)
γ-Phenyl-*n*-butyrate	*p*-azo	Landsteiner and van der Scheer (1934a)
δ-Phenyl-*n*-caproate	*p*-azo	Landsteiner and van der Scheer (1934a)
Cinnamate	*o*-azo	Landsteiner and Lampl (1918)
Cinnamate	*m*-azo	Landsteiner and Lampl (1918)
Cinnamate	*p*-azo	Landsteiner and Lampl (1918)
β-Benzoylpropionate	*p*-azo	Pressman and Siegel (1953b)
Oxanilate	*p*-azo	Landsteiner and van der Scheer (1934a)
Succinanilate	*p*-azo	Landsteiner and van der Scheer (1934a); Pressman and Siegel (1953a); Pressman *et al.* (1948)

(*continued*)

Group	Mode of attachment to protein	Reference
Succinanilate	*m*-azo	Landsteiner and van der Scheer (1938)
Adipanilate	*p*-azo	Landsteiner and van der Scheer (1932a, 1934a)
Suberanilate	*p*-azo	Landsteiner and van der Scheer (1932a, 1934a)
N-Methylsuccinanilate	*p*-azo	This book
Fumaranilate	*p*-azo	Siegel and Pressman (1954)
Maleanilate	*p*-azo	Siegel and Pressman (1954)
meso-Tartranilate (mixture of two isomers)	*p*-azo	Landsteiner and van der Scheer (1929)
l-Tartranilate	*p*-azo	Landsteiner and van der Scheer (1931)
d-Tartranilate	*p*-azo	Landsteiner and van der Scheer (1929)
l-Malanilate (mixture of two isomers)	*p*-azo	Landsteiner and van der Scheer (1932c)
d-Malanilate (mixture of two isomers)	*p*-azo	Landsteiner and van der Scheer (1932c)
5-Carboxysuccinanilate	3-azo	Landsteiner and van der Scheer (1938)
p-Phenylazohippurate	*p*-$NHCOCH_2$-SCH_2CH_2CH-$(NHCOCH_3)$-CO—	Saha *et al.* (1966)
l-Phenyl-(*p*-azobenzoylamino)-acetate	(azo as indicated)	Landsteiner and van der Scheer (1931); Karush (1956)
d-Phenyl-(*p*-azobenzoylamino)-acetate	(azo as indicated)	Karush (1956)
Benzoate	*o*-azo	Landsteiner and Lampl (1918); Landsteiner and van der Scheer (1931); Jacobs (1937); Pressman *et al.* (1954)
Benzoate	*m*-azo	Landsteiner and Lampl (1918); Landsteiner and van der Scheer (1931); Pressman *et al.* (1954)
Benzoate	*p*-azo	Landsteiner and Lampl (1918); Landsteiner and van der Scheer (1931); Hooker and Boyd (1941); Pressman *et al.* (1944); Pressman *et al.* (1954)
4-Methylbenzoate	3-azo	Landsteiner and Lampl (1918)
4-Chlorobenzoate	3-azo	Landsteiner and Lampl (1918)
4-Bromobenzoate	3-azo	Landsteiner and Lampl (1918)

(*continued*)

Group	Mode of attachment to protein	Reference
5-Nitrobenzoate	3-azo	This book
p-Phenylazobenzoate	*p'*-azo	Nisonoff and Pressman (1957a)
Phthalate	4-azo	Pressman and Siegel (1953a); Pressman and Pauling (1949)
Isophthalate	5-azo	This book
(3-Azo-5-succinylaminobenzoyl)*p*-aminobenzoate	(azo as indicated)	Landsteiner and van der Scheer (1938)

NONCARBOXYLIC ACID DERIVATIVES (Ions)

Group	Mode of attachment to protein	Reference
Benzenesulfonate	*o*-azo	Landsteiner and Lampl (1918)
Benzenesulfonate	*m*-azo	Landsteiner and Lampl (1918); Landsteiner and van der Scheer (1936); Haurowitz (1942)
Benzenesulfonate	*p*-azo	Landsteiner and Lampl (1918); Marrack and Smith (1932); Erlenmeyer and Berger (1933); Haurowitz (1942)
3-Methylbenzenesulfonate	4-azo	Landsteiner and Lampl (1918)
3-Methyl-5-bromobenzenesulfonate	4-azo	Landsteiner and Lampl (1918)
2-Methylbenzenesulfonate	5-azo	Landsteiner and Lampl (1918)
2-Bromobenzenesulfonate	5-azo	Jacobs (1937)
2-Chlorobenzenesulfonate	5-azo	Landsteiner and Lampl (1918)
2,4-Dimethylbenzenesulfonate	5-azo	Landsteiner and Lampl (1918)
3-Bromobenzenesulfonate	6-azo	Jacobs (1937); Landsteiner and Lampl (1918)
Azobenzenedisulfonate	*p*-azo	Landsteiner and Lampl (1918)
Naphthalene-1-sulfonate	4-azo	Landsteiner and Lampl (1918); Bronfenbrenner *et al.* (1931); Winkler (1962)
Benzenearsonate	*o*-azo	Pressman and Siegel (1953a)
Benzenearsonate	*m*-azo	Pressman *et al.* (1945); Pressman and Siegel (1953a)
Benzenearsonate	*p*-azo	Landsteiner and Lampl (1918); Pressman *et al.* (1945); Pressman and Siegel (1953a); Leskowitz (1963)
p-(Phenylazo)benzenearsonate	*p'*-azo	Pressman and Siegel (1953a)
(3-Azo-5-succinylaminobenzoyl)-*p*-aminophenylarsonate	(azo as indicated)	Landsteiner and van der Scheer (1938)
Benzenephosphonate	*p*-azo	Kreiter and Pressman (1964a)

(*continued*)

Group	Mode of attachment to protein	Reference
	POSITIVE CHARGED GROUPS	
Phenyltrimethylammonium	*p*-azo	Pressman *et al.* (1946)
Phenyltrimethylammonium	*m*-azo	Haurowitz (1942)
	HYDROCARBON AND UNCHARGED DERIVATIVES	
Benzene	azo	Landsteiner and Lampl (1918); Landsteiner and van der Scheer (1927); Mutsaars and Grégoire (1936); Jacobs (1937); Nisonoff and Pressman (1957b)
Benzene	carbamido	Hopkins and Wormall (1934); Mutsaars and Grégoire (1936)
Toluene	*p*-azo	Landsteiner and van der Scheer (1927); Bronfenbrenner *et al.* (1931)
Toluene	(α-direct)	Pillemer *et al.* (1939)
Ethylbenzene	*p*-azo	Landsteiner and van der Scheer (1934a)
Butylbenzene	*p*-azo	Landsteiner and van der Scheer (1934a)
Biphenyl	*p*-azo	Jacobs (1937)
Diphenylmethane	*p*-azo	Erlenmeyer and Berger (1932a)
Naphthalene	α-azo	Korosteleva and Skachkov (1964)
Naphthalene	β-azo	Korosteleva and Skachkov (1964)
Naphthalene	1-carbamido	Mutsaars and Grégoire (1936)
Anthracene	β-azo	Jacobs (1937)
1,2-Benzanthracene	10-carbamido	Creech *et al.* (1947a, b)
3,4-Benzpyrene	5-carbamido	Creech *et al.* (1947a, b)
1,2,5,6-Dibenzanthracene	9-carbamido	Creech *et al.* (1947a)
Chlorobenzene	*o*-azo	Landsteiner and van der Scheer (1927)
Chlorobenzene	*p*-azo	Landsteiner and van der Scheer (1927)
Nitrobenzene	*m*-azo	Nisonoff *et al.* (1959a)
Nitrobenzene	*p*-azo	Landsteiner and van der Scheer (1927); Nisonoff *et al.* (1959a); Froese and Sehon (1965)
3,5-Dinitrobenzene	1-azo	Nisonoff *et al.* (1959a)
2,4-Dinitrobenzene	direct	Eisen and Siskind (1964); Cheng and Talmage (1965)
2,4-Dinitrobenzene	1-azo	Eisen *et al.* (1954)

(*continued*)

Group	Mode of attachment to protein	Reference
1,3,5-Trinitrobenzene	2 direct	Little and Eisen (1965)
Methoxybenzene	*p*-azo	Bronfenbrenner *et al.* (1931)
Diphenylether	*p*-azo	Erlenmeyer and Berger (1932a); Jacobs (1937)
Diphenylamine	*p*-azo	Erlenmeyer and Berger (1932a)
Benzoylbenzene	*p*-azo	Jacobs (1937)
Phenylazobenzene	*p*-azo	Jacobs (1937)
Benzoylaminobenzene	*p*-azo (from aniline)	Erlenmeyer *et al.* (1933)
Deoxycorticosterone	21-hemisuccinyl	Beiser *et al.* (1959)
Progesterone	20-oxime *o*-carboxymethyl	Beiser *et al.* (1959)
Cholanyl	direct	Klopstock *et al.* (1964)
Cholesteryl	17-hemicarbonate ester	Klopstock *et al.* (1964)
1,3,5(10)-Estratriene-3-ol	17-carbamido	Goodfriend and Sehon (1961)
Cortisone	21-hemisuccinyl	Beiser *et al.* (1959)
Testosterone	17-hemicarbonate ester 3-oxime *o*-carboxymethyl	Beiser *et al.* (1959)
Fluorene	2-azo	Kitagawa *et al.* (1966)
4-Dimethylaminoazobenzene	4′-carbamido	Baldwin *et al.* (1960)
Acetanilide	*p*-azo	Landsteiner and van der Scheer (1934a)
Butyranilide	*p*-azo	Landsteiner and van der Scheer (1934a)
Caproanilide	*p*-azo	Landsteiner and van der Scheer (1934a)
4-Dimethylaminostilbene	4′-carbamido	Creech *et al.* (1953)
2′Methyl-4-dimethylaminostilbene	4′-carbamido	Creech *et al.* (1953)
Benzoyl	direct	Medveczky and Uhrovits (1931)
o-Acetoxybenzoyl (aspirin)	direct	Butler *et al.* (1940); Weiner *et al.* (1963)
Acetyl	direct	Landsteiner and Lampl (1917)
Propionyl	direct	Landsteiner and Lampl (1917)
Butyryl	direct	Landsteiner and Lampl (1917)
Isobutyryl	direct	Landsteiner and Lampl (1917)
Valeryl	direct	Landsteiner and Lampl (1917)
p-Iodobenzenesufonyl	direct	Merryman and Benacerraf (1963)
Benzenesulfonamide (sulfanilamide)	*p*-azo	Wedum (1942)
3-Nitro-4-hydroxy-5-iodophenylacetyl	direct	Brownstone *et al.* (1966)

(*continued*)

Group	Mode of attachment to protein	Reference
N-Benzyloxycarbonyltyrosyl	direct	Harington *et al.* (1940)
Benzyloxycarbonyl	direct	Gaunt and Wormall (1939)
p-Nitrobenzyloxycarbonyl	direct	Slobin (1966)
Colchicine	*p*-azobenzene-sulfonyl	Truhaut *et al.* (1965)
HETEROCYCLIC DERIVATIVES		
Pyridine	3-azo	Berger and Erlenmeyer (1935); Landsteiner and Pirie (1937); Nisonoff and Pressman (1957b)
4-Carboxypyridine	3-azo	Landsteiner and Pirie (1937)
2-Carboxypyridine	3-azo	Landsteiner and Pirie (1937)
Thiophenoylanilide	*p*-azo (from aniline)	Erlenmeyer *et al.* (1933)
Sulfathiazol	*p*-azo (from amino)	Wedum (1942)
Sulfapyridine	azo (from amino)	Wedum (1942)
Strychnine	5′-azo	Hooker and Boyd (1941)
Purine-6-oyl	direct	Butler *et al.* (1962); Butler *et al.* (1965)
Pyridoxyl	direct	Ungar-Waron and Sela (1966)
Uridine	through 5′-carboxyl	Sela *et al.* (1964)
Adenosine	through ribose	Estrada-Parra *et al.* (1965)
Adenosine-5′-phosphate	through ribose	Erlanger and Beiser (1964)
Thymidylic acid	through phosphate	Halloran and Parker (1966)
Tetrathymidylic acid	through phosphate	Halloran and Parker (1966)
Guanosine	through ribose	Erlanger and Beiser (1964)
Cytidine	through ribose	Erlanger and Beiser (1964)
5-Acetyluracil	direct at N	Tanenbaum and Beiser (1963)
Antipyrine	*p*-azo	Mulinos and Schlesinger (1937); Harte (1938)
Antipyrine	4-azo	Mulinos *et al.* (1938); Harte (1938)
CARBOHYDRATE DERIVATIVES		
Phenyl-α-glucoside	*p*-azo	Avery *et al.* (1932); Goebel *et al.* (1934b)
Phenyl-β-glucoside	*p*-azo	Avery *et al.* (1932); Goebel *et al.* (1934b); Yariv *et al.* (1962); Rude *et al.* (1966)
Benzyl-β-glucoside	*p*-azo	Goebel (1936); Goebel and Hotchkiss (1937)

(*continued*)

Group	Mode of attachment to protein	Reference
Phenyl-β-galactoside	*p*-azo	Avery and Goebel (1929); Beiser *et al.* (1960); Yariv *et al.* (1962)
Phenyl-acetyl-β-glucoside	p-azo	Goebel *et al.* (1934b)
Phenyl-N-acetyl-β-glucosaminide	p-azo	Westphal and Schmidt (1951)
o-β-Glucosido-N-carbobenzyloxytyrosyl	direct through carboxyl group	Clutton *et al.* (1938a); Humphrey and Yuill (1939)
Benzyl-β-cellobioside	*p*-azo	Goebel *et al.* (1934a); Goebel (1938); Allen (1965)
Phenyl-colitoside	*p*-azo	Lüderitz *et al.* (1960)
Phenyl-β-lactoside	*p*-azo	Goebel *et al.* (1934a); Karush (1957)
Benzyl-β-gentiobioside	*p*-azo	Goebel *et al.* (1934a); Goebel (1940)
Phenyl-β-maltoside	*p*-azo	Goebel *et al.* (1934a)
Pneumococcus Type 3 polysaccharide	*p*-azobenzylether	Avery and Goebel (1931)
	URONIC ACID DERIVATIVES	
Benzyl-β-glucuronoside	*p*-azo	Goebel (1936)
Benzyl-β-gentiobiuronoside	*p*-azo	Goebel (1940)
Benzyl-β-cellobiuronoside	*p*-azo	Goebel (1938)
Benzyl-β-galacturonoside	*p*-azo	Goebel and Hotchkiss (1937); Goebel (1940)
	AMINO ACID DERIVATIVES	
Benzoylglycine	*m*-azo	Landsteiner and van der Scheer (1938); Kreiter and Pressman (1964c)
Benzoylglycine	*p*-azo	van der Scheer and Landsteiner (1935); Landsteiner and van der Scheer (1936); Siegel and Pressman (1953)
Benzoyl-D,L-leucine	*m*-azo	Landsteiner and van der Scheer (1938); Kreiter and Pressman (1964c)
Benzoyl-D,L-leucine	*p*-azo	Landsteiner and van der Scheer (1936); van der Scheer and Landsteiner (1935)
Benzoyl-L-tryptophan	*p*-azo	van der Scheer and Landsteiner (1935)

(continued)

Group	Mode of attachment to protein	Reference
Benzoyl-D-glutamate	*p*-azo	van der Scheer and Landsteiner (1935); Ivánovics and Bruckner (1938)
Thyroxyl	direct through carboxyl group	Clutton *et al.* (1938b)
	PEPTIDE DERIVATIVES	
5-Azo-isophthalylglycine-D,L-leucine	(azo as indicated)	Landsteiner and van der Scheer (1938); Kreiter and Pressman (1964c)
Benzoylglycylglycine	*p*-azo	Landsteiner and van der Scheer (1930)
Benzoylglycyl-D,L-leucine	*p*-azo	Landsteiner and van der Scheer (1932b, 1936)
Benzoyl-D,L-leucylglycine	*p*-azo	Landsteiner and van der Scheer (1932b, 1936)
Benzoyl-D,L-leucyl-D,L-leucine	*p*-azo	Landsteiner and van der Scheer (1932b)
Benzoyl-D,L-leucylglycylglycine	*p*-azo	Landsteiner and van der Scheer (1934b)
Benzoyl-D,L-glutathione	*p*-azo	Landsteiner and van der Scheer (1934b)
Benzoylglycylglycylglycine	*p*-azo	Landsteiner and van der Scheer (1934b)
Benzoylglycylglycylglycylglycylglycine	*p*-azo	Landsteiner and van der Scheer (1939)
Benzoylglycylglycylglycylglycyl-D,L-leucine	*p*-azo	Landsteiner and van der Scheer (1939)
Benzoylglycylglycyl-D,L-leucylglycylglycine	*p*-azo	Landsteiner and van der Scheer (1939)
Benzoyl-D,L-leucyl-D,L-leucyl-D,L-leucylglycylglycine	*p*-azo	Landsteiner and van der Scheer (1939)
Poly-D,L-alanyl	direct	Brown *et al.* (1963); Sage *et al.* (1964); Schechter and Sela (1965b)
Lysine vasopressin	direct through carboxyl	Permutt *et al.* (1966)
Poly-D-alanyl	direct	Sage *et al.* (1964); Schechter and Sela (1965a)
Poly-L-alanyl	direct	Sage *et al.* (1964); Schechter and Sela (1965a)
Poly-L-lysine	direct	Arnon *et al.* (1965)

(*continued*)

Group	Mode of attachment to protein	Reference
Poly-L-tyrosine	direct	Schechter *et al.* (1964)
Poly-L-cyclohexylalanyl	direct	Sela and Arnon (1960b)
Bradykinin	direct through carboxyl	Goodfriend *et al.* (1964)
Angiotensin	carbamido and direct through carboxyl	Haber *et al.* (1964)
	OTHERS	
Nitro	(by nitration of protein)	Wormall (1930); Mutsaars (1939)
Iodo	direct	Wormall (1930); Snapper and Grunbaum (1936); Haurowitz and Appel (1939)
Benzylpenicilloyl	direct	Levine (1960); de Weck and Eisen (1960); Levine and Ovary (1961); Parker *et al.* (1962); Levine (1963)
Penicillenate	direct	Parker *et al.* (1962)
1,2-Naphthoquinone	reaction with protein	Ollodart and Rose (1962)
Dihydropsychosine	N-*p*-azobenzoyl	Takemori and Yamakawa (1963)
β,β'-Dichlorodiethylsulfide (mustard gas)	direct treatment	Berenblum and Wormall (1939)
β,β'-Dichlorodiethylsulfone	direct treatment	Berenblum and Wormall (1939)
Serotonin	*p*-azophenylazo	Filipp and Schneider (1964)

SUPPLEMENTARY READING

TEXTS

Boyd, W. C. (1956), *Fundamentals of Immunology.* Interscience, New York and London.

Campbell, D. H., Garvey, J. S., Cremer, N. E., and Sussdorf, D. H. (1963), *Methods in Immunology.* Benjamin, New York.

Eisen, H. N., Editor (1964), *Methods in Medical Research.* Year Book Medical Publishers, Chicago, Illinois.

Kabat, E. A., and Mayer, M. M. (1961), *Experimental Immunochemistry.* Charles C Thomas, Springfield, Illinois.

Kwapinski, J. B. (1965), *Methods of Serological Research.* John Wiley, New York.

Landsteiner, K. (1945), *The Specificity of Serological Reactions.* Harvard University Press, Cambridge, Massachusetts.

Sterzl, J., Hahn, P., and Rudinger, J. (1965), *Molecular and Cellular Basis of Antibody Formation.* Academic, New York and London.

Talmage, D. W., and Cann, J. R. (1961), *The Chemistry of Immunity in Health and Disease.* Charles C Thomas, Springfield, Illinois.

REVIEW ARTICLES

Eisen, H. N. (1964), in *The Harvey Lectures,* Series 60, p. 1. Academic, New York and London. The immune response to a simple antigenic determinant.

Eisen, H. N., and Pearce, J. H. (1962), *Ann. Rev. Microbiol.,* **16**, 101. The nature of antibodies and antigens.

Fleischman, J. B. (1966), *Ann. Rev. Biochem.,* **35**, 835. Immunoglobulins.

Fudenberg, H. H. (1965), *Ann. Rev. Microbiol.,* **19**, 301. The immune globulins.

Haurowitz, F. (1965), *Physiol. Rev.,* **45**, 1. Antibody formation.

Karush, F. (1962), *Advan. Immunol.,* **2**, 1. Immunologic specificity and molecular structure.

Lennox, E. S., and Cohn, M. (1965), *Ann. Rev. Biochem.,* **36**, 365. Immunoglobulins.

Nisonoff, A., and Thorbecke, G. J. (1964), *Ann. Rev. Biochem.,* **33**, 355. Immunochemistry.

Singer, S. J. (1965), in *The Proteins* (H. Neurath, ed.), Vol. III, p. 270. Academic Press, New York. Structure and function of antigen and antibody proteins.

Singer, S. J. (1967), *Advan. Protein Chem.* **22**, 1. Covalent labeling of active sites.

Talmage, D. W. (Ed. of Section I.), in *Immunological Diseases,* M. Samter, Editor. Little, Brown and Company, Boston, Massachusetts. Antigens and the immune response.

Tomasi, T. B., Jr. (1965), *Blood,* **25**, 382. Human gamma globulin.

REFERENCES

Allen, P. Z. (1965), *Immunochemistry,* **2**, 417. Immunochemical studies on some immune systems involving β(1,4)-linked glucose.

Alexander, J. (1931), *Protoplasma,* **14**, 295. Intracellular aspects of life and disease.

Almeida, J., Cinader, B., and Howatson, A. (1963), *J. Exptl. Med.,* **118**, 327. The structure of antigen-antibody complexes. A study by electron microscopy.

Anderer, F. A., and Schlumberger, H. D. (1966), *Biochim. Biophys. Acta,* **115**, 222. Cross reactions of antisera against the terminal amino acid and dipeptide of tobacco mosaic virus.

Arnon, R., Sela, M., Yaron, A., and Sober, H. A. (1965), *Biochemistry,* **4**, 948. Polylysine-specific antibodies and their reaction with oligolysines.

Arrhenius, S. (1907), *Immunochemistry,* Macmillan, New York.

Avery, O. T., and Goebel, W. F. (1929), *J. Exptl. Med.,* **50**, 533. Chemo-immunological studies on conjugated carbohydrate-proteins. II. Immunological specificity of synthetic sugar-protein antigens.

Avery, O. T., and Goebel, W. F. (1931), *J. Exptl. Med.,* **54**, 437. Immunological specificity of an antigen prepared by combining the capsular polysaccharide of type III pneumococcus with foreign protein.

Avery, O. T., Goebel, W. F., and Babers, F. H. (1932), *J. Exptl. Med.,* **55**, 769. Chemo-immunological studies on conjugated carbohydrate-proteins. VII. Immunological specificity of antigens prepared by combining α- and β-glucosides of glucose with proteins.

Baldwin, R. W., Beswick, J., Chayen, J., and Cunningham, G. J. (1960), *Acta Unio Intern. Contra Cancrum,* **16**, 47. Immunochemical studies of protein-carcinogen binding in rat liver during azo dye carcinogenesis.

Beiser, S. M., Burke, G. C., and Tanenbaum, S. W. (1960), *J. Mol. Biol.,* **2**, 125. Immunochemical studies on a galactosyl-protein conjugate.

Beiser, S. M., Erlanger, B. F., Agate, F. J., Jr., and Lieberman, S. (1959), *Science,* **129**, 564. Antigenicity of steroid-protein conjugates.

Beiser, S. M., Tanenbaum, S. W., and Erlanger, B. F. (1964), *Nature,* **203**, 1381. Purine- and pyrimidine-specific antibodies: precipitation with denatured deoxyribonucleic acid.

Benjamini, E., Young, J. D., Shimizu, M., and Cherry, Y. L. (1964), *Biochemistry,* **3**, 1115. Immunochemical studies on the tobacco mosaic virus protein. I. The immunological relationship of the tryptic peptides of tobacco mosaic virus protein to the whole protein.

Berenblum, I., and Wormall, A. (1939), *Biochem. J.,* **33**, 75. X. The immunological properties of proteins treated with β,β′-dichlorodiethylsulphone (mustard gas) and β,β′-dichlorodiethylsulphone.

Berger, E., and Erlenmeyer, H. (1935), *Klin. Wochschr.,* **14**, 536. Immunochemical studies on pyridine and pyridine derivatives.

Breinl, F., and Haurowitz, F. (1930), *Z. Physiol. Chem.,* **192**, 45. Chemical investigation of the precipitate from hemoglobin and anti-hemoglobin-serum and remarks on the nature of the antibodies.

Briegleb, G. (1949), *Z. Elektrochem.,* **53**, 350. Proton affinity, base strength, and resonance energy of simple nitrogen bases.

Bronfenbrenner, J., Hetler, D. M., and Eagle, T. O. (1931), *Science,* **73**, 455. Modification of therapeutic sera with a view of avoiding complications of allergic nature.

Brown, R. K. (1962), *J. Biol. Chem.,* **237**, 1162. Studies on the antigenic structure of ribonuclease. III. Inhibition by peptides of antibody to performic acid-oxidized ribonuclease.

Brown, R. K., Trzpis, M. A., Sela, M., and Anfinsen, C. B. (1963), *J. Biol. Chem.,* **238**, 3876. Studies on the antigenic structure of ribonuclease. IV. Polyalanyl ribonuclease.

Brownstone, A., Mitchison, N. A., and Pitt-Rivers, R. (1966), *Immunology,* **10**, 481. Biological studies with an iodine-containing synthetic immunological determinant 4-hydroxy-3-iodo-5-nitrophenylacetic acid (NIP) and related compounds.

Butler, G. C., Harington, C. R., and Yuill, M. E. (1940), *Biochem. J.,* **34**, 838. Studies in synthetic immunochemistry. 5. Observations on antiserums against aspirin-protein complexes.

Butler, V. P., Jr., Beiser, S. M., Erlanger, B. F., Tanenbaum, S. W., Cohen, S., and Bendich, A. (1962), *Proc. Natl. Acad. Sci. U.S.,* **48**, 1597. Purine-specific antibodies which react with deoxyribonucleic acid (DNA).

Butler, V. P., Jr., Tanenbaum, S. W., and Beiser, S. M. (1965), *J. Exptl. Med.,* **121**, 19. A study of the cross-reactivity of antipurin-6-oyl serum with deoxyribonucleic acid (DNA).

Campbell, D. H., Luescher, E., and Lerman, L. S. (1951), *Proc. Natl. Acad. Sci. U.S.,* **37**, 575. Immunologic adsorbents. I. Isolation of antibody by means of a cellulose-protein antigen.

Carsten, M. E., and Eisen, H. N. (1955), *J. Am. Chem. Soc.,* **77**, 1273. The specific interaction of some dinitrobenzenes with rabbit antibody to dinitrophenyl-bovine γ-globulin.

Cebra, J. J. (1961), *J. Immunol.,* **86**, 205. Studies on the combining sites of the protein antigen silk fibroin, III. Inhibition of the silk fibroin-antifibroin system by peptides derived from the antigen.

Cebra, J. J. (1964), *J. Immunol.,* **92**, 977. The effect of sodium dodecylsulfate on intact and insoluble papain hydrolyzed immune globulin.

Cebra, J. J., Givol, D., Silman, H. I., and Katchalski, E. (1961), *J. Biol. Chem.* **236**, 1720. A two-stage cleavage of rabbit γ-globulin by a water-insoluble papain preparation followed by cysteine.

Chen, C. C., Grossberg, A. L., and Pressman, D. (1962), *Biochemistry,* **1**, 1025. Effect of cyanate on several anti-hapten antibodies: evidence for the presence of an amino group in the site of anti-*p*-azobenzenearsonate antibody.

Cheng, W. C., and Talmage, D. W. (1965), *J. Biol. Chem.,* **240**, 3530. Isolation of anti-dinitrophenyl group antibodies with a triply substituted cross-reacting antigen.

Clutton, R. F., Harington, C. R., and Yuill, M. E. (1938a), *Biochem. J.,* **32**, 1111. Studies in synthetic immunochemistry. II. Serological investigation of o-β-glucosidotyrosyl derivatives of proteins.

Clutton, R. F., Harington, C. R., and Yuill, M. E. (1938b), *Biochem. J.,* **32**, 1119. Studies in synthetic immunochemistry. III. Preparation and antigenic properties of thyroxyl derivatives of proteins, and physiological effects of their antisera.

Cohen, S., and Porter, R. R. (1964), *Advan. Immunol.,* **4**, 287. Structure and biological activity of immunoglobulins.

Creech, H. J., Havas, H. F., and Andre, J. (1953), *Cancer Res.,* **13**, 335. Immunological properties of carcinogen-protein conjugates containing 4-dimethylaminostilbene and its 2′-methyl analog.

Creech, H. J., Oginsky, E. L., and Cheever, F. S. (1947a), *Cancer Res.,* **7**, 290. Immunological studies of hydrocarbon-protein conjugates. I. Precipitin reactions.

Creech, H. J., Oginsky, E. L., and Tryon, M. (1947b), *Cancer Res.,* **7**, 301. Immunological studies of hydrocarbon-protein conjugates. III. Inhibition reactions.

Crumpton, M. J., and Wilkinson, J. M. (1965), *Biochem. J.,* **94**, 545. The immunological activity of some of the chymotryptic peptides of sperm-whale myoglobin.

Czerlinksi, G., Diebler, H., and Eigen, M. (1959), *Z. Physik. Chem. (N.F.),* **19**, 246. Relaxation investigations on the kinetics of metal complex formation.

Day, L. A., Sturdevant, J. M., and Singer, S. J. (1962), *J. Am. Chem. Soc.,* **84**, 3768. The direct measurement of the rate of a hapten-antibody reaction.

Day, L. A., Sturdevant, J. M., and Singer, S. J. (1963), *Ann. N.Y. Acad. Sci.,* **103**, 611. The kinetics of the reactions between antibodies to the 2,4-dinitrophenyl group and specific haptens.

de Weck, A. L., and Eisen, H. N. (1960), *J. Exptl. Med.,* **112**, 1227. Some immunochemical properties of penicillenic acid. An antigenic determinant derived from penicillin.

Doolittle, R. F., and Singer, S. J. (1965), *Proc. Natl. Acad. Sci. U.S.,* **54**, 1773. Tryptic peptides from the active sites of antibody molecules.

Edelman, G. M. (1959), *J. Am. Chem. Soc.,* **81**, 3155. Dissociation of γ-globulin.

Edelman, G. M., Benacerraf, B., and Ovary, Z. (1963), *J. Exptl. Med.,* **118**, 229. Structure and specificity of guinea pig 7S antibodies.

Edelman, G. M., Olins, D. E., Gally, J. A., and Zinder, N. D. (1963), *Proc. Natl. Acad. Sci. U.S.,* **50**, 753. Reconstitution of immunologic activity by interaction of polypeptide chains of antibodies.

Ehrlich, P. (1906), *Studies on Immunity,* J. Wiley, New York.

Eisen, H. N. (1962), *Feder. Proc.,* **21**, 721. Antigenic determinants of conjugated proteins in relation to allergic responses.

Eisen, H. N. (1964a), in *Methods in Medical Research* (H. N. Eisen, ed.), Vol. 10, p. 106. Year Book Medical Publishers, Chicago, Illinois. VI. Equilibrium dialysis for measurement of antibody-hapten affinities.

Eisen, H. N. (1964b), *Ibid.,* p. 115. VII. Determination of antibody affinity for haptens and antigens by means of fluorescence quenching.

Eisen, H. N. (1964c), *Ibid.,* p. 94. IV. Preparation of purified anti-2,4-dinitrophenyl antibodies.

Eisen, H. N. (1966), in *The Harvey Lectures,* Series 60, 1964–65, p. 1. Academic, New York. The immune response to a simple antigenic determinant.

Eisen, H. N., Carsten, M. E., and Belman, S. (1954), *J. Immunol.,* **73**, 296. Studies of hypersensitivity to low molecular weight substances. III. The 2,4-dinitrophenyl group as a determinant in the precipitin reaction.

Eisen, H. N., and Karush, F. (1949), *J. Am. Chem. Soc.,* **71**, 363. The interaction of purified antibody with homologous hapten. Antibody valence and binding constant.

Eisen, H. N., Simms, E. S., Little, J. R., Jr., and Steiner, L. A. (1964), *Feder. Proc.,* **23**, 559. Affinities of anti-2,4-dinitrophenyl (DNP) antibodies induced by ε-41-mono-DNP-ribonuclease.

Eisen, H. N., and Siskind, G. W. (1964), *Biochemistry,* **3**, 996. Variations in affinities of antibodies during the immune response.

Erlanger, B. F., and Beiser, S. M. (1964), *Proc. Natl. Acad. Sci. U.S.,* **52**, 68. Antibodies specific for ribonucleosides and ribonucleotides and their reaction with DNA.

Erlenmeyer, H., and Berger, E. (1932a), *Biochem. Z.,* **252**, 22. Studies on the significance of structure of antigens for the production and the specificity of antibodies.

Erlenmyer, H., and Berger, E. (1932b), *Biochem. Z.,* **255**, 429. Relationship between structure of the antigens and the specificity of the antibodies.

Erlenmeyer, H., and Berger, E. (1933), *Biochem. Z.,* **262**, 196. Relation between the structure of antigens and the specificity of antibodies. V.

Erlenmeyer, H., Berger, E., and Leo, M. (1933), *Helv. Chim. Acta,* **16**, 733. Relationship between the structure of antigens and the specificity of antibodies.

Estrada-Parra, S., Schmill, A., and Martinez, R.-A. (1965), *Nature,* **208**, 1010. Reaction of adenine-specific antibodies with denatured deoxyribonucleic acid.

Farah, F. S., Kern, M., and Eisen, H. N. (1960), *J. Exptl. Med.,* **112**, 1195. Preparation and some properties of purified antibody specific for the 2,4-dinitrophenyl group.

Feinstein, A., and Rowe, A. J. (1965), *Nature,* **205**, 147. Molecular mechanism of formation of an antigen-antibody complex.

Ferguson, G., and Sim, G. A. (1961), *Acta Cryst.,* **14**, 1262. X-ray studies of molecular overcrowding. II. The crystal and molecular structure of *o*-chlorobenzoic acid.

Ferguson, G., and Sim, G. A. (1962), *Acta Cryst.,* **15**, 346. X-ray studies of molecular overcrowding. III. The crystal and molecular structure of *o*-bromobenzoic acid.

Fierz, H. E., Jadassohn, W., and Stoll, W. (1937), *J. Exptl. Med.,* **65**, 339. Anaphylactic sensitization with chemically definite compounds.

Filipp, G., and Schneider, M. (1964), *Acta Allerol.,* **19**, 216. The synthesis of serotoninazoprotein.

Fischer, E. (1894), *Chem. Ber.,* **27**, 2985. Influence of configuration on the action of enzymes.

Fischer, E. (1898), *Z. Physiol. Chem.,* **26**, 60. Importance of stereochemistry in physiology.

Fleischman, J. B., Pain, R. H., and Porter, R. R. (1962), *Arch. Biochem. Biophys.,* Suppl. 1, 174. Reduction of γ-globulins.

Fleischman, J. B., Porter, R. R., and Press, E. M. (1963), *Biochem. J.,* **88**, 220. The arrangement of the peptide chains in γ-globulin.

Fougereau, M., Olins, D. E., and Edelman, G. M. (1964), *J. Exptl. Med.,* **120**, 349. Reconstitution of antiphage antibodies from L and H polypeptide chains and the formation of interspecies molecular hybrids.

Franek, F., and Nezlin, R. S. (1963), *Biokhimiya,* **28**, 193. The role of different peptide chains of the antibody in the antigen-antibody reaction.

Froese, A., and Sehon, A. H. (1965), *Immunochemistry,* **2**, 135. Kinetic and equilibrium studies of the reaction between anti-*p*-nitrophenyl antibodies and a homologous hapten.

Froese, A., Sehon, A. A., and Eigen, M. (1962), *Can. J. Chem.,* **40**, 1786. Kinetic studies of protein-dye and antibody-hapten interactions with the temperature jump method.

Fuchs, S., and Sela, M. (1963), *Biochem. J.,* **87**, 70. Studies on the chemical basis of the antigenicity of proteins 6. Antigenic specificity of some synthetic polypeptides containing tyrosine.

Gaunt, W. E., and Wormall, A. (1939), *Biochem. J.,* **33**, 908. Immunological and chemical properties of carbobenzyloxy-proteins. I. Serum globulin and egg albumin derivatives. II. Insulin derivatives.

Gelzer, J., and Kabat, E. A. (1964), *J. Exptl. Med.,* **119**, 983. Specific fractionation of human antidextran antibodies. II. Assay of human anti-dextran serums and specifically fractionated purified antibodies by microcomplement fixation and complement fixation inhibition techniques.

Gill, T. J., III, and Doty, P. (1960), *J. Mol. Biol.,* **2**, 65. A strongly antigenic synthetic polypeptide.

Gill, T. J., III, and Doty, P. (1961), *J. Biol. Chem.,* **236**, 2677. Studies on synthetic polypeptide antigens. II. The immunochemical properties of a group of linear synthetic polypeptides.

Gill, T. J., III, Kunz, H. W., Friedman, E., and Doty, P. (1963), *J. Biol. Chem.,* **238**, 108. Studies on synthetic polypeptide antigens. VIII. The inhibition of the antibody-synthetic polypeptide reaction by amino acids, dipeptides, amines, alcohols, and dicarboxylic acids.

Givol, D., Fuchs, S., and Sela, M. (1962), *Biochim. Biophys. Acta,* **63**, 222. Isolation of antibodies to antigens of low molecular weight.

Givol, D., and Sela, M. (1964), *Biochemistry,* **3**, 444. Isolation and fragmentation of antibodies to polytyrosyl gelatin.

Gleich, G. J., and Allen, P. Z. (1965), *Immunochemistry,* **2**, 417. Immunochemical studies on some immune systems involving β(1,4) linked glucose.

Goebel, W. F. (1936), *J. Exptl. Med.,* **64**, 29. Chemo-immunological studies on conjugated carbohydrate-proteins. X. The immunological properties of an artificial antigen containing glucuronic acid.

Goebel, W. F. (1938), *J. Exptl. Med.,* **68**, 469. Chemo-immunological studies on conjugated carbohydrate-proteins. XII. The immunological properties of an artificial antigen containing cellobiuronic acid.

Goebel, W. F. (1940), *J. Exptl. Med.,* **72**, 33. Studies on antibacterial immunity induced by artificial antigens. II. Immunity to experimental pneumococcal infection with antigens containing saccharides of synthetic origin.

Goebel, W. F., Avery, O. T., and Babers, F. H. (1934a), *J. Exptl. Med.,* **60**, 599. Chemo-immunological studies on conjugated carbohydrate-proteins. IX. The specificity of antigens prepared by combining the *p*-aminophenyl glucosides of disaccharides with protein.

Goebel, W. F., Babers, F. H., and Avery, O. T. (1934b), *J. Exptl. Med.,* **60**, 85. Chemo-immunological studies on conjugated carbohydrate proteins. VIII. The influence of the acetyl group on the specificity of hexoside-protein antigens.

Goebel, W. F., and Hotchkiss, R. D. (1937), *J. Exptl. Med.,* **66**, 191. Chemo-immunological studies on conjugated carbohydrate-proteins. XI. The specificity of azo protein antigens containing glucuronic and galacturonic acids.

Goodfriend, T. L., Levine, L., and Fasman, G. D. (1964), *Science,* **144**, 1344. Antibodies to bradykinin and angiotensin: a use of carbodiimides in immunology.

Goodfriend, L., and Sehon, A. H. (1960), *Nature,* **185**, 764. Antigenicity of Cestrone-protein conjugates.

Goodfriend, L., and Sehon, A. H. (1961), *Can. J. Biochem. Physiol.,* **39**, 941. Antibodies to esterone-protein conjugates. I. Immunochemical studies.

Grabar, P. (1958), *Advan. Protein Chem.,* **13**, 1. The use of immunochemical methods in studies on proteins.

Grabar, P., and Williams, C. A., Jr. (1953), *Biochim. Biophys. Acta.,* **10**, 193; (1955) **17**, 67. Méthode immuno-electrophorétique d'analyse de mélanges de substances antigéniques.

Graf, L., Yariv, J., and Rapport, M. M. (1965), *Immunochemistry,* **2**, 145. Immunochemical studies of organ and tumor lipids—XV. The reactivity of anti-lactose sera with cytolipin H.

Grossberg, A. L., Chen, C. C., Rendina, L., and Pressman, D. (1962a), *J. Immunol.,* **88**, 600. Specific cation effects with antibody to a hapten with a positive charge.

Grossberg, A. L., Markus, G., and Pressman, D. (1965), *Proc. Natl. Acad. Sci. U.S.,* **54**, 942. Change in antibody conformation induced by hapten.

Grossberg, A. L., and Pressman, D. (1960), *J. Am. Chem. Soc.,* **82**, 5478. Nature of the combining site of antibody against a hapten bearing a positive charge.

Grossberg, A. L., and Pressman, D. (1963), *Biochemistry,* **2**, 90. Effect of acetylation on the active site of several antihapten antibodies: further evidence for the presence of tyrosine in each site.

Grossberg, A. L., and Pressman, D. (1964), in *Methods of Medical Research* (H. N. Eisen, ed.), Vol. 10, p. 103. Year Book Medical Publishers, Chicago, Illinois. V. Purification of anti-*p*-azobenzoate antibodies.

Grossberg, A. L., and Pressman, D. (1967), *Feder. Proc.,* **26**, 339. Chemical modification of arginine in the active sites of antibodies.

Grossberg, A. L., Radzimski, G., and Pressman, D. (1962b), *Biochemistry,* **1**, 391. Effect of iodination on the active site of several antihapten antibodies.

Grossberg, A. L., Stelos, P. and Pressman, D. (1962c), *Proc. Natl. Acad. Sci. U.S.,* **48**, 1203. Structure of fragments of antibody molecules as revealed by reduction of exposed disulfide bonds.

Gurvich, A. E., Kapner, R. B., and Nezlin, R. S. (1959), *Biokhimiya,* **24**, 144. Isolation of pure antibodies with the aid of antigens fixed on cellulose and studies on their properties.

Gurvich, A. E., Kuzovleva, O. B., and Tumanova, A. E. (1961), *Biokhimiya,* **26**, 934. Production of protein cellulose complexes (immunosorbents) in the form of suspensions able to bind great amounts of antibodies.

Gyenes, L., Rose, E., and Sehon, A. H. (1958), *Nature,* **181**, 1465. Isolation of antibodies on antigen-polystyrene conjugates.

Habeeb, A. F. S. A., Cassidy, H. G., and Singer, S. J. (1958), *Biochim. Biophys. Acta,* **29**, 587. Molecular structural effects produced in proteins by reaction with succinic anhydride.

Haber, E. (1964), *Proc. Natl. Acad. Sci. U.S.,* **52**, 1099. Recovery of antigenic specificity after denaturation and complete reduction of disulfides in a papain fragment of antibody.

Haber, E., Page, L. B., and Jacoby, G. A. (1964), *Clin. Res.,* **12**, 184. Synthetic copolymers of angiotensin and polyaminoacids.

Halloran, M. J., and Parker, C. W. (1966), *J. Immunol.,* **96**, 379. The production of antibodies to mononucleotides, oligonucleotides and DNA.

Harington, C. R., Humphrey, J., Yuill, M. E., and Clutton, R. F. (1940), *Rept. Proc. 3rd Intern. Congr. Microbiol.,* p. 822. Further work on the immunological properties of gelatin derivatives and problems arising therefrom.

Harte, R. A. (1938), *J. Immunol.,* **34**, 433. Serological tests with pyrazolone compounds.

Haurowitz, F. (1942), *J. Immunol.,* **43**, 331. Separation and determination of multiple antibodies.

Haurowitz, F., and Appel, G. (1939), *Z. Immunitaetsforsch.,* **95**, 478. Precipitation of iodized proteins of different iodine contents with specific antiserums.

Haurowitz, F., and Breinl, F. (1933), *Z. Physiol. Chem.,* **214**, 111. Chemical investigation of the specific binding of arsanil-protein and arsanilic acid to immune serum.

Heidelberger, M. (1935), *J. Exptl. Med.,* **61**, 563. A precipitin reaction between type III pneumococcus polysaccharide and homologous antibody. III. A quantitative study and a theory of the reaction mechanism.

Heidelberger, M. (1939), *Chem. Rev.,* **24**, 323. Chemical aspects of the precipitin and agglutinin reactions.

Heidelberger, M., Treffers, H. P., and Mayer, M. (1940), *J. Exptl. Med.,* **71**, 271. A quantitative theory of the precipitin reaction. VII. The egg albumin-antibody reaction in antisera from the rabbit and horse.

Hooker, S. B. (1937), *J. Allergy,* **8**, 113. Different determinants of antigenic specificity on single molecules.

Hooker, S. B., and Boyd, W. C. (1940), *J. Immunol.,* **38**, 479. Antibodies to strychnine.

Hooker, S. B., and Boyd, W. C. (1941), *J. Immunol.,* **42**, 419. A test of the alternation- ("lattice"-) hypothesis with divalent and trivalent haptens.

Hopkins, S. J., and Wormall, A. (1934), *Biochem. J.,* **28**, 228. Phenyl *iso*cyanate protein derivatives and their immunological properties. III. The amino acid derivatives and serological inhibition tests.

Humphrey, J. H., and Yuill, M. E. (1939), *Biochem. J.,* **33**, 1826. Studies in synthetic immunochemistry. IV. Further investigation of *o*-β-glucosidotyrosyl derivatives of proteins.

Isliker, H. C. (1953), *Ann. N.Y. Acad. Sci.,* **57**, 225. Purification of antibodies by means of antigens linked to ion exchange resins.

Ivánovics, G., and Bruckner, V. (1938), *Z. Immunitaetsforsch.,* **93**, 119. The specificity of anthrax immune sera toward coupled azo proteins.

Jacobs, J. (1937), *J. Gen. Physiol.,* **20**, 353. Serological reactions of azo-proteins derived from aromatic hydrocarbons and diaryl compounds.

Kabat, E. A. (1960), *J. Immunol.,* **84**, 82. The upper limit for the size of the human antidextran combining site.

Kabat, E. A. (1962), *Feder. Proc.,* **21**, 694. Antigenic determinants of dextrans and blood group substances.

Karush, F. (1956), *J. Am. Chem. Soc.,* **78**, 5519. The interaction of purified antibody with optically isomeric haptens.

Karush, F. (1957), *J. Am. Chem. Soc.,* **79**, 3380. The interaction of purified anti-β-lactoside antibody with haptens.

Karush, F., and Marks, R. (1957), *J. Immunol.,* **78**, 297. The preparation and properties of purified anti-hapten antibody.

Kendrew, J. C., Watson, H. C., Strandberg, B. E., and Dickerson, R. E. (1961), *Nature,* 190, 666. A partial determination by X-ray methods, and its correlation with chemical data.

Kitagawa, M., Tanigaki, N., Yagi, Y., Planinsek, J., and Pressman, D. (1966), *Cancer Res.*, **26**, 752. Carcinogen-binding antigens in rat liver microsomes.

Kitagawa, M., Yagi, Y., and Pressman, D. (1965a), *J. Immunol.*, **95**, 446. The heterogeneity of combining sites of antibodies as determined by specific immunoadsorbents. I. A rapid micromethod of fractionation of antibody.

Kitagawa, M., Yagi, Y., and Pressman, D. (1965b), *J. Immunol.*, **95**, 455. The heterogeneity of combining sites of antibodies as determined by specific immunoadsorbents. II. Comparison of elution patterns obtained with anti-*p*-azobenzoate antibodies by different kinds of immunoadsorbent and fluting hapten.

Kitagawa, M., Yagi, Y., and Pressman, D. (1965c), *J. Immunol.*, **95**, 991. The heterogeneity of combining sites of antibodies as determined by specific immunoadsorbents. III. Further characterization of purified antibody fractions obtained from anti-*p*-azobenzoate antibodies.

Klopstock, A., Pinto, M., and Rimon, A. (1964), *J. Immunol.*, **92**, 515. Antibodies reacting with steroid haptens.

Koshland, Daniel E., Jr. (1963), *Ann. N.Y. Acad. Sci.*, **103**, 630. Properties of the active site of enzymes.

Koshland, M. E., Englberger, F. M., and Gaddone, S. M. (1963), *J. Biol. Chem.*, **238**, 1349. Identification of tyrosine at the active site of anti-*p*-azobenzenearsonic acid antibody.

Koshland, M. E., Englberger, F. M., and Gaddone, S. M. (1965), *Immunochemistry*, **2**, 115. Evidence against the universality of a tyrosyl residue at antibody combining sites.

Koshland, M. E., Englberger, F., and Koshland, D. E., Jr. (1959), *Proc. Natl. Acad. Sci. U.S.*, **45**, 1470. General method for labeling of active site of antibodies and enzymes.

Korosteleva, T. A., and Skachkov, A. P. (1964), *Vopr. Onkol.*, **10**, 72. The study of carcinogenic aromatic amines as haptens.

Kreiter, V. P., and Pressman, D. (1964a), *Biochemistry*, **3**, 274. Differences among antibodies formed in response to the *p*-azobenzenephosphonate and *p*-azobenzenearsonate haptens.

Kreiter, V. P., and Pressman, D. (1964b), *Immunochemistry*, **1**, 91. Fractionation of anti-*p*-azobenzenearsonate antibody by means of immunoadsorbents.

Kreitter, V. P., and Pressman, D. (1964c), *Immunochemistry*, **1**, 151. Antibodies to a hapten with two determinant groups.

Lafferty, K. J., and Oertelis, S. (1963), *Virology* **21**, 91. The interaction between virus and antibody. III. Examination of virus-antibody complexes with the electron microscope.

Landsteiner, K. (1942), *J. Exptl. Med.*, **75**, 269. Serological reactivity of hydrolytic products from silk.

Landsteiner, K. (1945), *The Specificity of Serological Reactions*, Harvard University Press, Cambridge, Massachusetts.

Landsteiner, K., and Lampl, H. (1917), *Z. Immunitaetsforsch.*, **26**, 258. Antigens with various acyl groups.

Landsteiner, K., and Lampl, H. (1918), *Biochem. Z.*, **86**, 343. Antigens. XII. The relationship between serological specificity and chemical structure. (Preparation of antigens with specific groups of known chemical structure.)

Landsteiner, K., and Pirie, N. W. (1937), *J. Immunol.*, **33**, 265. Serological specificity in pyridine derivatives.

Landsteiner, K., and van der Scheer, J. (1927), *J. Exptl. Med.*, **45**, 1045. Influence of acid groups on the serological specificity of azo-proteins.

Landsteiner, K., and van der Scheer, J. (1928), *J. Exptl. Med.*, **48**, 315. Serological differentiation of steric isomers.

Landsteiner, K., and van der Scheer (1929), *J. Exptl. Med.*, **50**, 407. Serological differentiation of steric isomers (antigens containing tartaric acids).

Landsteiner, K., and van der Scheer, J. (1930), *Proc. Soc. Exptl. Biol. Med.*, **27**, 812. Antigens containing peptides of known structure and antigenic properties of azoalbumoses.

Landsteiner, K., and van der Scheer, J. (1931), *J. Exptl. Med.*, **54**, 295. Specificity of serological reactions with simple chemical compounds (inhibition reactions).

Landsteiner, K., and van der Scheer, J. (1932a), *Proc. Soc. Exptl. Biol. Med.*, **29**, 747. Precipitin reactions of immune sera with simple chemical substances.

Landsteiner, K., and van der Scheer, J. (1932b), *J. Exptl. Med.*, **55**, 781. Serological specificity of peptides.

Landsteiner, K., and van der Scheer, J. (1932c), *Proc. Soc. Exptl. Biol. Med.*, **29**, 1261. The serological differentiation of steric isomers.

Landsteiner, K., and van der Scheer, J. (1934a), *J. Exptl. Med.*, **59**, 751. Serological studies on azo proteins. Antigens containing azo components with aliphatic side chains.

Landsteiner, K., and van der Scheer, J. (1934b), *J. Exptl. Med.*, **59**, 769. Serological specificity of peptides. II.

Landsteiner, K., and van der Scheer (1936), *J. Exptl. Med.*, **63**, 325. On cross reactions of immune sera to azoproteins.

Landsteiner, K., and van der Scheer, J. (1938), *J. Exptl. Med.*, **67**, 709. Cross reactions of immune sera to azoproteins. II. Antigens with azo components containing two determinant groups.

Landsteiner, K., and van der Scheer, J. (1939), *J. Exptl. Med.*, **69**, 705. Serological specificity of peptides. III.

Lapresle, C., Kaminski, M., and Tanner, C. E. (1959), *J. Immunol.*, **82**, 94. Immunochemical study of the enzymatic degradation of human serum albumin: an analysis of the antigenic structure of a protein molecule.

Lapresle, C., and Webb, T. (1965), *Biochem. J.*, **95**, 245. Isolation and study of a fragment of human serum albumin containing one of the antigenic sites of the whole molecule.

Lerman, L. S. (1953), *Nature,* **172**, 635. Antibody chromatography on an immunologically specific adsorbent.

Lerman, L. S. (1953), *Proc. Natl. Acad. Sci. U.S.*, **39**, 232. A biochemically specific method for enzyme isolation.

Leskowitz, S. (1963), *Nature,* **199**, 291. Delayed hypersensitivity to a conjugate of polytyrosine and its inhibition by haptens.

Levine, B. B. (1960), *J. Exptl. Med.*, **112**, 1131. Studies on the mechanism of the formation of the penicillin antigen. I. Delayed allergic cross-reactions among penicillin G and its degradation products.

Levine, B. B. (1963), *J. Exptl. Med.*, **117**, 161. Studies on the dimensions of the rabbit anti-benzylpenicilloyl antibody-combining sites.

Levine, B. B., and Ovary, Z. (1961), *J. Exptl. Med.*, **114**, 875. Studies on the mechanism of the formation of the penicillin antigen. III. The N-(P-α-benzylpenicilloyl) group as an antigenic determinant responsible for hypersensitivity to penicillin G.

Levine, L. (1962), *Feder. Proc.*, **21**, 711. Determinants of specificity of proteins, nucleic acids, and polypeptides.

Little, J. R., and Eisen, H. N. (1965), *Feder. Proc.*, **24**, 333. Physical and chemical differences between antibodies to the dinitrophenyl and trinitrophenyl groups.

Lüderitz, O., Staub, A. M., and Westphal, O. (1966), *Bacteriol. Rev.*, **30**, 192. Immunochemistry of O and R antigens of salmonella and related enterobacteriaceae.

Lüderitz, O., Westphal, O., Staub, A. M., and Le Minor, L. (1960), *Nature,* **188**, 556. Preparation and immunological properties of an artificial antigen with colitose (3-deoxy-L-fucose) as the determinant group.

Manecke, G., and Gillert, K. E. (1955), *Naturwissenschaften,* **42**, 212. Serologically specific adsorbents.

Marrack, J. R. (1934), *The Chemistry of Antigens and Antibodies.* Report No. 194 to the Medical Research Council. His Majesty's Stationery Office, London.

Marrack, J. R. (1939), *The Chemistry of Antigens and Antibodies.* Report No. 230 to the Medical Research Council. His Majesty's Stationery Office, London.

Marrack, J. R., and Orlans, E. S. (1954), *Brit. J. Exptl. Pathol.*, **35**, 389. The effects of acetylation of amino groups on the reactions of antigens and antibodies.

Marrack, J. R., and Smith, F. C. (1932), *Brit. J. Exptl. Pathol.*, **13**, 394. Quantitative aspects of immunity reactions: the combination of antibodies with simple haptens.

Maurer, P. H. (1964), *Progr. Allergy,* **8**, 1. Use of synthetic polymers of amino acids to study the basis of antigenicity.

Maurer, P. H., Gerulat, B. F., and Pinchuck, P. (1964), *J. Biol. Chem.*, **239**, 922. Antigenicity of polypeptides (poly-α-amino acids). XI. Quantitative relationships among polymers and rabbit antisera.

Maurer, P. H., Subrahmanyam, D., Katchalski, E., and Blout, E. R. (1959), *J. Immunol.*, **83**, 193. Antigenicity of polypeptides (poly-α-amino acids).

Medveczky, A., and Uhrovits, A. (1931), *Z. Immunitaetsforsch.*, **72**, 256. Immunity experiments with benzoylated antigens.

Merryman, C., and Benacerraf, B. (1963), *Proc. Soc. Exptl. Biol. Med.*, **114**, 372. Studies on the structure of mouse antibodies.

Metzger, H., and Mannik, M. (1964), *J. Exptl. Med.*, **120**, 765. Recombination of antibody polypeptide chains in the presence of antigen.

Metzger, H., Wofsy, L., and Singer, S. J. (1964), *Proc. Natl. Acad. Sci. U.S.*, **51**, 612. The participation of A and B polypeptide chains in the active sites of antibody molecules.

Mudd, S. (1932), *J. Immunol.*, **23**, 423. A hypothetical mechanism of antibody formation.

Mulinos, M. G., and Schlesinger, E. (1937), *Proc. Soc. Exptl. Biol. Med.*, **35**, 305. A contribution to drug allergy: antipyrine.

Mulinos, M. G., Schlesinger, E., and Stein, D. B. (1938), *Proc. Soc. Exptl. Biol. Med.*, **37**, 583. Antigenic properties of some azo compounds of serum albumin and serum globulin.

Mutsaars, W. (1939), *Ann. Inst. Pasteur,* **62**, 81. Serologic study of the xanthoproteins.

Mutsaars, W., and Grégoire, P. E. (1936), *Compt. Rend. Soc. Biol.*, **123**, 144. Comparison of the antigenic properties of proteins conjugated with aromatic nuclei by ureid and diazo coupling.

Nisonoff, A., Markus, G., and Wissler, F. C. (1961), *Nature,* **189**, 293. Separation of univalent fragments of rabbit antibody by reduction of a single, labile disulphide bond.

Nisonoff, A., and Pressman, D. (1957a), *J. Am. Chem. Soc.*, **79**, 1616. Closeness of fit and forces involved in the reactions of antibody homologous to the *p*-(*p*'-azophenylazo)benzoate ion group.

Nisonoff, A., and Pressman, D. (1957b), *J. Am. Chem. Soc.*, **79**, 5565. The annular nitrogen of pyridine as a determinant of immunologic specificity.

Nisonoff, A., and Pressman, D. (1958a), *J. Immunol.*, **80**, 417. Heterogeneity and average combining constants of antibodies from individual rabbits.

Nisonoff, A., and Pressman, D. (1958b), *Science,* **128**, 659. Loss of precipitating activity of antibody without destruction of binding sites.

Nisonoff, A., and Pressman, D. (1958c), *J. Immunol.,* **81**, 126. Heterogeneity of antibody sites in their relative combining affinities for structurally related haptens.

Nisonoff, A., Shaw, A. R., and Pressman, D. (1959a), *J. Am. Chem. Soc.,* **81**, 1418. The nitro group as a determinant of immunologic specificity.

Nisonoff, A., Winkler, M., and Pressman, D. (1959b), *J. Immunol.,* **82**, 201. The similar specificity of the combining sites of an individual antibody molecule.

Obermayer, F., and Pick, E. P. (1904), *Wien. Klin. Wochschr.,* **17**, 265. Beitrage zur kenntnis der präzipitinbildung. Ueber den begriff der art- und zustandspezifizität (originäre und konstitutive gruppierung) und die beeinflussung der chemischen eigenart des tierkörpers.

Ollodart, R., and Rose, N. R. (1962), *Cancer Res.,* **22**, 689. Antibodies to 1,2-naphthoquinone.

Onoue, K., Yagi, Y., and Pressman, D. (1965), *Immunochemistry,* **2**, 181. Immunoadsorbents with high capacity.

Palmer, J. L., Mandy, W. J., and Nisonoff, A. (1962a), *Proc. Natl. Acad. Sci. U.S.,* **48**, 49. Heterogeneity of rabbit antibody and its subunits.

Palmer, J. L., Nisonoff, A., and Van Holde, K. E. (1962b), *Proc. Natl. Acad. Sci. U.S.,* **50**, 314. Dissociation of rabbit gamma globulin into subunits by reduction and acidification.

Pappenheimer, A. M., Lundgren, H. P., and Williams, J. W. (1940), *J. Exptl. Med.,* **71**, 247. Studies on the molecular weight of diphtheria toxin, antitoxin, and their reaction products.

Parker, C. W., de Weck, A. L., Kern, M., and Eisen, H. N. (1962), *J. Exptl. Med.,* **115**, 803. The preparation and some properties of penicillenic acid derivatives relevant to penicillin hypersensitivity.

Pauling, L. (1940), *J. Am. Chem. Soc.,* **62**, 2643. A theory of the structure and process of formation of antibodies.

Pauling, L. (1960), *The Nature of the Chemical Bond,* 3rd ed. Cornell University Press, Ithaca, New York.

Pauling, L., Campbell, D. H., and Pressman, D. (1943), *Physiol. Rev.,* **23**, 203. The nature of the forces between antigen and antibody and of the precipitation reaction.

Pauling, L., Pressman, D., and Campbell, D. H. (1944a), *J. Am. Chem. Soc.,* **66**, 330. The serological properties of simple substances. VI. The precipitation of a mixture of two specific antisera by a dihaptenic substance containing the two corresponding haptenic groups; evidence for the framework theory of serological precipitation.

Pauling, L., Pressman, D., and Grossberg, A. L. (1944b), *J. Am. Chem. Soc.,* **66**, 784. The serological properties of simple substances. VII. A quantitative theory of the inhibition by haptens of the precipitation of heterogeneous antisera with antigens, and comparison with experimental results for polyhaptenic simple substances and for azoproteins.

Permutt, M. A., Parker, C. W., and Utiger, R. D. (1966), *Endocrinol.,* **78**, 809. Immunochemical studies with lysine vasopressin.

Pillemer, L., Ecker, E. E., and Martiensen, E. W. (1939), *J. Exptl. Med.,* **70**, 387. The specificity of kerateine derivatives.

Polmar, S. H., and Steinberg, A. G. (1964), *Science,* **145**, 928. Dependence of a Gm(b) antigen on the quarternary structure of human gamma globulin.

Porter, R. R. (1959), *Biochem. J.,* **73**, 119. The hydrolysis of rabbit γ-globulin and antibodies with crystalline papain.

Porter, R. R. (1962), in *Basic Problems in Neoplastic Disease* (A. Gellhorn and E. Hirschberg, ed.), p. 177. Columbia University Press, New York. Structure of γ-globulin and antibodies.

Porter, R. R., and Weir, R. C. (1966), *J. Cell. Physiol.*, **67**: Suppl. 1, 51. Subunits of immunoglobulins and their relationship to antibody specificity.

Pressman, D. (1953), *Adv. Biol. Med. Phys.*, **3**, 99. Antibodies as specific chemical reagents.

Pressman, D. (1957), in *Molecular Structure and Biological Specificity* (L. Pauling and H. Itano, eds.). American Institute of Biological Sciences, Washington, D. C. Molecular complementariness in antigen-antibody systems.

Pressman, D. (1964), in *Methods in Medical Research* (H. N. Eisen, ed.), Vol. 10. p. 122. Year Book Publishers, Chicago, Illinois. VIII. Hapten-antibody combinations determined by inhibition of precipitation.

Pressman, D., Bryden, J. H., and Pauling, L. (1948), *J. Am. Chem. Soc.*, **70**, 1352. The reactions of antiserum homologous to the *p*-azosuccinanilate group.

Pressman, D., Grossberg, A. L., Pence, L. H., and Pauling, L. (1946), *J. Am. Chem. Soc.*, **68**, 250. The reactions of antiserum homologous to the *p*-azophenyltrimethylammonium group.

Pressman, D., Nisonoff, A., and Radzimski, G. (1961a), *J. Immunol.*, **86**, 35. Specific anion effects with antibenzoate antibody.

Pressman, D., Nisonoff, A., Radzimski, G., and Shaw, A. (1961b), *J. Immunol.*, **86**, 489. Nature of the active site of antibenzoate antibodies: further evidence for the presence of tyrosine.

Pressman, D., Pardee, A. B., and Pauling, L. (1945), *J. Am. Chem. Soc.*, **67**, 1602. The reactions of antisera homologous to various azophenylarsonic acid groups and the *p*-azophenylmethylarsinic acid group with some heterologous haptens.

Pressman, D., and Pauling, L. (1949), *J. Am. Chem. Soc.*, **71**, 2893. The reactions of antiserum homologous to the 4-azophthalate ion.

Pressman, D., and Roholt, O. A. (1961), *Proc. Natl. Acad. Sci. U.S.*, **47**, 1606. Isolation of peptides from an antibody site.

Pressman, D., and Siegel, M. (1953a), *J. Am. Chem. Soc.*, **75**, 686. The binding of simple substances to serum proteins and its effect on apparent antibody-hapten combination constants.

Pressman, D., and Siegel, M. (1953b), *J. Am. Chem. Soc.*, **75**, 1376. The steric configuration of β-benzoylpropionate ion in aqueous solution as determined by immunochemical means.

Pressman, D., and Siegel, M. (1957), *J. Am. Chem. Soc.*, **79**, 994. The hydration of the annular nitrogen group as a factor in the combination of hapten with antibody.

Pressman, D., Siegel, M., and Hall, L. A. R. (1954), *J. Am. Chem. Soc.*, **76**, 6336. The closeness of fit of antibenzoate antibodies about haptens and the orientation of the haptens in combination.

Pressman, D., and Sternberger, L. A. (1950), *J. Am. Chem. Soc.*, **72**, 2226. The relative rates of iodination of serum components and the effect of iodination on antibody activity.

Pressman, D., Swingle, S. M., Grossberg, A. L., and Pauling, L. (1944), *J. Am. Chem. Soc.*, **66**, 1731. The serological properties of simple substances. VIII. The reactions of antiserum homologous to the *p*-azobenzoic acid groups.

Robbins, P. W., and Uchida, T. (1962), *Feder. Proc.*, **21**, 702. Determinants of specificity in salmonella: changes in antigenic structure mediated by bacteriophage.

Roholt, O. A., Onoue, K., and Pressman, D. (1964), *Proc. Natl. Acad. Sci. U.S.*, **51**, 173. Specific combination of H and L chains of rabbit γ-globulins.

Roholt, O. A., Radzimski, G., and Pressman, D. (1963), *Science,* **141**, 726. Antibody combining site: the B polypeptide chain.

Roholt, O. A., Radzimski, G., and Pressman, D. (1965a), *Science,* **147**, 613. Polypeptide chains of antibody: effective binding sites require specificity in combination.

Roholt, O. A., Radzimski, G., and Pressman, D. (1965b), *J. Exptl. Med.,* **122**, 785. Preferential recombination of antibody chains to form effective binding sites.

Roholt, O. A., Radzimski, G., and Pressman, D. (1966), *J. Exptl. Med.,* **123**, 921. Specificity in the combination of F_D fragments with L chains to form hapten-binding sites.

Rowe, D. S., and Fahey, J. L. (1965), *J. Exptl. Med.,* **121**, 171 and 185. A new class of human immunoglobulins. I. A unique myeloma protein. II. Normal serum IgD.

Rude, E., Westphal, O., Hurwitz, E., Fuchs, S., and Sela, M. (1966), *Immunochemistry,* **3**, 137. Synthesis and antigenic properties of sugar-polypeptide conjugates.

Sage, H. J., Deutsch, G. F., Fasman, G. D., and Levine, L. (1964), *Immunochemistry,* **1**, 133. The serological specificity of the poly-alanine immune system.

Saha, K., Karush, F., and Marks, R. (1966), *Immunochemistry,* **3**, 279. Antibody Affinity—I. Studies with a large haptenic group.

Schechter, I., Bauminger, S., Sela, M., Nachtigal, D., and Feldman, M. (1964), *Immunochemistry,* **1**, 249. Immune response to polypeptidyl proteins in rabbits tolerant to the protein carriers.

Schechter, I., and Sela, M. (1965a), *Biochim. Biophys. Acta,* **104**, 298. Combining sites of antibodies to L-alanine and D-alanine peptide determinants.

Schechter, I., and Sela, M. (1965b), *Biochim. Biophys. Acta,* **104**, 301. Preferential immune response to D-amino acid residues in poly-DL-amino acid determinants.

Schlossman, S. F., and Kabat, E. A. (1962), *J. Exptl. Med.,* **116**, 535. Specific fractionation of a population of antidextran molecules with combining sites of various sizes.

Schoellman, G., and Shaw, E. (1962), *Biochem. Biophys. Res. Commun.,* **7**, 36. A new method for labelling the active center of chymotrypsin.

Schwarzenbach, G. (1936), *Z. Physik. Chem.,* **A176**, 133. The effect of an ionic charge upon the acidity of an acid.

Sela, M. (1966), *Advan. Immunol.,* **5**, 29. Immunological studies with synthetic polypeptides.

Sela, M., and Arnon, R. (1960a), *Biochim. Biophys. Acta,* **40**, 382. A specific synthetic polypeptide antigen.

Sela, M., and Arnon, R. (1960b), *Biochem. J.,* **77**, 394. Studies on the chemical basis of the antigenicity of proteins. 3. The role of rigidity in the antigenicity of polypeptidyl gelatins.

Sela, M., Arnon, R., and Jacobson, I. (1963), *Biopolymers,* **1**, 517. Synthesis of poly-L-lysine and poly-L-lysylalbumin via N^{ϵ}-trifluoroactyl-N^{α}-carboxy-L-lysine anhydride.

Sela, M., Fuchs, S., and Arnon, R. (1962), *Biochem. J.,* **85**, 223. Studies on the chemical basis of the antigenicity of proteins 5. Synthesis, characterization and immunogenicity of some multichain and linear polypeptides containing tyrosine.

Sela, M., Ungar-Waron, H., and Schechter, I. (1964), *Proc. Natl. Acad. Sci. U.S.,* **52**, 285. Uridine-specific antibodies obtained with synthetic antigens.

Siegel, M., and Pressman, D. (1953), *J. Am. Chem. Soc.,* **75**, 3436. The reactions of antiserum homologous to the *p*-azohippurate ion.

Siegel, M., and Pressman, D. (1954), *J. Am. Chem. Soc.,* **76**, 2863. The reactions of antiserum homologous to the *p*-azomaleanilate and *p*-azofumaranilate ion groups.

Singer, S. J. (1964), in *Methods of Medical Research* (H. N. Eisen, ed.), Vol. 10, p. 87.

Year Book Medical Publishers, Chicago, Illinois. II. Purification of antiprotein antibodies by thiolated antigen procedure.

Singer, S. J., and Doolittle, R. F. (1966), *Science,* **153**, 13. Antibody active sites and immunoglobulin molecules.

Singer, S. J., Fothergill, J. E., and Shainoff, J. R. (1960), *J. Am. Chem. Soc.,* **82**, 565. General method for isolation of antibodies.

Slobin, Lawrence I. (1966), *Biochemistry,* **5**, 2836. Preparation and some properties of antibodies with specificity toward *p*-nitrophenyl esters.

Snapper, I., and Grunbaum, A. (1936), *Brit. J. Exptl. Pathol.,* **17**, 361. On the immunity reactions of iodoproteins.

Takemori, T., and Yamakawa, T. (1963), *J. Biochem.,* **54**, 444. Immunochemical studies of lipids. I. Preparation and immunological properties of synthetic psychosine-protein antigens.

Tanigaki, N., Kitagawa, M., Yagi, Y., and Pressman, D. (1966), *Cancer Res.* (in press). The reaction of specific antibody with acetaminofluorene fixed in liver cells.

Tanenbaum, S. W., and Beiser, S. M. (1963), *Proc. Natl. Acad. Sci. U.S.,* **49**, 662. Pyrimidine-specific antibodies which react with deoxyribonucleic acid (DNA).

Truhaut, R., German, A., and Schuster, J. (1965), *Compt. Rend.,* **261**, 602. Immunological investigation of colchicine derivatives.

Ungar-Waron, H., and Sela, M. (1966), *Biochim. Biophys. Acta,* **124**, 147. Pyridoxal-specific antibodies obtained with a synthetic pyridoxal-polypeptide conjugate.

Utsumi, S., and Karush, F. (1964), *Biochemistry,* **3**, 1329. The subunits of purified rabbit antibody.

Utsumi, S., and Karush, F. (1965), *Biochemistry,* **4**, 1766. Peptic fragmentation of rabbit γG-immunoglobulin.

van der Scheer, J., and Landsteiner, K. (1935), *J. Immunol.,* **29**, 371. Serological tests with amino acids.

Velick, S. F., Parker, C. W., and Eisen, H. N. (1960), *Proc. Natl. Acad. Sci. U.S.,* **46**, 1470. Excitation energy transfer and the quantitative study of the antibody hapten reaction.

Wasserman, E., and Levine, L. (1961), *J. Immunol.,* **87**, 290. Quantitative micro-complement fixation and its use in the study of antigenic structure by specific antigen-antibody inhibition.

Wedum, A. G. (1942), *J. Infect. Diseases,* **70**, 173. Immunological specificity of sulfonamide azoproteins.

Weiner, L. M., Rosenblatt, M., and Howes, H. A. (1963), *J. Immunol.,* **90**, 788. The detection of humoral antibodies directed against salicylates in hypersensitive states.

Weir, R. C., and Porter, R. R. (1966), *Biochem. J.,* **100**, 69. The antigen-binding capacity of the peptide chains of horse antibodies.

Westphal, O., and Schmidt, H. (1951), *Ann.,* **575**, 84. N-Acetyl-glucosamine as the determinant group in artificial antigens.

Whitney, P. L., and Tanford, C. (1965), *Proc. Natl. Acad. Sci. U.S.,* **53**, 524. Recovery of specific activity after complete unfolding and reduction of an antibody fragment.

Winkler, M. H. (1962), *J. Mol. Biol.,* **4**, 118. A molecular probe for the antibody site.

Wofsy, L., Metzger, H., and Singer, S. J. (1962), *Biochemistry,* **1**, 1031. Affinity labeling. A general method for labeling the active sites of antibody and enzyme molecules.

Wofsy, L., and Singer, S. J. (1963), *Biochemistry,* **2**, 104. Effects of the amidination reaction on antibody activity and on the physical properties of some proteins.

Wormall, A. (1930), *J. Exptl. Med.*, **51**, 295. The immunological specificity of chemically altered proteins: halogenated and nitrated proteins.

Yagi, Y., Engel, K., and Pressman, D. (1960), *J. Immunol.*, **85**, 375. Quantitative determinations of small amounts of antibody by use of solid adsorbents.

Yagi, Y., Maier, P., and Pressman, D. (1962), *J. Immunol.*, **89**, 736. Immunoelectrophoretic identification of guinea pig anti-insulin antibodies.

Yagi, Y., Maier, P., and Pressman, D. (1965), *Science,* **147**, 617. Antibodies against the component polypeptide chains of bovine insulin.

Yariv, J., Rapport, M. M., and Graf, L. (1962), *Biochem.* J., **85**, 383. The interaction of glycosides and saccharides with antibody to the corresponding phenylazo glycosides.

INDEX

THE STRUCTURAL BASIS OF ANTIBODY SPECIFICITY

DAVID PRESSMAN
ALLAN L. GROSSBERG

ROSWELL PARK MEMORIAL INSTITUTE

Microbial and Molecular Biology Series

This monograph brings together a quantitative appraisal of research on the chemical nature of antibody specificity since the earlier studies described by Landsteiner. It will be useful as a text for senior-graduate level courses on chemical immunology or immunochemistry, and as a reference for immunologists, pharmacologists, enzymologists, and allergists.

The text treats those structural features of haptens or antigens and of antibodies which provide the basis for their specific interaction. The first two chapters introduce the chemical concepts which are involved in antibody-antigen interaction. Chapter 3 discusses a large number of anti-hapten systems in depth in terms of the structural details important for antibody-hapten combination. The following chapters discuss the basis of the heterogeneity of antibody molecules, and the use of antibodies to map out structures of small and large molecules in aqueous solution.

Liberal use is made of drawings of chemical structures together with their names, so that biology students can easily grasp and follow the discussion of chemical principles involved, and an extensive bibliography and appendix gives access to a large number of studies of anti-hapten systems.

BENJAMIN BOOKS OF RELATED INTEREST

GENETIC COMPLEMENTATION

J. R. S. FINCHAM / *John Innes Institute*

A critical and unified account of genetic complementation, this monograph describes the evolution of the idea of the gene, the gene as described by complementation tests, and the complications which arise due to anomalous complementation between mutant derivatives of the same gene.

1966, 144 pages   Hardbound   ISBN 0-805-32550-6

TETRAPYRROLE BIOSYNTHESIS AND ITS REGULATION

JUNE LASCELLES / *Oxford University*

This research monograph treats the whole field of the biosynthetic pathway of tetrapyrrole pigments. The path of chlorophyll synthesis and its integration with the specific proteins and cell structures with which the pigments are associated *in vivo* is covered, and its regulation is described in detail.

1964, 132 pages   Hardbound   ISBN 0-805-36000-X

THE MITOCHONDRION

ALBERT L. LEHNINGER / *Johns Hopkins University*

This is the first comprehensive monograph to bring together the results of confluent studies on enzymatic mechanisms of the oxidative cycles, of electron transport, of oxidative phosphorylation, and of the cell biology and ultrastructure of the mitochondrion.

1965, 263 pages   Hardbound   ISBN 0-805-36110-3

CONTROL OF MACROMOLECULAR SYNTHESIS

OLE MAALOE, NIELS O. KJELDGAARD
/ *University of Copenhagen*

The protein and nucleic acid syntheses in bacteria, and the rules governing these syntheses in intact growing bacteria, are described in this graduate monograph. The contents are arranged to emphasize the necessity of balancing results of *in vitro* experiments against *in vivo* studies of the mechanisms.

1966, 284   Hardbound   ISBN 0-805-36680-6

W. A. BENJAMIN, INC.
ADVANCED BOOK PROGRAM
READING, MASSACHUSETTS

DAVID PRESSMAN is Research Professor of Chemistry in the Roswell Park Division of the State University of New York at Buffalo, and Director of Cancer Research in Biochemistry at Roswell Park Memorial Institute. He has served as Head of the Immunochemistry Section of the Sloan-Kettering Division of Cornell Medical School.

Dr. Pressman received his B.S. and Ph.D. degrees from the California Institute of Technology, and his M.A. from the University of California at Los Angeles. He has held the Gordon Memorial Lectureship of the Long Island College of Medicine (1951) and he received the Bertha Teplitz Award of the Ann Langer Cancer Research Foundation (1958), the Schoellkopf Medal of the American Chemical Society (1965), and the Morely Medal of the American Chemical Society (1967). Dr. Pressman has served on the editorial boards of *Transplantation Bulletin, Cancer Research, Journal of Immunology, Journal of Medicinal and Pharmaceutical Chemistry,* and *Immunochemistry.*

ALLAN L. GROSSBERG is Associate Research Professor of Chemistry in the Roswell Park Division of the State University of New York at Buffalo, and Associate Cancer Research Scientist in Biochemistry at Roswell Park Memorial Institute. He received his B.S. and M.S. degrees from the California Institute of Technology, and his Ph.D. from McGill University.

Dr. Grossberg has been Collip Fellow at the McGill University School of Medicine, Lecturer in Physiology at McGill, and a Research Biochemist at the School of Medicine of Temple University. His main research interests include the chemical nature of the active sites of antibodies, structural features of haptens and of antibody sites important for this interaction, methods of labeling active sites of antibodies, methods of chemical modification of proteins, and the study of protein conformation.